RADIONUCLIDES IN THE OCEANS

Inputs and Inventories

Coordinators:

P. Guéguéniat, P. Germain and H. Métivier

les éditions de physique

Avenue du Hoggar
Zone Industrielle de Courtabœuf
BP 112
91944 Les Ulis cedex A, France

Book series coordinated by Henri Métivier

Books already published:

Agriculture, Environnement et Nucléaire : comment réagir en cas d'accident

Auteurs : René Coulon, Jacques Delmas, Gérard Griperay, Philippe Guetat, René Loyau, Claude Madelmont, Rémy Maximilien, Jean-Claude Rottereau

Traitement de la contamination interne accidentelle des travailleurs

Auteurs : M.H. Bhattacharyya, B.D. Breistenstein, H. Métivier, B.A. Muggenburg, G.N. Stradling, V. Volf

Approche de la sûreté des sites nucléaires

Auteur : Jean Fauré

Circonstances et conséquences de la pollution radioactive dans l'ancienne Union soviétique

D. Robeau, Coordinateur.
Auteurs : Jean-Claude Nénot, Christian Chenal, Sabine Charmasson, Daniel Robeau, M. Bertin, Philippe Renaud, Henri Maubert, André Jouve, Alexandre Grebenkov

Éléments de sûreté nucléaire
Elements of Nuclear Safety (Russian version in preparation)

Auteur : Jacques Libmann

Le tritium – de l'environnement à l'Homme

Yves Belot, Monique Roy et Henri Métivier, Coordinateurs.
Auteurs : Y. Belot, M. Roy, H. Métivier, P. Pihet, Ph. Duport, A. Flüry-Hérard, E. Rabin, Ph. Boucquey, F. Briot, P. Giroux, J.Y. Hervé, J.P. Le Goff et G. Pescayre

Radionuclides in the Oceans

P. Guéguéniat, P. Germain and H. Métivier, Coordinators

ISBN : 2-86883-285-7

© Les Editions de Physique 1996

Contributors

A. Aarkrog
Risø National Laboratory,
P.O. Box 49,
4000 Roskilde, Denmark

Y. Bourlat
SMSRB
B.P. 208
91311 Montlhéry Cedex, France

P. Bailly du Bois
IPSN
Rue Max-Pol Fouchet
B.P. 10
50130 Octeville, France

K. Buesseler
National Science Fondation
Division of Ocean Sciences Room 725
4201 Wilson Blvd,
Arlington VA 22230, U.S.A.

Y. Baron
G.E.A. Marine Nationale
B.P. 19
50115 Cherbourg - Naval, France

S. Charmasson
IPSN/SERE/LRM Toulon
B.P. 330
83507 La Seyne Cedex, France

J.M. Bewers
Bedford Institute of Oceanography
P.O. Box 1006, Darthmouth,
N.S. B2Y 4 A2, Canada

A.A. Cigna
ENEA – CRE
13040 Saluggia VC, Italy

J.C. Bourguignon
SMSRB
B.P. 208
91311 Montlhéry Cedex, France

H. Dahlgaard
Riso National Laboratory
MIL-114
4000 Roskilde, Denmark

R. Delfanti

ENEA C.R. Ambiente Marino -
S. Terasa
C.P. 316
19100 La Spezia, Italy

C. Gascó-Leonarte

CIEMAT
Avenuda Complutense 22
28040 Madrid, Spain

P. Guéguéniat

IPSN
Rue Max-Pol Fouchet
B.P. 10
50130 Octeville, France

T.F. Hamilton

Lawrence Livermore, National Lab.
P.O. Box 808-L453
CA-94551-9900 Livermore, U.S.A.

J. Hermann

Bundesamt für Seeschiffahrt und
Hydrographie,
Bernhard - Nocht Strasse 78
20305 Hamburg, Germany

E. Holm

Department of Radiation Physics
Lund University
Lasarettet
22185 Lund, Sweden

G.H. Hong

Korea Ocean Research and
Development Institute
Ansan, Korea

D. Josefsson

Department of Radiation Physics
Lund University
Lasarettet
22185 Lund, Sweden

P.J. Kershaw

MAFF/DFR
Pakefield road
Suffolk
NR33 OHT Lowestoft, U.K.

L. León Vintró

Department of Experimental
Physics – University College
Belfied
Dublin 4, Ireland

G. Le Petit

SMSRB
B.P. 208
91311 Montlhéry Cedex, France

H.D. Livingston

Woods Hole
Oceanographic Institution
360 Woods Hole Rd,
MS25 Woods Hole,
MA 02543-1541, U.S.A.

S. Magnusson

Islandic Radiation Protection
Institute
Laugavegur 118D
IS-150 Island

J.C. Milliès-Lacroix
SMSRB
B.P. 208
91311 Montlhéry Cedex, France

P.I. Mitchell
Department of Experimental
Physics – University College
Belfield
Dublin 4, Ireland

S. Nielsen
RISO National Laboratory
P.O. Box 49
4000 Roskilde, Denmark

H. Nies
Bundlesamt für Seeschiffahrt und
Hydrographie,
Bernhard-Nocht Strasse 78
20305 Hamburg, Germany

F. Nyffeler
Institut of Geology
University of Neuchâtel
Groupe Prosper
11 rue Emile Argend
2003 Neuchâtel, Switzerland

C. Papucci
ENEA C.R. Ambiente Marino -
S. Terasa
C.P. 316
19100 La Spezia, Italy

B. Persson
Department of Radiation Physics
Lund University
Lasarettet
22185 Lund, Sweden

P. Roos
Department of Radiation Physics
Lund University
Lasarettet
22185 Lund, Sweden

J.A. Sánchez-Cabeza
Servei de Fisica de les Radiacions
Balleterra
8193 Barcelona, Spain

M. Sickel
Norwegian Radiation
Protection Authority
P.O. Box 55
1345 Østerås, Norway

P. Strand
Norwegian Radiation
Protection Authority
P.O. Box 55
1345 Østerås, Norway

Yu. Tsaturov
Roshydromet,
Novovagan' kovsky str. 12,
123242 Moscow, Russia

Foreword

This book is a collection of papers given on the first day of the international symposium *Radionuclides in the Oceans* (RADOC 96-97). This symposium was organized by the Nuclear Safety and Protection Institute (IPSN) and the Ministry of Agriculture, Fisheries and Food (MAFF). It was divided into two parts. The first part, « Inventories, Behaviour and Processes », took place at Octeville-Cherbourg, France (7-11 October 1996) and dealt with the same themes as the 1987 Cherbourg symposium (Radionuclides as a tool for oceanography) and the 1991 Norwich symposium (Radionuclides in the study of marine processes). The second part, « Impacts on Man and the environment », will take place at Norwich and Lowestoft (7-11 April 1997), and will cover the themes of radiological and environmental protection and modelling.

Ten years after Chernobyl, after the French decision to end nuclear weapon testing in the Pacific Ocean, after the end of the OECD-NEA Coordinated Research and Environmental Surveillance Programme related to low-level waste dumping in deep sea, and one hundred years after the discovery of radioactivity, IPSN has considered it useful to assemble the available information on artificial radioactivity levels in the seas and oceans. The objective is to address scientific and public concerns about the use of the sea as a « waste repository », and to answer regarding the radioactive contamination of the seas and oceans. Therefore, international experts have been invited to describe and quantify, during the first day of the symposium (Part I), the inputs and inventories of artificial radionuclides released in seas and oceans by civil and military activities.

In the different chapters of this book, radionuclides are studied in geographical areas of different size, and varying physical and biological features. Therefore, some presentations deal with oceans taken as a whole (Atlantic, Pacific and Indian oceans). Some sources of radionuclides, such as atmospheric fallout, both before and after Chernobyl, have a large scale impact, whereas others, such as marine dumping sites, sites for nuclear weapon tests, and damaged submarines provide more localised inputs of artificial radionuclides.

Others presentations focus on of particular interest seas from the point of view of specific radionuclide sources and the particular processes which govern radionuclide behaviour. The Channel, the North Sea and the Irish Sea are quite shallow and receive, directly or indirectly a small fraction of the wastes released by reprocessing plant wastes. The Baltic Sea has been strongly affected by Chernobyl, and is subject to a high salinity pressure gradient. The Black Sea has also been marked by Chernobyl and is strongly anoxic. The Mediterranean Sea receives an input of radionuclides from the Rhone River outflow into the western basin and has exchanges with the Atlantic Ocean. Dumped radioactive wastes, radionuclide inputs from the Ob and Yenisei river basins, radionuclides from European reprocessing plants transported by ocean currents, and radionuclide transport by ice must be considered in the Arctic, Barents, Kara and Laptev Seas.

It appears that such a comprehensive review of all the available data has not been made in recent years and it is the aim of this book to provide it.

The production of this book was made possible by the collaborative efforts of the international experts in providing, within a tight schedule, the inputs requested by IPSN; they deserve our gratitude. Our thanks also go to J.F. Hémidy, Director of the « École d'Ingénieurs de Cherbourg », and J. Lemière of the « Institut Universitaire de Technologie, Cherbourg – Manche », who have very kindly made available their premises for the *Radionuclides in the Oceans* Symposium. We also would like to thank M. Masson, D. Boust, P. Bailly du Bois, D. Maro for their review of the manuscripts and proofs, as well as Mrs C. Leconte, S. Le Cavelier, Mrs I. Le Corre who have devoted much efforts to the organization of this event.

We are very grateful to the Minister of the Environment, Mrs Corinne Lepage, who has accepted to open the session devoted to inputs and inventories of radionuclides in seas and oceans.

Coordinators
P. Guéguéniat, P. Germain, H. Métivier

Summary

1 Radionuclides in the Atlantic Ocean: A Survey

F. Nyffeler, A.A. Cigna,
H. Dahlgaard and H.D. Livingston

The knowledge of the distribution of radionuclides in the ocean is gradually being updated through a continuous flow of data, ranging from the periodical monitoring records issued by national authorities to the results of local and ocean scale scientific cruises, carried out within the framework of large international programs. This paper tries to summarize and to update the state of our knowledge regarding the Atlantic Ocean, by scaling some prominent features. We consider successively the ocean scale distribution of radionuclides from bomb testing fallout, compared with the natural background, the regional inputs from land-based sources and from the adjacent seas. Finally, the controlled or uncontrolled dumping practice and the accidents like the Chernobyl case are also taken into account to estimate the collective doses to the world population.

1.1. Introduction

Anthropogenic radionuclides have been introduced to the Atlantic Ocean from a variety of sources since the advent of the nuclear age. The sources include fallout from atmospheric nuclear weapon's tests, nuclear waste dumping/disposal activities and accidents, in particular, the Chernobyl accident in April 1986. The temporal and spatial nature on these inputs has affected greatly the past, present and future distributions of the various radionuclides involved. The natural radionuclides resulting from the non-nuclear industry (*e.g.*, the fertilisers plants) should also be considered in comparison with those of primordial or of cosmogenic origin. However, the natural radionuclides are ubiquitous in the ocean in significant concentrations, and the anthropogenic contribution to the natural stock is not expected to be comparatively relevant.

Three categories of man-made radionuclides can be noted according to their time and space scales.

a) *All ocean inputs:* this applies chiefly to fallout from atmospheric nuclear weapon's tests which took place in the late 50's and early 60's in both the North and South Atlantic. About 3/4 of the Atlantic input was to the North Atlantic and 1/4 to the South Atlantic. In each hemisphere, the delivery was maximal at mid-latitudes and minimal at the equator and at the poles. The input of ^{238}Pu from the burn-up of the U.S. SNAP 9A satellite over the Southern Hemisphere in 1964 was also widely introduced to the Atlantic but, in this case, the latitudinal distribution was reversed, with the large fraction of the input going into the South Atlantic.

b) *Point sources and regional inputs:* these inputs include the point sources from nuclear fuel reprocessing discharges such as Sellafield (UK) and Cap de la Hague (France). Because it was randomly distributed, the fallout to Western European coastal waters after the Chernobyl accident enters the same category of inputs. In all three cases, the soluble fraction of the radionuclides introduced were largely transported into the Arctic and sub-Arctic seas.

c) *Dumping and accidents:* these include the planned dumping of packaged low level nuclear waste at a variety of sites and by several countries, the accidental losses in deep water of nuclear powered submarines, as well as the disposal of reactors with their fuel in the shallow water of the Northern Seas by the Former Soviet Union (FSU). In all these cases, any releases which have occurred have lead to extremely localized contamination to date.

For each of these categories, the type of radionuclides released, their isotopic ratios and the ratio between species can be used to determine their origin. The ratios also provide new opportunities to gain an understanding of processes as the large scale transport associated with the global ocean circulation, the vertical mixing, the biological accumulation and the short-circuit mechanisms. The wide spectrum of half-lives of radionuclides allows to use them for a variety of scientific applications, from the local study of the sediment and the processes in the seabed to the changes in the ocean scale circulation over decades. Some of these issues have been addressed in the proceedings of a previous symposium on the use of radionuclides in the study of marine processes (Kershaw *et al.*, 1991). The aim of the present paper is to review and update the actual level of knowledge by putting emphasis on some prominent features associated with the three categories of inputs indicated above.

1.2. Field Measurements and Databases

Measurements of man-made radionuclides have been performed throughout the North East Atlantic and the Arctic since the 1960's. The most comprehensive suite of measurements in the Atlantic was made in 1972/1973 as part of GEOSECS, the « Geochemical Ocean Sections program » (National Science Foundation, 1987). The next two large programmes were, « Transient Tracers in the Ocean » (TTO) and the « South Atlantic Ventilation Experiment » (SAVE) in 1981 and 1987-1989 respectively. In addition, numerous data reports and review papers were issued by the German Hydrographic Institute (Kautsky, 1980; 1987), the Obninsk laboratory, Russia (Vakulovskii *et al.*, 1985), the Woods Hole Oceanographic Institution, USA (Livingston, 1988), the Lowestoft laboratory, UK, (Kershaw and Baxter, 1995), the Bedford Institute of Oceanography, Canada (Smith *et al.*, 1990), Lund University, Sweden (Roos and Holm, 1993), the Risoe National Laboratory, (Aarkrog *et al.*, 1983; 1986; 1987; Dahlgaard, 1984; 1994; 1995a) and the French IPSN-CEA laboratory at Octeville (Guéguéniat *et al.*, 1995). During the past decade, programs aiming at improving the use of the national radiological data bases available in the riparian countries of the northern seas have been launched under the aegis of the European Community (CEC, 1990) and of the IAEA (Povinec, 1994).

Radioactive waste was dumped in the north-east Atlantic until 1982 and the operations have been supervised by the NEA (Nuclear Energy Agency). In 1981, the Agency set-up the CRESP programme (Co-ordinated research and Environmental Surveillance Programme), to increase knowledge of the processes controlling the transfer of radionuclides in the environment (NEA, 1982), which provided a significant amount of original site specific data.

The disposal of radioactive waste in the shallow Arctic areas have recently triggered concerns, which resulted in a temporarily boosted scientific effort. The inventory of the radioactive waste disposed in the Arctic region by the FSU has been reported in the so-called « White Report » (Yablokov *et al.*, 1993), and the consequences of such dumping operations are presently assessed within the framework of the IASAP programme (Sjoeblom and Linsley, 1995). As an outcome, a significant amount of site specific data are presently accumulated in the polar areas, which are of vital environmental concern (Strand and Holm, 1993).

1.3. The Ocean Scale Distribution of Radionuclides

Other than in the Arctic and sub-Arctic seas and their southern deep water overflows, virtually all of the anthropogenic signal throughout the North and South Atlantic derives from fallout from atmospheric nuclear weapon's tests. Hence the ocean scale distribution of anthropogenic radionuclides in the Atlantic is, in reality, that of the fallout signal (plus the ^{238}Pu from the satellite power source). The fate of this signal is determined by a number of factors, *viz.* the original input pattern, physical mixing of affected water masses, chemical properties with respect to particle and biological removal, and radioactive decay.

1.3.1. Principal Radionuclides

The principal nuclides involved fall into two broad categories based on their behaviour in respect to association with particles:
a) soluble, b) reactive. Also, for convenience, we shall break down the discussion into other components, a) surface waters, b) the ocean water column and c) the sediments.

1.3.1.1. Soluble Radionuclides

These include ^{137}Cs, ^{90}Sr and ^{3}H. ^{14}C is also largely a soluble tracer but has both bomb-produced and pre-bomb cosmogenic origins. ^{129}I has been shown to serve as a soluble tracer of nuclear fuel reprocessing discharges but its large scale fallout distributions have not been studied. The first four have been extensively studied in the Atlantic in several large programs and other studies. They have found wide use as tracers of ocean circulation and used in model validation as well as in studies of physical processes such as deep sea ventilation. The fission products, ^{137}Cs and ^{90}Sr, have been shown to maintain the same constant ratio of about 1.5 to each other (Bowen *et al.*, 1974) throughout the Atlantic Ocean (and as such characterised their input ratio in fallout) – other than the slight ratio change with time associated with their slightly different half-lives – ^{90}Sr ($T_{1/2}$ = 28.8 years), ^{137}Cs ($T_{1/2}$ = 30.0 years).

1.3.1.2. Reactive Radionuclides

The principal reactive radionuclides studied in the Atlantic resulting from fallout are the Pu isotopes, ^{238}Pu, ^{239}Pu and ^{240}Pu, and ^{241}Am. In the water column, in addition to studies of their basic behaviour in the ocean, they have been used to study the nature of the scavenging process by which metals are incorporated into the pool of sinking particulates, fractionated from other soluble species and eventually transferred to the ocean sediments. In sediments, as well as providing an index of the current extent of removal from the water column, the transuranic elements have advanced the interpretation of bioturbation, the biologically driven physical mixing process in marine sediments.

1.3.2. Horizontal Distribution and Penetration

GEOSECS and TTO provided the most extensive opportunity to observe the fallout transient's distribution and penetration throughout Atlantic waters.

Unfortunately, only ^3H and ^{14}C were measured, as resources for fallout studies had become scarce. The distribution patterns of ^3H, especially, can be used to infer the approximate evolution of the distribution of ^{137}Cs and ^{90}Sr. This approximation follows from the fact that the ratio of ^3H to ^{137}Cs or ^{90}Sr increased over time - during the input to the ocean - because of the continuing input of ^3H from the troposphere due to hydrological recycling, including re-evaporation of terrestrial freshwater sources (Livingston, 1985). Currently in the mid-90's, the World Ocean Circulation Experiment (WOCE) is completing a survey of the Atlantic Ocean as part of the WOCE Hydrographic Program (WHP). Again this will provide ^3H and ^{14}C data, amongst other tracers, and can be used only to approximate the evolution of ^{137}Cs and ^{90}Sr.

Other than these large programs, information for the large scale evolution of fallout radionuclides in the Atlantic has to be pieced together from individual studies on a variety of short cruises by many laboratories. There is much more information in the two decades following the arrival of fallout in the ocean than in recent years, so the long term evolution is not well described.

1.3.3. The Vertical Distribution of the Radionuclides in the Atlantic

1.3.3.1. Surface Waters

In surface waters, the variation in the Atlantic in space and time is reasonably well characterised due to the larger number of surface water samples which have been collected and analysed. The situation for ^{137}Cs has been reported very recently as part of an IAEA Co-ordinated Research Program report (MARDOS) (Povinec, 1994). By inference, this can be used to derive ^{90}Sr distributions also – by dividing ^{137}Cs concentrations by 1.5. The key data sets showing the variation of the N/S distributions of surface ^{137}Cs concentrations over time come from the GEOSECS Atlantic expedition in 1972/1973 (National Science Foundation, 1987), a Polish cruise from Europe to Antarctica in 1977-1978 and a Swedish Antarctic expedition in 1988-1989 (Holm *et al.*, 1991). Other data sets were provided by several other MARDOS program participants.

Inspection of these data confirms the expected reduction in surface water concentrations over time due to both radiogenic decay and by physical mixing. What is interesting, however, is that the overall pattern of the N/S distribution, with concentration maxima in the mid-latitudes on both hemispheres, has been largely maintained – presumably because of the dominant large circulation gyres in both the North and South Atlantic Ocean. The total change in Atlantic surface ^{137}Cs concentrations, from the maximum values observed after the fallout input in the mid-60's to the values reported for 1990 in the MARDOS report, can be derived from comparison of the MARDOS data with data from the RIME report (National Academy of Sciences, 1971). For this comparison, RIME report of ^{90}Sr concentrations were converted to ^{137}Cs by multiplication by the factor of 1.5 mentioned above (Bowen *et al.*, 1974). In brief, concentrations have declined by a factor of 7. When radioactive decay is considered, the decline by mixing is about 3.5.

A similar approach was used by Holm *et al.* (1991), who contrasted the change in surface Pu concentrations from 1972 (Geosecs) to 1988 (Swedish expedition). They noted a 4-5 fold decline in surface Pu concentrations over this period. An even greater change can be presumed to have occurred from the concentrations associated with ^{137}Cs maxima in the high fallout years. Derived Pu concentrations from the RIME report data (converting from ^{90}Sr by multiplying by 0.018), the ratio of ^{239,240}Pu/^{90}Sr in fallout (Harley, 1975), suggest a decline in surface Pu from the mid-60's to 1988 of a factor of 31. As noted by Holm *et al.* (1991), the more rapid decline in surface Pu concentrations is in consequence of its removal on particles which sink out of the surface layer. Much of this removal is subsequently released to subsurface, intermediate and deep waters through demineralisation.

1.3.3.2. The Ocean Water Column

As mentioned above, there are no large scale measurements of fallout nuclides in the Atlantic after Geosecs (other than ^{3}H or ^{14}C). The evolution of the fallout transient has to be inferred from the scattered stations occupied subsequent to Geosecs or, in the case of the soluble species, from the evolution of the ^{3}H signal as mapped by the TTO, SAVE and WOCE programs. The situation is much worse in the South Atlantic – where the data for subsurface fallout concentrations other than Geosecs are minimal.

Ostlund (1985) noted several features of the fallout transient traced by ^{3}H, between 1972 (Geosecs) and 1981 (TTO). In intermediate waters and deep waters, the signal had significantly deepened and moved south due to ventilation processes – as illustrated by changes in the 0.2, 1 and 2 isolines of tritium concentration (expressed in TU81N – tritium units as at 1981). In addition, tritium could be detected as far south as 26°N in the southward flowing deep western boundary current fed from dense water overflows from the Greenland and Norwegian Seas (see Fig. 1.1.).

It was on the TTO expedition that the first evidence of Sellafield ^{137}Cs was observed in this dense overflow water as far south as Labrador in the boundary current (Livingston, 1988). Other Sellafield components, such as ^{90}Sr, ^{129}I and ^{99}Tc must also characterize this stream, but were not determined at all then or detected.

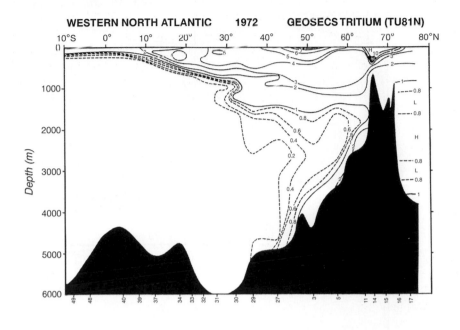

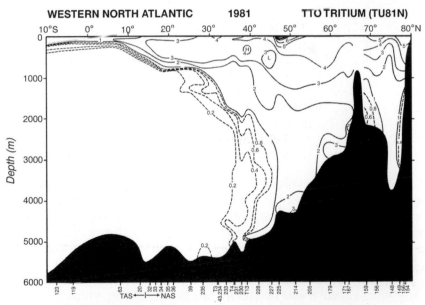

Fig. 1.1. Tritium sections across the Western North Atlantic.

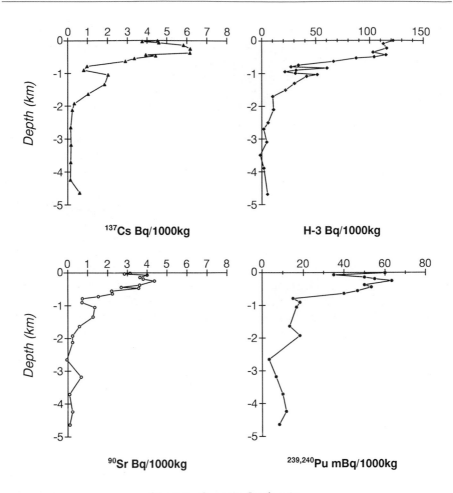

Fig. 1.2. Geosecs Station 29.

Some sense of the evolution of the penetration into deep waters of nuclear age tracers can be realized by comparison of artificial radionuclide profiles from the mid-latitude central North Atlantic 1972 (Geosecs) with those observed at sites in the deep western abyssal plains (Nares and Hatteras) in 1980-1984. For example, consider the situation at Geosecs station 29 at about 36°N. Profiles of ^{137}Cs, ^{90}Sr and ^{3}H are closely correlated (Fig. 1.2.).

Essentially none of these tracers can be seen much below 2000 m. There is, however, a small tracer maximum just below 1000 m which derives from Mediterranean deep water outflow. A small but detectable ^{239,240}Pu signal is found throughout the deep water below 2000 m, which has to have resulted from Pu removed from surface waters on sinking particles, being released to deep water by oxidation of the sinking organic particles. Profiles a decade later at the Hatteras and Nares sites (Cochran *et al.*, 1987) permit a glimpse of changes with time of these nuclide distributions. In the upper part of the water column there are tracer maxima which derive from upper water ventilation by so called 18° water formed to the north each winter. But the Pu profile relative to that of the soluble tracers can be shown to have changed little from the Geosecs pattern. For example, the Pu/^{137}Cs ratio (corrected for ^{137}Cs decay to 1981) at around 400 m (the depth of the 18° water) is essentially unchanged in 8 years – going from 0.010 in 1972 to 0.009 in 1981. But in the deep water at the Hatteras and Nares sites, measurable amounts of ^{137}Cs were observed in addition to the Pu signal. The clear implication is that the gradual ventilation of deep water along the western boundary is responsible for these changes. Cochran et al. (1987) also reported water column data for ^{241}Am which indicate that this nuclide has a deeper water column distribution than its Pu parent (^{241}Pu), and confirms that Am is being more rapidly transported towards ocean sediments on sinking particles.

The vertical transport of Pu by sinking particle is confirmed by the full depth profiles of ^{239,240}Pu and ^{137}Cs obtained by Nies (1989) in the northeast Atlantic (Fig. 1.3.). The trends are quite similar to those observed elsewhere in the North Atlantic, but the slight increase in concentration observed close to the bottom is attributed to bottom nepheloid layers with higher particle concentrations, resuspended from the enriched sediment.

1.3.3.3. The Sediments

There is no systematic large scale information of anthropogenic radionuclides in Atlantic sediments over time. In addition, the majority of available information tends to be found in coastal or shelf/slope sediments. Some of the latter has been discussed in relatively recent papers and references therein (Sholkovitz, 1983; Buesseler and Sholkovitz, 1987). Because of the higher productivity and suspended particulates found in the shelf and slope regions, significant removal of reactive species such as transuranics has taken place to fine grained sediment sinks there. But, relative to the huge open ocean areas, these represent rather minor sinks on an oceanic basis.

It can be stated unequivocally that much of Atlantic fallout transuranic inventory is still in the water column and is not moving rapidly towards the sea floor. The water column profiles observed in the Geosecs program and the later profiles (Cochran et al., 1987; Nies, 1989) all confirm this and, in fact, that more than 2/3rd of the Pu inventory is in the upper 2000 m. Reported fluxes of Pu in deep North Atlantic sediment traps in the period 1978-1981 were much smaller than the underlying sediment inventories (Bacon et al., 1985). 17 years of delivery at these rates accounted for as little as 25% of observed sediment inventories. Sediment cores at the Nares and Hatteras abyssal plain sites contained 3-4% of the Pu and 7-20% of the ^{241}Am of the total in the water column and sediments at these locations (Cochran et al., 1987). These data confirm that ^{241}Am is being removed faster

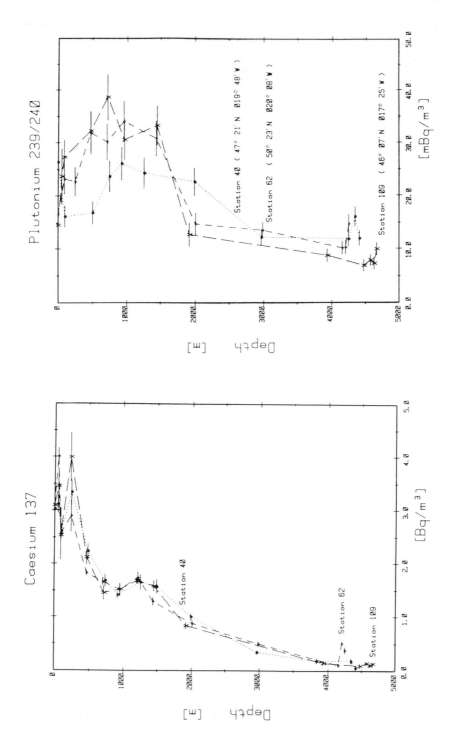

Fig. 1.3. Profiles of Pu, Cs in the NE Atlantic (from Nies, 1989).

than Pu and suggest that most of the observed Pu, at least, in these deep sediments was delivered to the seafloor soon after its fallout delivery to the surface ocean.

1.3.4. Natural and Anthropogenic Radionuclides

It is worth comparing and contrasting the observed Atlantic levels of bomb fallout radionuclides with those which are found for the naturally occurring radionuclides which can be viewed as analogues. For ^{137}Cs, the natural analogue is ^{40}K, an alkali metal, which behaves as a true soluble element and varies in proportion to salinity. At average ocean salinity, ^{40}K has a concentration of about 11 Bq l^{-1} (National Academy of Sciences, 1971). In contrast, in the same report, the maximum levels of North Atlantic ^{137}Cs (converted from ^{90}Sr data as described above), were no more than 0.021 Bq l^{-1}. Uranium is a naturally occurring alpha emitting element which is probably much more soluble than Pu, but is worth comparing since at present most fallout Pu is still in the water column. Typical ^{238}U levels are about 42 mBq l^{-1} (National Academy of Sciences, 1971). In contrast, peak fallout surface Pu values, derived from ^{90}Sr as described earlier, were not likely higher than 0.25 mBq l^{-1} and contemporary subsurface maximum values are less than 0.05 mBq l^{-1} (Harley, 1975).

In deep Atlantic sediments, Pu and ^{241}Am levels can most appropriately be compared with U and Th isotopes – as chemical and physical analogues. Marine sediment levels of ^{238}U (56 mBq g^{-1}) and ^{232}Th (280 mBq g^{-1}) have been reported (National Academy of Sciences, 1971). Sediments in the deep NW Atlantic have maximum superficial ^{239,240}Pu concentrations of 0.68 mBq g^{-1} and ^{241}Am levels less than half this number (Sayles and Livingston, 1988).

1.4. Point Sources and Regional Inputs in the North Atlantic Area

The total amount of radioactivity released from the nuclear industry into the marine environment is small compared to the burden of natural radioactivity, and the concentrations measured in seawater are orders of magnitude lower than those for natural radionuclides. Despite this, the man-made radionuclides released as point sources are extremely valuable tracers for the transport and dispersion of coastal pollution from Europe to the Arctic. Reasons for this are that the sources are few and relatively well defined. The specific man-made radionuclides, in particular ^{99}Tc, ^{137}Cs, ^{134}Cs, ^{90}Sr, ^{125}Sb, ^{129}I and ^{239,240}Pu can be analysed accurately at extremely low concentrations, *i.e.*, orders of magnitude lower than several natural elements in the sea.

A rather wide survey of the sources of radionuclides into the North Atlantic ocean was carried on within the framework of the project MARINA set-up in the second half of the '80s by the Direction General XI of the Commission of the European Communities (CEC, 1990). Discharge data from a total of 72 sites which release directly or indirectly into the Northern European waters have been collected and collated for MARINA. The period covered extends from the start of discharges up to the end of 1984 for all sites and up to the end of 1986 for the reprocessing plants. The sites comprise 57 nuclear power stations, 2 uranium enrichment plants and 8 research establishments. The nuclear stations represent an installed capacity around 220 GW(e) years, the power generation in 1984 being 35 GW(e). The results summarised in Tables 1.I. and 1.II. are taken from Mc Coll *et al.* (1989).

Table 1.I. Total liquid discharges of Alpha and Beta emitters.

Alpha emitters	%	Beta emitters	%
^{239}Pu	50.8	^{137}Cs	27.5
^{241}Am	39.1	^{106}Ru	21.3
^{238}Pu	4.8	^{241}Pu	13.9
Th	2.5	^{144}Ce	5.2
Cm	1.0	^{90}Sr	4.7
U	0.9	^{134}Cs	3.9
^{237}Np	0.9	Remainder	4.4

Table 1.II. Site contribution to the total discharges.

Type of facility	Alpha emitters (%)	Beta emitters (%)	^{3}H Tritium (%)	Collective dose to year 2500 (man Sv)
Reprocessing	97.4	98.6	69.7	5150
Power stations	0.2	0.5	19.6	87
Research	0.01	0.02	10.8	3.4
Other	2.4	0.9	0	14
Sites				
Sellafield	95.2	86.9	52.9	4600
La Hague	0.52	5.3	16.4	430
Dounreay	1.8	6.7	0.33	120
TOTAL	PBq	PBq	PBq	man Sv
(to end of 1984)	1.4	150	46	
(to year 2500)				5254

1.4.1. Characterization of the Sources of Radionuclides

As said before, the ratio between nuclides as well as their isotopic ratios were used to characterize the various sources. For instance, the global fall-out from atmospheric nuclear test explosions during the 1950s and 1960s had a characteristic ^{137}Cs /^{90}Sr ratio of ~1.5 (Livingston, 1988). Later, European nuclear fuel reprocessing plants, especially Sellafield in the United Kingdom, became a larger contributor to anthropogenic radioactivity in the North East Atlantic (Kershaw and Baxter, 1995). Compared to global fallout, the ^{137}Cs /^{90}Sr ratio was around 4 times higher, and the ^{99}Tc/^{137}Cs ratio 10-20 times higher. Throughout the 1980s, the Sellafield contribution therefore gradually increased the ^{137}Cs /^{90}Sr ratio in the North East Atlantic, including the Arctic Ocean and the East Greenland Current (Aarkrog *et al.*, 1987; Livingston, 1988). In the same period, the ^{99}Tc/^{137}Cs ratio increased by an order of magnitude in the East Greenland Current Polar Water (Dahlgaard, 1986; Charles *et al.*, 1989).

Table 1.III. Characteristics for some of the discussed man-made radionuclides in the Arctic. Percentages quoted are for East Greenland Current Polar Water around 1990 (Dahlgaard, 1995a).

Isotope	$T_{1/2}$ (yr)	Radiation	Sources (ranked by importance)
^{99}Tc	0.21×10^6	β	~85 % European coastal discharges ~15 % weapons tests
^{137}Cs	30	γ, β	Atmospheric weapons tests ~35% European coastal discharges ~15% Chernobyl Russian sources
^{134}Cs	2.1	γ, β	Chernobyl
^{90}Sr	28	β	Atmospheric weapons tests Russian sources ~15% European coastal discharges
^{129}I	16×10^6	γ, β*	European coastal discharges Weapons tests Russian? Natural
$^{239,240}Pu$	24×10^3 6×10^3	α	Weapons tests European coastal discharges Russian?

* Radiation from environmental levels of ^{129}I too low to measure. Measured by AMS (Raisbeck *et al.*, 1995).

The Chernobyl Nuclear Power plant accident in April/May 1986 provided significant injections of ^{137}Cs and ^{134}Cs, especially in the Baltic Sea, but also at various locations throughout the North East Atlantic. The radioactive contamination was detectable all over the European countries (CEC, 1990). Although most of the activity was deposited on land, northern European waters received significant amounts of radio caesium. The total amounts of ^{137}Cs and ^{134}Cs deposited on these waters were around 10 PBq and 5 PBq, respectively (Aarkrog *et al.*, 1988). The contributions directly to the Barents Sea and the Arctic ocean are largely unknown, although they are thought to be low. Like Sellafield discharges, Chernobyl activity was transported to the Arctic by ocean circulation. Chernobyl did not contribute to the ^{99}Tc contamination in the Atlantic (Aarkrog *et al.*, 1988). As an example, Table 1.III. indicates the relative importance of different sources for a series of man-made radionuclides in the East Greenland Polar Water draining the Arctic Ocean.

1.4.2. Currents, Dispersion, Transit Times

By contrast with fallout, the land based sources discharge radionuclides in well defined locations, which are usually shallow and dynamically active. The radionuclides released in such areas are transported by advection and dispersed by eddy diffusion. Simultaneously, they are submitted to a series of complex processes as concentration by living organisms, adsorption on settling particulate material, but also remobilization from the sediment during storms and rough sea conditions. A transit time from a source to a specified location is thus not a well-defined unique number: a measured concentration will consist of variable fractions of past discharges, and the duration of the transport may vary with time as it is influenced by meteorological conditions. Nevertheless, combining circulation models and observational data related to specific events provided realistic first order estimates for the transit times from Sellafield and La Hague to the Arctic region.

1.4.3. Transfer Factors

Having estimated a representative transport time, T years, a Transfer Factor (TF) is calculated as the quotient between observed concentrations in the environment and an average discharge rate T years earlier. The unit for the transfer factor, Bq m^{-3} / PBq yr^{-1}, is equal to 10^{-15} yr m^{-3}. In other words, a TF value of 1 indicates that one Bq m^{-3} are present per annual unit of discharge of one PBq. Expressed in weight units (TF = ng m^{-3} / ton yr^{-1}) a TF value of 1 indicates that for each ton discharged to the coastal waters per year, 1 ng m^{-3} is observed in the environment T years later. A set of transfer factors reviewed in Dahlgaard (1995a) is provided in Table 1.IV.

Table 1.IV. Transfer factors, TF = Bq m^{-3} / PBq yr^{-1} = ng m^{-3} / ton yr^{-1}, from Sellafield to various surface waters.

Location	Transport time (years)	TF (ng m^{-3} / ton yr^{-1})
Kattegat	4	15
N-W. Norwegian C.	3-4	10-50
S-SE Barents Sea	5-6	5-10
Kara Sea	5-6	5-10
W. Spitzbergen	~5	~5
Arctic Ocean	~6-10	~1-10
East Greenland C.	7-10	1-2
North Atlantic Current Faroe islands	~14-17	>> 0.3

Given the approximation included in the various parameters, the transfer factors should not be considered as exact unique numbers, but rather as estimates of the transfer. The data given for the Arctic Ocean and for the North Atlantic Current should be considered particularly preliminary as they are based on few observations, in addition to the uncertainty concerning « background » concentrations from other sources. However, the values provide the actual best estimate of the order of magnitude of the transfer. Combining the Transfer Factor for the North Atlantic Current and the stipulated transit time suggest a re-circulation of water and contaminants back to the North Atlantic from the Arctic and Nordic Seas. According to Dickson *et al.* (1988), the further transport from the East Greenland Current is based on the « Great Salinity Anomaly », where a lowering of the salinity could be traced from the East Greenland Current through the Labrador Current and the North Atlantic Current back to the Nordic Seas and the Arctic.

The large Sellafield discharges until the mid 1980's illustrated the use of the transfer factor for the evaluation of the impact of the actual sources. It has thus been seen that only a negligible fraction of the present ^{137}Cs concentration in the Barents and Kara Seas originates from a direct transport of the present discharges. A much larger part comes from resuspension of previously sedimented ^{137}Cs after earlier discharges and from the outflow of Chernobyl-derived radio-caesium from the Baltic Sea (Dahlgaard, 1995c). The least conservative of the applied radioactive tracers is caesium, with a Kd of 3×10^3 for coastal sediments (IAEA, 1985). For ^{99}Tc and ^{90}Sr, Kd values are at least an order of magnitude lower. However, it has been demonstrated that a fraction of the non-conservative element plutonium discharged from Sellafield has been transported to the Arctic (Kershaw and Baxter, 1995). Plutonium is accorded a Kd value of 10^5 in coastal sediments (Nielsen and Strand, 1995), and most of the discharged material is presumably present in the sediments of the Irish Sea. The presence of Sellafield-derived plutonium in the Arctic thus demonstrates that even non-conservative pollutants are undergoing long-distance transport from the European coastal waters.

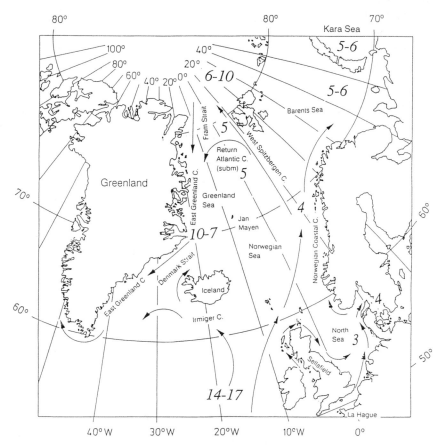

Fig. 1.4. Major currents and transit time (Dahlgaard, 1994).

1.5. Radioactive Waste in the Arctic and Sub-Arctic Areas

The polar areas and ecosystems are known to be vulnerable to any form of anthropogenic pollution, which can be transported there by atmospheric processes, ocean currents and rivers. But the Arctic areas have also been used to dispose radioactive waste, in liquid form, packaged containers or even large pieces of decommissioned ships as nuclear reactors, with and without spent fuel.

1.5.1. Disposal of Radioactive Waste in the Barents and Kara Seas

From the early 1960s until 1991, the former Soviet Union has dumped relevant amounts of radioactive waste into the Barents and Kara Seas. In Table 1.V. the main characteristics of these wastes, for a total amount of 5,300 TBq, are reproduced from (Yablokov *et al.*, 1993; Sjoeblom and Linsley, 1995).

The collective doses to the world population have been calculated from ingestion of radionuclides in contaminated seafood, by a dispersion model. By assuming that radionuclides in solid waste are released over a period of 100 years from the time of dumping and all liquid wastes are available for dispersion at the time of discharge, the collective dose (calculated to 1000 years) is about 100 man Sv.

Table 1.V. Radioactive waste dumped into the Kara Sea.

Waste Category	Waste material	Number of objects	Total activity 1993/1994 (TBq)
High level (with spent fuel)	Reactors or containers	7	4,700
Intermediate and low level	Containers Large objects Vessels	6,508 154 15	580
Intermediate level	Reactors without spent fuel	10	20

A comparison with the results from the MARINA Project shows that the collective dose per unit discharge of ^{137}Cs by FSU into the Barents and the Kara Seas is about one order of magnitude lower (4 man Sv PBq^{-1}) than that of discharges of ^{137}Cs into the Irish Sea (50 man Sv PBq^{-1}). This difference is mainly due to the low production of seafood for human consumption in the polar waters compared with that in the European coastal waters (Nielsen *et al.*, 1995).

1.5.2. Inputs from the Siberian Rivers

In addition to the disposal of liquid and packaged radioactive waste, the Arctic seas collects the inputs of large rivers which drain extended land areas (3×10^6 km^2 for the Ob river for instance) and which are known to be contaminated by radioactive discharges upstream. Recent measurements showed for instance that the Techa river contains enhanced levels of ^{90}Sr,

^{137}Cs, ^{239,240}Pu, ^{241}Am and ^{60}Co. The levels upstream are several orders of magnitude higher than those expected from global fallout (Trapeznikov *et al.*, 1993) but a noticeable fraction of the activity is deposited in the sediment, trapped in reservoirs and weak current areas. The light fraction of that sediment may be released as bursts events during the floods, and may flocculates or precipitate at the interface between brackish and sea water. The high values of the ^{90}Sr/^{137}Cs ratio in the north east Kara Sea strongly correlate to the salinity, which confirms the relevance of the input of ^{90}Sr from the rivers. But in view of the complexity of the river's network and of the scattered measurements, it becomes rather critical to assess the amplitude of the sources and the inventory of the nuclides still contained in the sediment of the overall river system. Most on the data available to date are limited to ^{137}Cs and to ^{90}Sr contents.

1.6. Dumping of Packaged Radioactive Waste in the Atlantic

Dumping of packaged low and medium level radioactive waste into the ocean has occurred since the end of World War II when the nuclear energy industry began. Between 1949 and 1982, radioactive waste disposal operations in the Northeast Atlantic were carried out at several locations by Belgium, France, the Federal Republic of Germany, Italy, the Netherlands, Sweden, Switzerland and the United Kingdom, within the co-operative framework of the Nuclear Energy Agency since 1967. Uniform operational procedures and safety assessments were established internationally within that NEA framework.

The total amount of radionuclides dumped in the Northeast Atlantic by European Countries are reported in Table 1.VI. (NEA, 1985). The collective dose truncated at the year 2500 to the European Union population from the sea dumping of solid radioactive waste is about 50 man Sv and, therefore, negligible in comparison with any of the other sources (fallout or natural nuclides).

Table 1.VI. Total amount of radionuclides dumped into north-east Atlantic (1949-1982).

Category	Amount (TBq)
Alpha emitters	666
Beta-gamma emitters	26,150
Tritium*	15,500

* Separate figures are available for disposals from 1976 onwards. In earlier years tritium disposals were included in the beta-gamma figures.

1.6.1.   Composition of the Waste and Packaging

Data on the radionuclide composition of the waste were provided by the dumping countries, and have been used to distinguish the two broad categories of alpha and beta-gamma emitters. In both categories, twelve nuclides were displayed, based on their relative abundance in the waste. Pu isotopes and ^{241}Am account for over 96% of the alpha activity dumped, whereas ^{3}H and ^{241}Pu account for over 87% of the beta-gamma activity. The rest of the long-lived beta-gamma activities comprises essentially the fission product ^{90}Sr and ^{137}Cs and the activation product ^{60}Co (NEA, 1985).

While the dumped waste contains a variety of radio-isotopes, basic considerations and experiments on the matrix suggested that only very low level of activity could be expected in the area of dumping. First, the waste form and their containment drastically limit the leaching in the marine environment. Second, some of the radionuclides are present in the waste in such low quantities that they are unlikely to be detectable in the water or in the sediment with standard methods of measurements. Third, the background from weapons test fallout is not negligible.

1.6.2 .   Monitoring within the Framework of the CRESP Programme

The Co-ordinated Research and Environmental Surveillance Programme (CRESP) was established in 1980 by the NEA to strengthen the scientific and technical basis of the assessment of the Atlantic dumpsite. In addition to the evaluation of the radionuclide transfer mechanisms, CRESP was requested to increase the site-specific data base related to the oceanographic and biological characteristics of the dumping area, through radio-analyses of sediment, biota and water.

From considerations about the waste form, the following criteria were adopted to identify radionuclides worth measuring in samples collected at the dumpsite or in its surroundings for comparison:
• Long half-life (> 5 y).
• High fission or activation yields.
• Measuring using radio analytical techniques.
• Significantly present in the dumped waste.

Using these criteria, the most relevant candidate radionuclides were judged to be ^{137}Cs, ^{90}Sr, ^{239,240}Pu, ^{238}Pu, ^{240}Am and ^{3}H. As these nuclides are also present in global fallout, the background level was established both in the vicinity of the dumpsite and in region outside having similar bio-geo-chemical characteristics.

Levels of Radioactivity at the Dumpsite

In spite of the monitoring effort over a period of about 15 years, measurements on samples taken at the dumpsite did not show a dramatic increase for any of the representative radionuclides. However, some releases from the containers can be inferred from the analysis of water and from the concentration in typical living organisms (sea cucumbers). In 1993, ^{90}Sr and ^{137}Cs concentrations in the range of 38-128 mBq m^{-3} were observed in the near bottom water at the dumpsite, while the concentrations at a remote control site were below detection limits. About all the tritium was dumped in vented drums and it was considered the most likely radionuclide to be released in quantity. Indeed, from the field data, it was estimated that 10-50% of the dumped tritium was present in the bottom 1000 m of the water column within about 650 km of the dumpsite. The vertical dispersion is attributed to the effect of topography which controls the deep-sea flow. While the inventories (Bq m^{-2}) and the concentrations of ^{239,240}Pu in the sediment within the dumpsite were similar to those of the control site (thus compatible with a fallout origin), the increase of the ratio ^{238}Pu/^{239,240}Pu in the upper few mm of sediment would suggest a limited contamination by reprocessing waste but could also be a consequence of the SNAP burn-up.

Compared to the total amount of material dumped, the actual levels of activity are very low. This is not surprising as a photographic survey by Sibuet and Coic (1989) showed that most of the dumped containers are in good condition. Some damaged drums may have released radionuclides by dissolution of the matrix, but this is a very slow process. Furthermore, due to dilution and mixing, the level of activity is expected to decrease rapidly with distance away from the drums down to a level which is not even distinguishable from background levels. In terms of radiological impact, the dumping operations performed in the deep north-east Atlantic can thus be considered as negligible compared to the fallout or to the releases from land base sources in the shallow water.

1.7. Accidents and Radioactive Contamination

From the official statistics, accidents which did lead to the radioactive contamination of the marine environment are happily not frequent. Their impact may significantly differ according to the type of accident, the vehicle and the radioactive material involved. The consequences of the loss of a nuclear submarine in the deep-sea can hardly be compared with the crash of an aircraft carrying nuclear weapons or the burn-up of a satellite. We review briefly below some of the major accidents reported during the last three decades. We should emphasize that because of its location, the Thule accident offered the most suitable facilities to monitor the consequence of an accident scenario.

1.7.1. The Thule Accident

In January 1968 a crash on sea-ice, involving four unarmed nuclear weapons, occurred 11 km west of the Thule Air Base in Greenland. Most of the plutonium released to the environment was recovered from the ice. However, a radio-ecological study carried out in the summer of the same year detected ^{239}Pu in the marine environment of Thule (Aarkrog, 1972). In 1979 the estimated inventories of plutonium and americium in the marine sediments from the Thule accident were: 1 TBq of $^{239+240}$Pu, 17 GBq of ^{238}Pu, 2 TBq of ^{241}Pu and 0.1 TBq of ^{241}Am. From 1974 to 1979 the horizontal transport of the accident of plutonium was 0.4 km y^{-1} and the median depth in sediment increased by approximately 6 mm during these five years. No indication of accident plutonium was detected in surface sea water or sea plants, therefore bio-accumulation of plutonium from lower to higher trophic levels was expected to be irrelevant.

Seawater collected close to the sea bottom at the point of impact contained plutonium concentrations four times higher than surface seawater; however, all the surplus activity was found in particulates (Aarkrog *et al.*, 1984). Therefore, the contribution of the Thule accident to an increase of global plutonium in the Atlantic Ocean outside few ten of kilometres from the impact point, is negligible.

1.7.2. Other Accidents

In 1963 a US nuclear submarine, the Thresher, sank in the Atlantic Ocean 100 miles North-east of Cape Cod. Surveys carried out in 1983 and 1986 detected a minor contamination by ^{60}Co and ^{63}Ni in sediments only (Sheldon and Michne, 1993; IAEA, 1991).

As mentioned in the introduction, in 1964 an isotope powered unit (SNAP-9A) in a satellite which underwent burn-up during re-entry, dispersed into the atmosphere about 0.6 PBq of ^{238}Pu. In the Northern hemisphere nearly 0.1 PBq were deposited, corresponding to about one half of the ^{238}Pu due to the fallout produced by nuclear weapons tests (Hardy *et al.*, 1972).

In 1969 a US nuclear submarine, the Scorpion, sank in the Atlantic Ocean 400 miles SW of Azores. Surveys carried out in 1978 and 1979 detected a minor contamination by ^{60}Co and ^{63}Ni in sediments only (Sheldon and Michne, 1993; IAEA, 1991).

In 1970 and 1986 also two USSR nuclear submarines sank in the Atlantic Ocean (IAEA, 1991; Yablokov *et al.*, 1993).

In 1989 a fire broke out in the stern section of the USSR nuclear submarine « Komsomolets »; after several hours' struggle, it sank in the Norwegian Sea (Baxter *et al.*, 1995). While no significant radiological impact has been reported to date, remedial solutions or recovery are actually being examined at the international level.

The inputs from such accidents are summarized in Table 1.VII. Other accidents, which have not been officially confirmed, were not taken into account.

Table 1.VII. Radioactive sources in the Atlantic Ocean from various accidents.

Date	Object	Location	Depth	Source	Estimated radio-activity in (TBq)
April 1963	Thresher	Atlantic Ocean	2590	reactor	1,147
April 1964	SNAP-9A	(W Indian Ocean) (?)	=	^{238}Pu	110
May 1968	Scorpion	Atlantic Ocean	> 3000	1 reactor + weapons	1,295
Aug. 1970	USSR submarine	Bay of Biscay	4000	2 reactors + weapons	9,000
June 1986	USSR submarine	Bermuda Is.	5500	2 reactors + weapons	9,000
July 1989	Komsomolets	Norwegian Sea	1685	1 reactor + weapons	3,600

1.8. Conclusions

The estimated inventories in the North Atlantic, updated for the radioactive decay to 1995, are reported in Table 1.VIII. (Aarkrog, 1989). The highest concentrations from nuclear reprocessing plants are observed in the marginal seas of North Western Europe. The Baltic Sea contained the highest radio-caesium concentrations after the Chernobyl accident.

The collective doses to the population of the European Union *via* marine pathways from the different sources concerning the Northern European waters are summarized in Table 1.IX. (CEC, 1990). It is interesting to note

Table 1.VIII. Estimated inventories in the North Atlantic in 1995.

Source	^{137}Cs (PBq)	^{90}Sr (PBq)	$^{239+240}$Pu (PBq)
Civil nuclear site discharges	26	4	
Weapons test fallout	130	90	3
Chernobyl accident	17	–	–

that the contribution from natural radionuclides in two years is nearly equivalent to the whole contribution from anthropogenic sources up to the year 2500.

The global amount from confirmed accidents and the amount of radioactive wastes dumped into the North East Atlantic are rather similar. Therefore it can be estimated that also the corresponding doses delivered to humans should be similar, while the natural radionuclides remain the major contributors to the collective dose.

Table 1.IX. Collective exposure of the population of the European Union up to the year 2500 from radionuclides in the Northern European waters.

Source	Collective dose (man Sv)	
Civil nuclear site discharges	5,300	The collective doses are calculated for discharges occurring from the start of operations up until the end of 1984.
Weapons test fallout	1,600	This excludes the contribution from ^{14}C which is difficult to quantify due to lack of data but could be up to several hundreds man Sv.
Chernobyl fallout	1,000	
Sea dumping of of solid radio- active waste	50	
Sea dumping into the Arctic Seas	100	This value is referred to the world population (up to the year 3000).
Other accidents	~ 50	
Natural radionuclides	1,700,000	The collective doses rate from natural radionuclides in seawater is 3400 man Sv per year and the collective dose is calculated over 500 years.

References

Aarkrog A. (1972) A re-examination of plutonium at Thule, Greenland, in 1970. In: *CEC - Radioecology applied to the protection of man and its environment.*, Proc. Seminar Roma 7-10 September 1971, (Report EUR 4800) pp. 1213-1219. Luxembourg.

Aarkrog A. (1989) Chernobyl related monitoring and comparison with fallout data. In: *CEC - The radiological exposure of the population of the European Community from radioactivity in North European Marine Waters - Project MARINA*, Bruges 14-16 June 1989 (Report XI/4669/89-EN) pp. 229-249. Luxembourg.

Aarkrog A., Boelskifte S., Dahlgaard H., Duniec S., Hallstadius L., Holm E. and Smith J.N. (1987) Technecium-99 and caesium-134 as long distance tracers in Arctic waters. *Estuar. Cstl. Shelf Sci.* **24**, 637-647.

Aarkrog A., Carlsson L., Chen Q.J., Dahlgaard H., Holm E., Huynh-Ngoc L., Jensen K.H., Nielsen S.P. and Nies H. (1988) Origin of technetium-99 and its use as a marine tracer. *Nature* **335**, 338-340.

Aarkrog A., Dahlgaard H., Hallstadius L., Hansen H. and Holm E. (1983) Radio caesium from Sellafield effluents in Greenland waters. *Nature* **304**, 49-51.

Aarkrog A., Dahlgaard H., Hallstadius L., Holm E., Mattsson S. and Rioseco J. (1986) Time Trend of ^{99}Tc in Seaweed from Greenland Waters, Technetium in the Environment Cadarache, France, October 1984 (G. Desmet and M. Myttenaere, Eds.), pp. 69-78. Elsevier Applied Science Publishers, London.

Aarkrog A., Dahlgaard H., Nilsson K. and Holm E. (1984) Further studies of plutonium and americium at Thule, Greenland. *Health Physics* **46**, 29-44.

Bacon M.P., Huh C.A., Fleer A.P. and Deuser W.G. (1985) Seasonality in the flux of natural radionuclides and plutonium in the deep Sargasso Sea. *Deep Sea Res.* **32**, 273-286.

Baxter M.S., Ballestra S., Gastaud J., Hamilton T.F., Harms I., Huynh-Ngoc L., Liong Wee Kwong L., Osvath I., Parsi P., Petterson H., Povinec P.P. and Sanchez A. (1995) Marine radioactivity studies in the vicinity of sites with potential radionuclides releases. pp. 125-141. Environmental Impact of Radioactive Releases, IAEA, Vienna 1995.

Bowen V.T., Noshkin V.E., Volchok H.L., Livingston H.D. and Wong K.M (1974) ^{137}Cs to ^{90}Sr ratios in the Atlantic Ocean 1966 through 1972. *Limnol. Oceanogr.* **19**, 670-681.

Buesseler K.O. and Sholkovitz E.R. (1987) The geochemistry of fallout plutonium in the North Atlantic: ^{240}Pu/^{239}Pu ratios and their significance. *Geochim. Cosmochim. Acta* **51**, 2623-2637.

Camplin W.C. and Aarkrog A. (1990) Radioactivity in North European Waters, The radiological exposure of the population of the European Community from radioactivity in North European Marine Waters.

Project MARINA. Bruges 14-16 June 1989, Radiation Protection-47. (Report EUR 12483) pp. 197-338. Luxembourg.

CEC (1990) The radiological exposure of the population of the European Community from radioactivity in North European Marine Waters. Project MARINA. Bruges 14-16 June 1989, Radiation Protection-47. (Report EUR 12483) pp. 1-566. Luxembourg.

Charles D., Jones M. and Cooper J.R. (1989) The Radiological Impact on the ECMember States of Routine Discharges to North European Waters. In: *The radiological exposure of the population of the European Community from radioactivity in North European Marine Waters Project MARINA*. Bruges 14-16 June 1989, Radiation Protection-47. (Report EUR 12483) pp. 415-560. Luxembourg.

Cochran J.K., Livingston H.D., Hirschberg D.J. and Surprenant L.D. (1987) Natural and anthropogenic radionuclide distributions in the north west Atlantic Ocean. *Earth Planet. Sci. Lett.* **84**, 135-152.

Dahlgaard H. (1994) Source of ^{137}Cs, ^{90}Sr and ^{99}Tc in the East Greenland current. *J. Environ. Radioact.* **25**, 37-55.

Dahlgaard H. (1995a) Transfer of European coastal pollution to the Arctic: Radioactive tracers. *Mar. Pollut. Bull.* **31,** 3-7.

Dahlgaard H. (1995b) On the background level of ^{99}Tc, ^{90}Sr and ^{137}Cs in the North Atlantic. *J. Marine Systems* **6**, 571-578.

Dahlgaard H. (1995c) On ^{99}Tc, ^{137}Cs and ^{90}Sr in the Kara Sea. Environmental Radioactivity in the Arctic. Norwegian Radiation Protection Authority, Oesteraas, 1995 (P. Strand and A. Cooke, Eds.) pp. 91-94.

Dahlgaard H., Aarkrog A., Hallstadius L., Holm E. and Rioseco J. (1986) Radio caesium transport from the Irish Sea *via* the North Sea and the Norwegian coastal current to East Greenland. *Rapp. P. v. Reun. Cons. int. Explor. Mer* **186**, 70-79.

Dickson R.R., Meincke J., Malmberg S.A. and Lee A.J. (1988) The «great salinity anomaly» in the North Atlantic. *Prog. Oceanog.* **20**, 103-151.

Guéguéniat P., Salomon P.B., Masson M. and Cabioch L. (1995) FLUX-MANCHE radiotracers measurements: a contribution to the dynamics of the English Channel and North Sea. *J. Marine systems* **6**, 483-494.

Hardy E.P., Krey P.W. and Volchok H.L. (1972) Global inventory and distribution of Pu-238 from SNAP-9A. Report HASL-250. U.S. Atomic Energy Commission, New York.

Harley J.H. (1975) Transuranium elements on land. Health and Safety Laboratory, Q. Rep. HASL-291 pp. 1-104.

Holm E., Roos P., Persson R.B.R., Bojanowsky R., Aarkrog A., Nielsen S.P. and Livingston H. D. (1991) Radio-caesium and plutonium in Atlantic surface waters from 73°N to 72°S. In: *Radionuclides in the study of marine processes*. Proceedings of an International Symposium, pp. 3-11, Norwich, UK 1991.

IAEA (1985) Sediment Kds and Concentration Factors for Radionuclides in the Marine Environment. STI/DOC/10/247, International Atomic Energy Agency, Vienna.

IAEA (1991) Inventory of radioactive material entering the marine environment: accidents and losses at sea involving radioactive materials. IAEA, Vienna (draft working document).

Kautsky H. (1980) Distribution of radioactive fallout products in the water of the North Atlantic and the Barents Sea during the year 1972. Isotope Marine Chemistry, Uchdo Rokakuho, Tokyo (E.D. Goldberg *et al.*, Eds.) pp. 9-23.

Kautsky H. (1987) Investigations on the distribution of ^{137}Cs, ^{134}Cs and ^{90}Sr and the water mass transport times in the northern North Atlantic and the North sea. *Dt. Hydrogr. Zeit.* **40**, 49-69.

Kershaw P. and Baxter A. (1995) The transfer of reprocessing wastes from north-west Europe to the Arctic. *Deep Sea Res. II - Topical Studies in Oceanography* **42**, 1413-1448.

P. Kershaw and D. Woodhead, Eds. (1991) Radionuclides in the Study of Marine Processes. Proceedings of an International Symposium, Norwich (Elsevier Applied Science, 1991, ISBN 1-85166-707-5).

Livingston H.D. (1988) The use of Cs and Sr isotopes as tracers in the Arctic Mediterranean Sea. *Philos. Trans. R. Soc. Lond. A* **325**, 161-176.

Livingston H.D. (1985) Anthropogenic radiotracer evolution in the Central Greenland Sea. Rit Fiskideildar 9, 43-54. Proceedings of a Nordic Symposium on Chemical Tracers for Studying Water Masses and Physical Processes in the Sea, Reykjavik, Iceland.

McColl N.P., Cooper J.R. and Van Weers A.W. (1989) Civil Nuclear Discharges into North European Waters. The radiological exposure of the population of the European Community from radioactivity in North European Marine Waters. Project MARINA. Bruges 14-16 June 1989, Radiation Protection-47. (Report EUR 12483) pp. 39-195, Luxembourg.

National Academy of Sciences (1971) Radioactivity in the Marine Environment (RIME). Report. National Academy of Sciences, Washington DC. USA.

National Science Foundation (1987) GEOSECS Atlantic, Pacific and Indian Ocean Expeditions. Shorebased Data and Graphics, NSF (1987), Washington DC, USA.

NEA (1982) Programme de Recherches et de Surveillance du Milieu Marin lié à l'immersion de déchets radioactifs en Mer. OECD, Paris.

NEA (1985) Review of the continued suitability of the dumping site for the radioactive waste in North-East Atlantic. OECD-NEA, Paris.

Nielsen S.P. and Strand P. (1995) Potential doses to man from the dumping of radioactive waste in the Arctic Seas. Environmental Impact of Radioactive Releases, IAEA, Vienna pp. 732-734.

Nies H. (1989) Plutonium and ^{137}Cs in the water column of the Northeast Atlantic. In: *Interim Oceanographic description of the North-East Atlantic site for the disposal of low-level radioactive waste.*, pp. 77-81 (OCDE, Paris, 1989).

Ostlund H.G. (1985) Tritium and Radiocarbon in the North Atlantic Ocean an overview. Rit Fiskideildar 9, Nordic Symposium on Chemical Tracers for Studying Water Masses and Physical Processes in the Sea, pp. 13-19, Reykjavik, Iceland.

Povinec P.P. (1994) Sources of radioactivity in the marine environment and their relative contributions to overall dose assessment from marine radioactivity (MARDOS). International Atomic Energy Agency, Marine Radioactivity Laboratory Report IAEA-MEL-R2/94 Monaco.

Raisbeck G.M., Yiou F., Zhou Z.Q. and Kilius L.R. (1995) [129]I from nuclear fuel reprocessing facilities at Sellafield (UK) and La Hague (France); Potential as oceanographic tracer. *J. Marine Systems* **6**, 561-570.

Roos P. and Holm E. (1993) Distribution of radiocesium and plutonium in Arctic water and sediments. Results from the Swedish Oden Expedition, 1991. International Conference on Environmental Radioactivity in the Arctic and Antarctic, Kirkenes, Norway, 23-27 August 1993 (P. Strand and E. Holm, Eds.) pp. 157-160. Norwegian. Radiation Protection Authority, Oesteraas, Norway.

Sayles F.L. and Livingston H.D. (1988) The distribution of Pu-239,240, Cs-137 and Fe-55 in continental margin sediments: Relation to sedimentary redox environment. Oceanic Processes in Marine Pollution, 2(15) (I. Duedall, Ed.) pp. 175-195. Plymouth, UK.

Sheldon R.B. and Michne J.D. (1993) Deep sea radiological environmental monitoring conducted at the site of the nuclear-powered submarine Scorpion sinking. *Knolls Atomic Power Laboratory, Schenectady, NY, Report KAPL-4749.*

Sholkovitz, E.R. (1983) The geochemistry of plutonium in fresh and marine water environments. *Earth Sci. Rev.* **19**, 95-161.

Sibuet M. and Coic D. (1989) Photographic prospection of the NEA dumpsite in the north-east Atlantic: quantitative distribution of epibenthic megafauna. In: *Interim Oceanographic description of the North-East Atlantic site for the disposal of low-level radioactive waste.*, pp. 167-178 (OCDE, Paris).

Sjoeblom K.-L. and Linsley G.S. (1995) The International Arctic Seas Assessment Project (IASAP). Interim progress report. Proc. Int. Symp. Environmental Impact of Radioactive Releases, IAEA, Vienna, pp. 155-164.

Smith J.N., Ellis K.M. and Jones E.P. (1990) Caesium 137 transport into the Arctic through the Fram Strait. *J. Geophys. Res.* **95**, 1693-1701.

Strand P. and Holm E. (1993) Environmental Radioactivity in the Arctic and Antarctic. Kirkenes, Norway, 23-27 August 1993, pp. 1-433.

Trapeznikov A., Aarkrog A., Kulikov N., Nielsen S.P., Pozolotina V., Polikarpov G., Trapeznikova V., Chebotina M., Chukanov V. and Yushkov P. (1993) Radioactive contamination of the Ob river system from the nuclear enterprise Majak in the Urals. Environmental Radioactivity in the Arctic and Antarctic, Kirkenes, Norway, 23-27 August 1993, pp. 135-150.

Vakulovskii S.M., Nikitin A.I. and Chumichev V.B. (1985) Pollution of Arctic seas by radioactive wastes from West European nuclear reprocessing plants. *Translated from Atomnaya Energiya* **58**, 445 449.

Yablokov A.V., Karasev V.K., Rumyantsev V.M., Kokeyev M.E., Petrov O.J., Lystov V.N., Yemelyanenkov A.F. and Rubtsov P.M. (1993) Facts and problems related to radioactive waste disposal in seas adjacent to the territory of the Russian Federation. Report by a Government Commission, Decree N° 613 of the Russian Federation President, Moskow. (English transl. Small World Publishers, Inc., Albuquerque, NM).

2 ^{137}Cs (^{90}Sr) and Pu Isotopes in the Pacific Ocean: Sources and Trends

T.F. Hamilton, J.-C. Milliès-Lacroix
and G.H. Hong

The main source of artificial radioactivity in the world's oceans can be attributed to worldwide fallout from atmospheric nuclear weapons testing. Measurements of selected artificial radionuclides in the Pacific Ocean were first conducted in the 1960's where it was observed that fallout radioactivity had penetrated the deep ocean. Extensive studies carried out during the 1973-1974 GEOSECS programme provided the first comprehensive data on the lateral and vertical distributions of ^{90}Sr, ^{137}Cs and Pu isotopes in the Pacific on a basin wide scale. Estimates of radionuclide inventories in excess of amounts predicted to be delivered by global fallout alone were attributed to close-in fallout and tropospheric inputs from early U.S. tests conducted on Bikini and Enewetak Atolls in the Equatorial Pacific. In general levels of fallout radionuclides (including ^{90}Sr, ^{137}Cs and Pu isotopes) in surface waters of the Pacific Ocean have decreased considerably over the past 4 decades and are now much more homogeneously distributed. Resuspension and the subsequent deposition of fallout radionuclides from previously deposited debris on land has become an important source term for the surface ocean. This can be clearly seen in measurements of fallout radionuclides in mineral aerosols over the Korean Peninsula (Yellow dust events). Radionuclides may also be transported from land to sea in river runoff, these transport mechanisms are more important in the Pacific Ocean where large quantities of river water and suspended solids/fluvial sediments reach the coastal zone. Another unique source of artificial radionuclides in the Pacific Ocean is derived from the slow resolubilization and transport of radionuclides deposited in contaminated lagoon and slope sediments near U.S. and French test sites. Although there is a small but significant flux of artificial radionuclides depositing on the sea floor, > 80% of the total ^{239,240}Pu inventory and > 95% of the total ^{137}Cs inventory remains in the water column. Studies conducted through the 1980's appear to be consistend with earlier findings and indicate that radionuclides inventories in mid-northern latitudes are at least a factor of two above those expected from global fallout alone. The long term persistence of close-in and/or stratospheric fallout from nuclear weapons testing in the Marshall Islands still appears to be the only plausible explanation for this anomaly.

2.1. Introduction

The widespread introduction of artificial radioactivity into the marine environment arose initially from denotation of nuclear devices in the atmosphere. There were reportedly 423 atmospheric nuclear weapons tests conducted between 1956 and 1980 with a total yield of 545 MT equivalent (UNSCEAR, 1982). Injection of radioactive debris into the global atmosphere and subsequent deposition on the earth's surface has varied in space and time. The nature and partitioning of radioactive debris between the local environment, the troposphere and stratosphere are determined by the type and location of test, the yield and the quantity and type of environmental material interacting with the device. This has particular significance for the Pacific Ocean because of possible contributions from close-in fallout as a result of atmospheric tests conducted by the United States on Bikini and Enewetak Atolls in the Equatorial Pacific and, to a lesser extent, from French tests carried out in the Tuamotu Archipelago in the South Pacific. Apart from the potential immediate impact of close-in and/or tropospheric fallout in the hours and days following any particular event, it is conceivable that local residual radioactive debris deposited in lagoon and continental slope sediments formed a reservoir and source term for the equatorial and/or South Pacific regions for the years following.

World-wide deposition of long-lived fission products (*e.g.* ^{137}Cs, ^{90}Sr) has largely resulted from stratospheric fallout. Peak periods of deposition occurred in 1964 with the levels having now dropped to near or below detection limits (Monetti, pers. comm.). The occasional detection of ^{137}Cs in air samples appears to be the result of tropospheric resuspension of previously deposited debris (Larsen *et al.*, 1995). Hence, it is expected that the present-day airborne flux of fallout radioactivity is partially attributed to dispersion of mineral aerosols. Indirect source terms such mineral aerosols and river run-off will continue to transfer fallout radionuclides from land to sea.

Other important long-lived radionuclides to enter the marine environment as a result of global fallout from nuclear weapons testing have included ^{3}H ($T_{1/2}$ = 12.3 years), ^{14}C ($T_{1/2}$ = 5 730 years) and the transuranic elements: ^{241}Pu ($T_{1/2}$ = 14.2 years); ^{239}Pu ($T_{1/2}$ = 2.4 × 10^4 years) present as a product of neutron capture of ^{238}U or as unreacted fissile material; ^{240}Pu ($T_{1/2}$ = 6580 years); ^{238}Pu ($T_{1/2}$ = 86.4 years); ^{241}Am ($T_{1/2}$ = 458 years); and ^{237}Np ($T_{1/2}$ = 2.14 × 10^6 years). Long-lived activation products such as ^{3}H, ^{14}C, ^{152}Eu and ^{60}Co were also formed from neutron capture from weapons structures, soil, water and air. The global deposit of plutonium over the earth's surface has been significantly modified by plutonium present in the U.S. satellite SNAP 9A which burned up in 1964 upon reentry into the atmosphere. About 75% of the total SNAP ^{238}Pu deposit fall in the Southern Hemisphere whereas only about 20% of the total weapons ^{238}Pu fallout occurred in that hemisphere (Hardy et al., 1973).

The cumulative deposition of stratospheric fallout over land has been monitoring by direct measurement of radionuclides in wet and dry precipitation collections and soil profiles. ^{90}Sr was initially chosen as the primary fallout radionuclide of interest because of its long half-life ($T_{1/2}$ = 28.5 years), relatively high fission yield (~3.7 PBq per MT of fission energy) and concerns about the potential incorporation of ^{90}Sr into the biosphere. Data on annual and cumulative depositions of ^{90}Sr have been published in series of Environmental Measurement Laboratory (EML) reports (Hardy, 1977; Larsen, 1984; 1985; Monetti, 1996). The U.K. Atomic Energy Authority (UKAEA) has also conducted a worldwide fallout programme since the early 1950's with integrated fallout records in excellent agreement with EML estimates (see Monetti, 1996). Real-time fallout data over the oceans are seriously lacking and it is generally assumed that the integrated latitudinal fallout patterns over land and sea are comparable. It should be keep in mind that more than 90% of weapons fallout was deposited prior to 1970 and radionuclides that enter the marine environment are redistributed by a large range of different physical, chemical and biological processes.

Much of the early literature on oceanic distributions of artificial radionuclides is devoted to ^{90}Sr and ^{137}Cs and was summarized by Volchok et al. (1971). The expected ^{137}Cs/^{90}Sr activity ratio in global fallout, as computed by Harley et al. (1965), should be about 1.45. In the compilation by Volchok et al. (1971) for all available data reported up until 1967, the weighted average ^{137}Cs/^{90}Sr activity ratio was 1.6±0.3 in good agreement with the theoretical value. As such, discussions involving ^{90}Sr may be considered as applying to ^{137}Cs as well. In this report and for simplicity in comparing data, ^{90}Sr measurements have been converted to ^{137}Cs by multiplying the ^{90}Sr data × 1.5.

Interpretation of early data from the Pacific Ocean is complicated by the non-uniformity of observed seasonal variations of ^{90}Sr fallout over the oceans and the geographic variability in the depth distribution. In addition, interpretation is made difficult because of the lack of interlaboratory comparisons or quality control. No consensus could be reached about the significance of ^{90}Sr penetration into the deep ocean or on the total oceanic inventory (Volchok et al., 1971). However, these early studies did highlight the need for more systematic and long-term studies, and raised expectation about the value of fallout radionuclides as tools to study oceanic processes. The first serious attempt to address these issues came with the GEOSECS programme in 1973-1974 where very carefully collected, large volume sample, hydrographic stations were occupied and fractions of these samples made available for analysis of ^{3}H, ^{14}C, ^{90}Sr, ^{137}Cs and the transuranic elements (Bowen et al., 1980). In many respects, this programme lead to the birth of modern day 'radionuclide oceanography'.

In the sections that follow an effort has been made to summarize much of the data and some of the new issues which have arisen since the early GEOSECS cruises and improved our understanding of the levels, fluxes and behaviours of artificial radioactivity in the Pacific Ocean. Our discussion has been limited to selected radionuclides – namely ^{137}Cs and plutonium isotopes. The behaviour of ^{137}Cs and plutonium in the oceans are expected to be quite different as ^{137}Cs is largely a conservative element with « water » properties whereas plutonium is regarded as a « particle » reactive radionuclide.

2.2. Natural Radioactivity in the Oceans

Inputs of radionuclides into the ocean needs to be considered with respect to natural baseline levels of marine radioactivity. Sea water contains about 12 600 Bq m^3 of natural radioactivity of which over 90% is due to ^{40}K (Burton, 1985). Other major natural occurring radionuclides in sea water include ^{87}Rb, U and Th decay series radionuclides, ^{14}C and ^{3}H. The total inventory of natural radioactivity in the Pacific Ocean (excluding ocean sediments) is about $\sim 9 \times 10^6$ PBq. Using data presented by Baxter (1983) the corresponding surface sediment inventory (over the top 10 m) in the Pacific Ocean is estimated to be about 1.6×10^7 PBq. As a further comparison, between 1967 and 1992 an estimated 1.3 PBq of mainly solidified (and some liquid) radioactive waste was dumped into the Pacific Ocean (IAEA, 1991; White Book, 1993) much of which still remains on the seafloor.

2.3. Atmospheric Global Fallout

A total of 423 nuclear weapons tests have been conducted between 1945 and 1980 with an estimated fission yield of 217 MT (Tab. 2.I.). Large-scale atmospheric test programmes were conducted in 1954-1958 and 1961-1962 before a partial test-ban treaty was agreed by the USA, the former USSR and the UK in 1963. The combined fission yield of the « late phase » test series conducted by France (1966-1974) and China (1964-1980) represents only about 10% of the total (Tab. 2.I.).

Stratospheric fallout accounts for most world-wide contamination by fission products. The lower stratosphere is assumed to range from 9 to 17 km in the polar regions and from 17 to 24 km in the equatorial regions (UNSCEAR, 1982). Exchange of tropospheric air between hemispheres is limited. Until 1952 all nuclear weapons detonations occurred in the Northern Hemisphere and were sufficiently low yield for the debris to have been largely confined to that hemisphere as tropospheric fallout. Circulation and mixing in the troposphere is driven by hemispheric circulation cells (Hadley Cells) which tend to change in size and shift latitudinally with season (Newell, 1971). Aerosols in the upper atmosphere descend gravitationally with a residence time up to 24 months – the long residence times of aerosols in the stratosphere leads to a significant time delay before fallout of stratospheric origin reaches the lower stratosphere (or upper troposphere) and eventually deposit on the earth's surface. Residence times of aerosols in the lower stratosphere vary between 3 to 12 months in the polar regions and 8 to 24 months in the equatorial regions (UNSCEAR, 1982). The transfer to the troposphere occurs mainly through gaps in the tropopause which frequently occur in winter at mid-latitudes giving rise to a « spring influx » of stratospheric fallout. Removal of aerosols from the troposphere occurs by wet (wash-out + rain-out) and dry deposition.

Table 2.I. Estimated fission yield of atmospheric tests.

Year	Country	Number of tests	Fission yield (~MT)
1945	USA	3	0.05
1946	USA	2	0.04
1948	USA	3	0.1
1949	USSR	1	0.02
1951	USA/USSR	17	0.54
1952	UK/USA	11	6.62
1953	UK/USA	13	0.29
1954	USA/USSR	7	30.1
1955	USA/USSR	17	1.67
1956	UK/USA/USSR	27	12.3
1957	UK/USA/USSR	45	10.89
1958	UK/USA/USSR	83	28.94
1960	France	3	0.11
1961	France/USSR	51	25.42
1962	USA/USSR	77	76.55
1964	China	1	0.02
1965	China	1	0.04
1966	France/China	8	1.3
1967	France/China	5	1.92
1968	France/China	6	5.3
1969	China	1	2
1970	France/China	9	4.55
1971	France/China	6	1.97
1972	France/China	5	0.24
1973	France/China	6	1.65
1974	France/China	8	1.55
1976	China	3	2.37
1977	China	1	0.02
1978	China	2	0.04
1980	China	1	0.45
Total		423	217

Source: UNSCEAR (1982).

Estimates of the annual deposition and cumulative global deposit of stratospheric fallout have come from direct measurements of ^{90}Sr deposition (Monetti, 1996). The annual deposition and cumulative deposit of ^{90}Sr for the period between 1958 and 1990 are shown in Table 2.II. The peak in weapons testing during 1962 produced a peak annual ^{90}Sr deposition during 1963 in the Northern Hemisphere and during 1964 in the Southern Hemisphere. The integrated annual global deposit of ^{90}Sr at the end of 1980 was 603 PBq (UNSCEAR, 1982) compared with 609 PBq at the end of 1990. About 1.4 PBq of the ^{90}Sr deposit was associated with the Chernobyl accident. The cumulative global ^{90}Sr deposit increased sharply though the early 1960's reaching a maximum of 451 PBq in 1966. Since 1972, the cumulative ^{90}Sr deposit has decreased because the annual loss from radioactive decay has been greater that the annual deposit. The cumulative global ^{90}Sr deposit at the end of 1990 was 311 PBq. The latitudinal distribution of the global ^{90}Sr deposit at this time is shown in Figure 2.1a. About 24% of the ^{90}Sr deposit occurs in the Southern Hemisphere where less than 10% of weapons tests were conducted. The majority of fallout occurs in the 30-60° latitude band with much less towards the polar regions. Figure 2.1b. contains a plot of the measured cumulative global ^{90}Sr burden along with the total theoretical ^{90}Sr production (~3.7 PBq per MT of fission yield) corrected for decay. The cumulative deposit in 1990 accounts for about 78% of the theoretical decay corrected production. As a first approximation the remaining 22% (or 177 PBq of ^{90}Sr produced in atmospheric nuclear weapons tests) provides the source-term for close-in or tropospheric fallout. No corrections have been made for Chernobyl inputs. The measured cumulative ^{90}Sr deposit (609 PBq) for 1990 is in good agreement with estimates based on stratospheric partitioning of nuclear debris and cumulative fission yields (660 Bq) (Bennet, 1978; UNSCEAR, 1982). The correlation between the temporal pattern of ^{90}Sr deposition and the annual fission yield from atmospheric nuclear weapons tests is illustrated in Figure 2.2. for selected locations in the Pacific region.

The Pacific Ocean occupies an area of about 1.72×10^8 km^2 or about 33% of the earth's surface (Baumgartner and Reichel, 1975) and has a total volume of about 7.07×10^8 km^3. The expected input of fallout radionuclides into the Pacific Ocean can be estimated from data presented in Figure 2.1. (for ^{137}Cs) and the distribution of fallout plutonium in soil profiles (for [239,240]Pu, after Hardy, 1973). The latitudinal distribution of the expected fallout deposit and total inventories of ^{137}Cs and [239,240]Pu in the Pacific Ocean are given in Table 2.III. The expected ^{137}Cs and [239,240]Pu inventory at the end of 1990 (excluding additional removal terms) is 147 PBq and about 3.8 PBq, respectively.

Table 2.II. Annual deposition and cumulative deposit of ^{90}Sr.

Year	Northern Hemisphere		Southern Hemisphere		Global	
	Annual deposition (PBq)	Cumulative deposit (PBq)	Annual deposition (PBq)	Cumulative deposit (PBq)	Annual deposition (PBq)	Cumulative deposit (PBq)
1945-58	67#	63#	24#	22.2#	90.5#	85#
1958	23	85	9.6	29.6	32.6	115
1959	39	122	6.7	37	45.9	159
1960	9.6	126	6.3	40.7	15.9	170
1961	13	137	6.3	48.1	19.2	185
1962	53	185	9.6	55.5	63.3	244
1963	97	278	12	66.6	108.4	344
1964	61	333	16	81.4	77.0	411
1965	29	352	13	92.5	41.8	444
1966	12	355	7.8	96.2	20.0	451
1967	6.3	352	4.1	96.2	10.4	451
1968	7.4	352	3.7	99.9	11.1	451
1969	5.6	348	5.2	103.6	10.7	451
1970	7.8	348	4.8	103.6	12.6	451
1971	7	344	5.6	107.3	12.6	451
1972	3.2	340	3.6	107.3	6.7	448
1973	1.2	333	1.2	107.3	2.3	440
1974	4.5	329	1.4	103.6	5.9	433
1975	2.2	322	1.3	103.6	3.4	426
1976	1	315	0.8	103.6	1.8	418
1977	3	311	0.8	99.9	3.8	411
1978	3.7	307	0.7	99.9	4.4	407
1979	1.1	303	0.4	96.2	1.5	400
1980	0.6	296	0.3	96.2	0.9	392
1981	1.6	289	0.3	92.5	1.9	381
1982	0.5	283	0.2	91	0.7	374
1983	0.3	277	0.2	89	0.5	366
1984	0.3	270	0.1	87	0.4	357
1985	0.1	264	0.1	85	0.2	349
1986	1.5	259	0.2	83.2	1.7	343
1987	0.1	253	0.2	81.3	0.3	334
1988	0.1	247	0.1	79.7	0.2	326
1989	0.1	241	0.2	77.8	0.2	319
1990	0	235	0.1	76.2	0.1	311
1995	(0)	213#	(0)	68.9#	(0)	282#

Source: Updated from UNSCEAR (1982) using Monetti (1996). # estimates only.

Table 2.III. Expected deposit and total inventory of ^{137}Cs
and ^{239,240}Pu in the Pacific Ocean from global fallout.

Latitude Band (°)	Area (10³km²)	^{137}Cs deposit (GBq km⁻²)	^{239,240}Pu deposit (GBq km⁻²) (1970)@	^{239,240}Pu deposit (GBq km⁻²) (1990)#	^{137}Cs inventory (PBq)	^{239,240}Pu inventory (PBq)
60-90	749	0.94	0.037	0.040	0.70	0.03
30-60	25 976	2.16	0.067	0.072	56	1.9
0-30	54 665	0.92	0.016	0.017	50	0.93
				Subtotals =	107	2.8
0-30	50 760	0.39	0.011	0.012	20	0.58
30-60	30 355	0.60	0.012	0.014	18	0.40
60-90	9 203	0.23	0.0024	0.0028	2.1	0.024
				Subtotals =	40	1.00
				Total	**147**	**3.83**

@ data from Hardy, 1973; # extrapolated from ^{90}Sr deposit (see Tab. 2.II.).

2.4. ^{137}Cs Concentrations in the Surface Ocean

Artificial radionuclides in the Pacific Ocean and adjacent seas have been extensively studied since the first measurements of radioactive contamination were made off Bikini Atoll in 1954 (Miyake *et al.*, 1955). Following the early GEOSECS cruises of 1973-1974 artificial radionuclides have been measured in large numbers of samples from most parts of the North Pacific but with much less coverage of the South Pacific (Fig. 2.3.). ^{137}Cs concentration data in Pacific Ocean surface waters for the period 1960-1995 have been summarized in Table 2.IV. (Bowen *et al.*, 1980; Hirose *et al.*, 1992; Hong (pers. comm.); Milliès-Lacroix (pers. comm.); Miyake *et al.*, 1988; Nakanishi *et al.*, 1995; Nagaya and Nakamura, 1993; 1992; 1987; 1984; 1976; 1975; Nakanishi *et al.*, 1984; Nakamura and Nagaya, 1985). Pre-1970 data was taken from the compilation of Volchok *et al.* (1971). Data for the Marshall Islands and French Polynesia have been excluded and will be discussed separately. For convenience, the Pacific Ocean has been divided into the western North Pacific Ocean, the eastern North Pacific Ocean and South Pacific Ocean along three latitude bands (0-10°, 10-30° and 30-60°). It does not appear to be justified to use a finer resolution due to the lack of data collected for certain geographical areas.

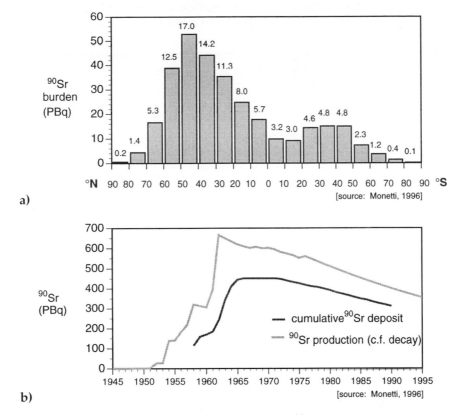

a)

[source: Monetti, 1996]

b)

[source: Monetti, 1996]

Figure 2.1. a) Latitudinal distribution of the global ^{90}Sr deposit at the end of 1990.
b) Temporal variation in the estimated ^{90}Sr production from atmospheric
weapons testing and the measured cumulative global deposit.

^{137}Cs concentrations in surface waters of the North Pacific have decreased steadily since the early 1960's to present-day levels of about 2 to 4 Bq m^{-3} (Tab. 2.IV.). Early measurements showed clear latitudinal zones as expected from fallout patterns with higher concentrations in the mid latitudes but with some regional exceptions. One anomaly observed around 32° N and 146° W in 1970 was attributed to transport of contaminated surface waters from the Columbia River (Nagaya and Nakamura, 1976). Similar findings were reported by Vdovenko et al. (1972) and Saruhashi et al. (1975). Large quantities of artificial radioactivity entered the lower Columbia River from the operation of plutonium production reactors located at Hanford, Washington between 1944 and 1971. Data on the total quantity of ^{137}Cs reaching the sea from the Hanford facilities are not readily available.

However, during peak periods of production, the plume of short lived radionuclides (*i.e.* ^{51}Cr) could be clearly identified up to several hundred kilometers offshore (Osterberg *et al.*, 1965). Other regional anomalies have been attributed to upwelling of cold waters of low concentration and inputs from Pacific Atoll tests sites (Nagaya and Nakamura, 1981; Noshkin and Wong, 1979, 1980; Noshkin *et al.*, 1987).

Table 2.IV. ^{137}**Cs concentrations in Pacific Ocean surface waters for the period 1960-1995.**

Location/period	^{137}Cs concentration (Bq m^{-3})			0-60° (median±S.D.)
	30-60° N	10-30° N	0-10° N	
North-Western Pacific				
pre-1960	50-132 (3)	16-171 (5)	88 (1)	NA
1960-61	7-11 (14)	4-22 (23)	3-20 (6)	NA
1962-64	12-29 (9)	9-27 (22)	5-11 (15)	NA
1965-66	11-19 (117)	4-12 (22)	4.5-6 (10)	~9[1]
1967-71	10-14.6 (5)	–	–	10.9 ± 2.5
1972-79	4-11 (42)	4.8-11.8 (49)	2.1-7.6 (19)	7.1 ± 1.9
1980-85	2-8 (15)	3.5-10.9 (25)	2.8-6.5 (12)	4.8 ± 1.5
1986-90	2.7-7.7 (12)	2.6-7 (12)	3.6-7 (9)	5.5 ± 1.8
1991-95	2.1-3.4 (9)	–	–	3.1 ± 0.3
North-Eastern Pacific				
pre-1960	50-132 (3)	16-171 (5)	88 (1)	NA
1960-61	3-11 (67)	4-22 (55)	2-10 (17)	NA
1962-64	11-28 (40)	9-17 (24)	8-16 (16)	10
1965-66	17-37 (197)	9-36 (131)	6-8 (9)	~18[1]
1967-71	5.6-23 (45)	5-22 (67)	3.5-4.5 (29)	~11[1]
1972-79	5-10 (18)	5-10 (5)	3-4 (2)	7.9 ± 1.8
1980-85	2.4-4.2 (2)	4.2 (1)	–	4.2 ± 1.0
1986-90	2-2.8 (3)	–	14.8 (1)#	2.7 ± 6.1
South Pacific	0-10°S	10-30°S	30-60°S	
pre-1960	–	–	–	
1960-61	2-15 (20)	1.5-8 (15)	0.7-3 (11)	NA
1962-64	2-18 (31)	1-18 (11)	–	NA
1965-66	3-8 (27)	3-9 (42)	2-14 (65)	~4[1]
1967-71	2-3 (33)	2-3 (30)	–	~2.5[1]
1972-79	2.3-6.5 (8)	3.7-6.8 (15)	2.6 (19)	4.6 ± 1.4
1980-85	–	–	–	–
1986-90	9.4-9.6 (2)	–	–	9.5 ± 0.1
(for additional data, see Fig. 2.4.)				

( ) number in parentheses refers to the number of samples analyzed. # high value. [1] estimate of average values only.

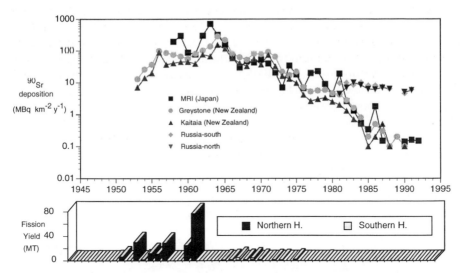

Figure 2.2. Temporal pattern of total annual ^{90}Sr deposition on the earth's surface at selected locations within the Pacific region (top) and the annual fission yield from atmosphere weapons testing (bottom).

^{137}Cs concentrations in the South Pacific have generally been much lower than those reported for northern latitudes as expected from global fallout patterns (Tab. 2.IV.). High quality analyses performed by the Service Mixte de Sécurité Radiologique (SMSR/CEA/DIRCEN-France) in surface waters of French Polynesia indicate that ^{137}Cs concentrations have decreased with an apparent half-life of about 14 years (Fig. 2.4., Bourlat and Martin, 1992). This appears to be fairly consistent with general trends observed in the North Pacific and demonstrate that ^{137}Cs is being actively removed from surface waters by processes other than radioactive decay.

2.5. Comparative Behaviour of ^{137}Cs (^{90}Sr) and ^{239,240}Pu

Reliable measurements of fallout radionuclides in the deep ocean during the 1960' and 1970's are relatively few because of the technical difficulties associated with sampling large volumes of water at depth and obtaining precise analytical results at low concentrations. Vertical distributions of ^{137}Cs and ^{90}Sr showed a rapid decrease with increasing depth-deep waters being one to two orders of magnitude lower in concentration compared with surface values (Nagaya and Nakamura, 1976; 1981; 1984). Sharp ^{137}Cs (^{90}Sr) gradients extended down to depths of 1000 to 2000 m below which concentrations were relatively uniform (Nagaya and Nakamura, 1976). The vertical distribution patterns were similar to those measured for fallout ^{3}H over the same period (Roether, 1974) and were indicative of the conservative nature of fallout ^{137}Cs. However, a significant fraction of fallout ^{137}Cs and ^{90}Sr rapidly penetrated the deep ocean and there was no clear understanding of the processes involved. The most probable explanation was thought to be active particle transport processes as reported my several workers (Martin, 1970; Honjo, 1980; Iseki, 1981). ^{137}Cs and ^{90}Sr are thought to behave similarly — in sediments, however, the two radionuclides show evidence of considerable separation. Future studies may reveal that specific biological

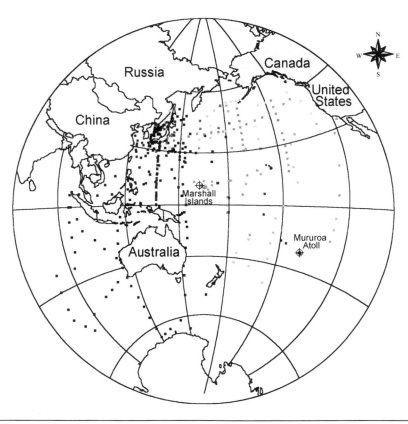

	Ocean (1994)		R/V Ryofu Maru (1979-88)		Hakuho-Maru (1976-79)
	CREAMS 1993		Miyake 1988 et al.		Hakuho-Maru (1980-82)
	SMSRB (France)		Hakuho-Maru (1987)		Hakuho-Maru (1988)
	Tansei and Hakuho (1969-73)		Hakuho-Maru (1984-86)		Hakuho-Maru (1992)
					LLNL Study Area

Figure 2.3. A map showing the geographical coverage of major sampling cruises (1973-1995) were ^{137}Cs (and/or ^{90}Sr) measurements were made.

processes may be responsible for differences in the behaviour and fate of radionuclides in the oceans. As an example, acantharians are abundant marine planktonic protists and are the only marine organism that use Sr as a major structural component (Bernstein and Betzer, 1991). Therefore, the vertical transport of ^{90}Sr in the water column should be partially controlled by the abundance and the settling/dissolution rates of acantharian skeletons cysts. Elevated levels of ^{137}Cs are also observed in waters immediately above the sea floor. This phenomenon appears to be associated with preferential scavenging of ^{137}Cs into bottom sediments and remobilization processes and/or horizontal inflow of nuclide rich waters from adjacent regions (Noshkin and Bowen, 1973; Nakamura and Nagaya, 1985; 1975).

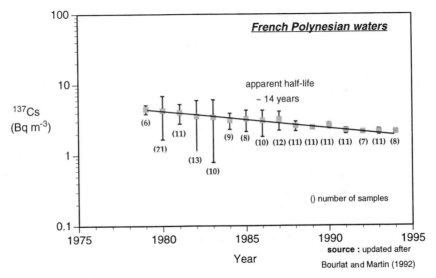

Figure 2.4. Temporal variation in the ^{137}Cs concentration
of French Polynesian surface ocean waters (± 2σ)

Long-term measurements of ^{239,240}Pu in surface waters of the western North Pacific show a gradual decrease during the period between 1979 and 1987 (Hirose et al., 1992). The total surface ^{239,240}Pu concentration along 137° E longitude decreased from 0.027-0.031 Bq m^{-3} to about 0.0055 Bq m^{-3} above 25° N and from 0.011 to 0.0024 Bq m^{-3} near the equator – through which the latitudinal distribution has remained with higher concentrations measured in mid-latitudes compared with those from tropical regions. ^{137}Cs concentrations showed no decrease through the same period (Hirose et al.,

1992) with the latitudinal difference apparently becoming more obscure with time. The deposition of ^{239,240}Pu in Japan decreased from a maximum of 0.27 MBq km^{-2} y^{-1} in 1981 to 0.0027 MBq km^{-2} y^{-1} in 1986 or about two orders of magnitude (see Fig. 2.5.). Therefore, the rate at which ^{239,240}Pu is removed from surface waters is longer than the atmospheric residence time. Using a simple box model, Hirose et al. (1992) estimated that the residence times of ^{239,240}Pu and ^{137}Cs in the surface mixed layer of the western North Pacific were 4 and 9.1 years, respectively. The residence time of plutonium in the upper 80 m of an eastern North Pacific water column was estimated by Fowler et al. (1983) using sediment traps to be 2.4 years. A short residence time and higher affinity for removal of plutonium on sinking particles is supported by the general finding that particulate ^{239,240}Pu concentrations range up to 21% of the total compared with less than 1% for ^{137}Cs (Hirose et al., 1992; Fowler et al., 1983; Noshkin and Wong, 1980). Hence it appears that vertical processes may be more important than horizontal transport in controlling the spatial distributions of plutonium. The surface mixed layer of the western North Pacific contains between 30 and 60% of the total ^{137}Cs inventory in the water column and only 1-6% of the ^{239,240}Pu inventory. This also implies that plutonium is being preferentially scavenged from the upper water column. As a result, the present-day surface ocean will tend to carry the recent input signatures of ^{239,240}Pu while, by contrast, the present-day ^{137}Cs inputs will be strongly masked by the pre-existing radionuclide pool. It is therefore not surprising that the ^{239,240}Pu surface distributions have shown a latitudinal fallout pattern at least through until the late 1980's (Nagaya and Nakamura, 1984).

The concentrations of ^{137}Cs and ^{239,240}Pu measured in lagoons waters from U.S. and French test sites in the Pacific are shown in Table 2.V. Lagoon waters from the Marshall Islands (Bikini and Enewetak Atolls) in the Equatorial Pacific and from Mururoa Atoll in the South Pacific show elevated levels of ^{239,240}Pu from the slow solubilization of plutonium held in the underlying sediments. Comparable concentrations of ^{239,240}Pu are found in all three atolls with the soluble fraction ranging between 0.3 Bq m^{-3} (Mururoa) and 2 Bq m^{-3} (Bikini). The concentration of ^{239,240}Pu in lagoon waters is 50 to 500 times higher that those observed in the open ocean. Waters in the lagoon exchange with the open ocean water and therefore provide a continuous source term for plutonium. The concentration of dissolved ^{239,240}Pu in Mururoa lagoon waters appears to have decreased slightly between 1985 and 1991 with an apparent residence time of 9 years (Bourlat et al., 1995). This is apparently due to the slow depletion of plutonium in the top layers of sediment. It also appears that ^{137}Cs has already equilibrated with the open ocean.

The vertical distributions of ^{90}Sr, ^{137}Cs and ^{239,240}Pu as recently measured in the water column at 22° S in the Tuamotu Archipelago (off Mururoa Atoll) are very similar to those previously observed in northern latitudes (see Fig. 2.6.). One of the general and interesting features of ^{239,240}Pu concentration profiles in the Pacific Ocean is a distinct subsurface maximum at depths ranging from 250 to 1000 m (Nakanishi *et al.*, 1995; 1984; Nagaya and Nakamura, 1987; 1984; Bowen *et al.*, 1980; Noshkin and Wong, 1979). The general distribution patterns of ^{90}Sr, ^{137}Cs and ^{239,240}Pu in the Pacific Ocean does not appear to have changed significantly over the past 25 years although there is some evidence to suggest that the depth of the ^{239,240}Pu maximum and the proportion of the total water column radionuclide inventory held in deep water has increased over time (Nakanishi *et al.*, 1984; Bowen *et al.*, 1980; Noshkin and Wong, 1979). Early transport models based on irreversible particle scavenging processes predicted a more rapid transfer of radionuclides to the deep ocean than what has actually been observed.

The relative distribution, behaviours and transport of ^{137}Cs and ^{239,240}Pu in the oceans can be explained by a reversible process of biologically mediated scavenging which varies in space and time. Highly productive surface waters will tend to enhance the vertical transport of radionuclides and provide a possible mechanism whereby fallout radionuclides are preferentially transported to the deep ocean or onto the seafloor. There is increasing evidence that the main transport vectors to the deep ocean are large, rapidly sinking zooplankton faecal pellets (Fowler *et al.*, 1983; Fisher and Fowler, 1983). Smaller particles and micropellets sink slowly and, hence, are more subject to biogeochemical cycling. The appearance of a subsurface maximum for plutonium may therefore be a function of the dynamics of these types of transformation processes.

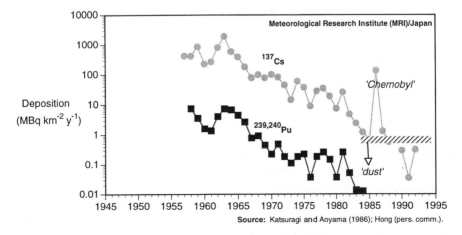

Source: Katsuragi and Aoyama (1986); Hong (pers. comm.).

Figure 2.5. Temporal pattern of ^{137}Cs and ^{239,240}Pu deposition over Japan.

**Table 2.V. Concentration of ^{137}Cs and ^{239,240}Pu
in surface waters near Pacific Ocean test sites.**

Location/period	^{137}Cs (Bq m^{-3})	^{239,240}Pu (Bq m^{-3})	
	dissolved	dissolved	particulate
Mururoa Lagoon (140 km^2; average depth = 30 m)			
1982	5.9 (46)	–	–
1983	6.2 (31)	–	–
1984	5.6 (70)	–	–
1985	4.7 (35)	0.54 (37)	0.2 (37)
1986	4.6 (35)	0.62 (37)	< 0.13 (37)
1987	3.9 (10)	0.42 (10)	< 0.007 (10)
1988	3.4 (34)	0.52 (10)	0.07 (10)
1989	2.7 (10)	0.46 (10)	< 0.10 (10)
1990	2.7 (10)	0.39 (10)	0.05 (10)
1991	–	0.32 (10)	0.08 (10)

[French Polynesian surface waters (1990); ^{137}Cs = 2.7 ± 0.3 Bq m^{-3} (n = 11); ^{239,240}Pu (1991) = < 0.0016-0.0017 Bq m^{-3} (n = 4)].

Location/period	dissolved	dissolved	particulate
Enewetak Atoll (933 km^2, average depth = 49 m)			
1972	–	0.81 (35)	0.37 (35)
1974	16 (9) #	0.93 (71)	0.70 (71)
1976	–	0.59 (29)	0.48 (29)
1982	19 (4) #	0.63 (23)	–
1994	10 (3) #	0.70 (3) #	–
Bikini Atoll (629 km^2; average depth = 45 m)			
1972	–	1.55 (17)	0.48 (17)
1977	–	1.81 (26)	–
1982	–	2.04 (5)	–

[Northern Equatorial Pacific ocean waters – ^{137}Cs = 2-7 Bq m^{-3}; ^{239,240}Pu = 0.015 ± 0.007 Bq m^{-3}]

Number in parentheses is the number of samples analyzed. *Source:* Boulat *et al.*, 1995; Bourlat and Martin (1992); Noshkin *et al.*, 1987. # off Runit Island only.

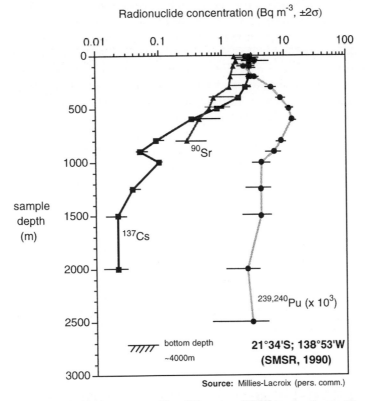

Radionuclide concentration (Bq m^{-3}, ±2σ)

Figure 2.6. Depth distribution of ^{90}Sr, ^{137}Cs and ^{239,240}Pu in the Pacific Ocean (taken off Mururoa Atoll in the Tuamotu Archipelago).

2.6. Resuspension of Previously Deposited Debris

One of the main sources of ^{137}Cs and ^{239,240}Pu depositing on the earth's surface can be attributed to tropospheric resuspension of previously deposited debris (Monetti, 1996; Nakanishi *et al.*, 1995). Seasonal patterns in the deposition of ^{137}Cs and ^{239,240}Pu over Japan and Korea can now be directly linked to « yellow » dust events (Katsuragi and Aoyama, 1986; Lee, 1994). The mean flux of « yellow » dust into the Japan Sea is about 13 000 kg km^{-2} y^{-1} (Irino and Tada, 1994). Precise estimates for the wider North Pacific are not available but there is strong evidence for transport of large quantities of Asian dust westward across the North Pacific (Parrington *et al.*, 1983). Dust events are also known to occur off the principal desert regions of Australia and Mexico-California. Windom (1975) estimates that 10-30% of deep sea deposits consists of eolian material. It has also been estimated that about 50% of fallout radionuclides associated with mineral aerosols will be in a soluble form (Hodge *et al.*, 1978). Using an average ^{137}Cs concentration for undisturbed soil on the Korean Peninsula of 60 Bq kg^{-1}, Hong (pers. comm.) estimated that the « yellow » dust ^{137}Cs flux into the Japan Sea will be about 0.8 MBq km^{-2} y^{-1}, which is comparable with the measured annual ^{137}Cs deposit for this region since 1985 (excluding 1986 Chernobyl inputs) (see Fig. 2.5.). Using a ^{239,240}Pu/^{137}Cs activity ratio of about 0.03 the equivalent ^{239,240}Pu mineral aerosol flux would be around 0.02 MBq km^{-2} y^{-1}. Again, this is similar to the leveling off depositional flux measured by MRI in Japan (Fig. 2.5.).

The estimated total atmospheric flux of mineral aerosol in the North Pacific Ocean is 4.73×10^{11} kg y^{-1} (GESAMP, 1989). This would lead to a total annual ocean deposit of 28 and 1 TBq of ^{137}Cs and ^{239,240}Pu, respectively. We estimate that over the past 30 years, resuspension of previously deposited fallout debris and mineral aerosol deposition in the North Pacific may have contributed up to 1.2 PBq of ^{137}Cs and about 0.03 PBq of ^{239,240}Pu. These inputs represent only about 1% of the total expected inventory from global fallout but nonetheless the cumulative effect of these processes will become increasingly important.

2.7. Land-Based Sources of Radioactivity

Land-based sources of artificial radionuclides are transferred to the coastal marine environment by rivers and as controlled releases from the nuclear industry. The combined present-day input from these sources into the Pacific Ocean is expected to be small compared with existing ocean inventories (see Sect. 2.10.) but nonetheless remobilization of previously deposited radionuclides by erosional and associated processes will ultimately lead to their export by rivers to the sea. Particle reactive radionuclides (*e.g.* Pu isotopes & ^{241}Am) delivered to shallow coastal regions in river runoff will largely be associated with suspended solids and/or colloids. Most of these particles (and any associated radionuclides) will be deposited or settle with fine coastal sediments. Colloidal and/or finely divided material will be transported offshore with surface currents. Radionuclides entering the coastal marine environment are subject to a wide range of different chemical, physical and chemical processes which will tend to redistribute different elements in space and time, *i.e.*, advection, diffusion, biogeochemical interactions, particle scavenging processes, adsorption-desorption reactions, redox reactions, sedimentation and mixing processes, sediment diagenesis, etc.

Many of the world's rivers with the largest suspended load are located into the S.E. Asian region – Ganges-Brahmaputra, the Huang He or Yellow River, the Irrawaddy and the Chang Jiang being the largest – and along with supply from large oceanic islands deliver more than 6000×10^6 t of suspended matter annually to nearshore coastal regions of S.E. Asia and the western Pacific Ocean (Eisma, 1993 and references therein). This material remains mostly in nearshore areas and on the inner continental shelf with less than 10% transported to the deep ocean (Drake, 1976). Similarly, the average annual discharge of suspended sediment from various drainage basins in the eastern Pacific is about 750×10^6 t (Milliman and Meade, 1983). It is expected that these inputs would have increased radionuclide inventories in adjacent coastal sediments over that expected from direct atmospheric fallout. In contrast, Livingston and Bowen (1979) have observed strong inventory deficiencies in nearshore and shelf sediments on the northeastern coast of the United States. These differences may, however, be explained by postdepositional redistribution processes and variations in the nature and type of sediment.

Detailed information on the transport of artificial radionuclides from land to sea is limited especially for the Pacific Ocean. Beasley *et al.* (1981a) estimated between 150 and 300 GBq of ^{239,240}Pu and between 40 and 80 GBq of ^{241}Am entered the eastern North Pacific between the 1950's and mid-1978 as of consequence of Columbia River runoff. Less than 10% of this contribution originated from Hanford-derived plutonium where ^{239}Pu was produced by the decay of ^{239}Np present in reactor effluent water (Beasley *et al.*, 1981a; 1981b). These authors suggest that plutonium export from the Columbia River, representing between 0.3 and 0.5% of the total catchment deposit for that time, would have increased the transuranic element inventory of coastal sediments by at most 2.5 times that expected from direct atmospheric fallout. Over the same time period, estimates of plutonium export from the Hudson River (Simpson *et al.*, 1976) represent about 0.5% of the total fallout delivery to the surrounding catchment. This suggests that a reasonable estimate of the total export of fallout radionuclides from river catchments to the oceans would be around 1% but in reality may range considerably between different river systems and drainage basins. Detailed information on catchment areas was not available at time of publication but it is informative to make a crude calculation assuming plutonium export in river runoff is controlled by suspended particles having an average ^{239,240}Pu specific activity of 0.05-0.5 Bq kg^{-1} (estimate only) and based on a total annual discharge of suspended matter to the Pacific Ocean of 6500×10^6 t (after Milliman and Meade, 1983). Based on these calculations the annual ^{239,240}Pu export by river runoff into the Pacific Ocean would range between 0.3 and 3 TBq. The maximum cumulative input over the past 50 years would be about 160 TBq providing an additional 4% of ^{239,240}Pu above the expected oceanic inventory from global fallout alone (Tab. 2.III.). Inputs of dissolved plutonium isotopes from river runoff are expected to be considerably less.

Parallel measurements of ^{137}Cs and ^{90}Sr in river and rain-waters from Japan during the period between February 1960 and July 1962 were used by Yamagata *et al.* (1963) to provide initial runoff estimates. About 1.3% of the ^{137}Cs and 7.2% of ^{90}Sr deposited on the land from global fallout were carried by the Tonegawa River to the sea. These estimates are consistent with reported average ^{137}Cs and ^{90}Sr concentrations in the Japanese river waters during 1961 (Miyake and Tsubota, 1963). Hence it appears that ^{90}Sr is more effectively transported from land to sea – the relative transport factor being about 5-6 times greater than that of ^{137}Cs. This also implies that transfers of different radionuclides from land to sea may have varied in time so it would be difficult to obtain an accurate retrospective estimate of land-sea runoff inventories. We propose that the immediate runoff export of land-derived radionuclides plus the cumulative effects of erosional transport over the past fifty years have contributed no more than 10% above the expected oceanic inventory from global fallout.

2.8. Remobilization of ^{137}Cs and ^{239,240}Pu from Test Sites in the Pacific

Bikini and Enewetak Atolls form part of the Western (Ralik) chain of the Marshall Islands in the equatorial Pacific and were used by the United States as testing grounds for nuclear devices from 1946 until 1958. Of the 66 nuclear devices detonated in the Marshall Islands most were coral surface, tower or barge bursts. The remaining tests included 4 airbursts and three underwater explosions. Surface bursts conducted over coral islands or over shallow waters produced highly localized input (Joseph *et al.*, 1971) because large quantities of soil were incorporated in the ensuring fireball and cloud. In these cases different types and sizes of high specific activity particles were formed consisting of mixtures of partially hydrated CaO, $Ca(OH)_2$ and $CaCO_3$ formed by high-temperature vaporization and subsequent condensation processes (Schell *et al.*, 1980). In the years that following, contaminated particles deposited in lagoon and surrounding slope and basin sediments formed a reservoir and source term for the marine environment through solubilization and water transport. The mean exchange rate for Enewetak lagoon waters is approximately one month and estimates for Bikini lagoon waters vary between 30 and 140 days (Noshkin *et al.*, 1987).

Mururoa Atoll is located in the central part of the South Pacific Ocean and is one of the largest atolls in the Tuamota Archipelago (Bourlat *et al.*, 1995). The lagoon has a surface area of 140 km^2 and an estimated volume of 4.5 km^3. About 3% of the lagoon water is exchanged with the open ocean on a daily basis through a 4 km wide passage. A number of barge, ballon and safety shots were conducted in the near surface environment of the atoll.

Inventories of ^{239,240}Pu and ^{241}Am in excess of global fallout levels persisting in these Pacific atoll sediments are continuously mobilizing into solution and providing a source term to the surrounding ocean. Analyses of grab and core samples collected from Enewetak Atoll in 1972 were used to give an estimate of the total sediment inventory for plutonium of 44.4 TBq (Noshkin and Wong, 1979). The estimated plutonium inventory for Bikini sediments was 54.4 TBq. Using the residence times of lagoon waters and the average soluble inventories, it was estimated that the annual discharge of ^{239,240}Pu from Enewetak and Bikini Atolls is 0.10 and 0.12 TBq, respectively. Such that, the cumulative export to the equatorial Pacific Ocean over the past 35-40 years has been about 8.3 TBq. By comparison, the annual discharge rate for ^{239,240}Pu from Mururoa lagoon sediment to the open ocean is about 0.02 TBq (Bourlat *et al.*, 1995). Hence the total cumulative export to the ocean from this source over the past 20-25 years would be around 0.45 TBq.

We can also provide a crude estimate for ^{137}Cs export from the lagoon environments using ^{137}Cs/^{239,240}Pu activity ratios. Typical present-day ^{137}Cs/^{239,240}Pu inventory ratios on contaminated islands in the Marshall Islands range between 1.8 and 19 (Robison, pers. comm.). This implies that a maximum of about 2 PBq of the present Pacific Ocean inventory was derived from ^{137}Cs that was initially deposited on or around the lagoons. This represents less than 2% of the total ^{137}Cs deposit in the North Pacific Ocean from global fallout. Export into the South Pacific from the Mururoa Atoll lagoon are expected to be similar.

2.9.   Impacts of Chernobyl on the Pacific

Radioactive debris from the 1986 Chernobyl accident caused widespread contamination over much of Europe. Chernobyl-derived radionuclides were also detected in Japan, across North America and in the north Pacific region (Aoyama *et al.*, 1986; Larsen *et al.*, 1986). ^{137}Cs deposition in Tokyo (Japan) in the weeks following the accident totaled about 74 MBq km^{-2} or approximately 2% of the cumulative ^{137}Cs deposit from global fallout (Aoyama *et al.*, 1986). The total annual ^{137}Cs deposit in Japan during 1986 was over 200 times higher than pre-Chernobyl values (Fig. 2.5.). The presence of Chernobyl-derived ^{137}Cs in marginal seas around Japan was inferred by measurement of ^{134}Cs detected in surface waters north of about 30° N (Aoyama and Hirose, 1995). These authors estimated that 10 to 46% of the total ^{137}Cs surface water concentration was directly attributable to Chernobyl inputs while the vertical transport of Chernobyl-derived ^{134}Cs (^{137}Cs) was largely controlled by the vertical extension of the surface mixed layer. These results confirmed earlier findings that Cs isotopes delivered to the surface ocean may remain in the upper mixed layer for up to several decades.

Debris from the Chernobyl nuclear reactor explosion appears to have made no detectable contribution to atmospheric ^{137}Cs levels in New Zealand (Matthews, 1995) and presumably to the South Pacific Ocean.

2.10. Radionuclide Inventories in Waters and Sediments from the North Pacific

[137]Cs and [239,240]Pu inventories in sea water and sediment are shown in Figures 2.7. and 2.8. for water and sediment column profiles measured in the Pacific Ocean during and after the GEOSECS cruises. The total inventories can be compared with global fallout estimates in Table 2.V. It is also noted that total oceanic inventories are influenced by inter-ocean exchange (Toggweiler and Trumbore, 1985; Livingston et al., 1984) but these processes have not been addressed in this article.

2.11. Discussion

It can be seen that calculated inventories of ^{137}Cs and [239,240]Pu exceed mean global fallout inputs at the corresponding latitudes. Between 95 and 99% of ^{137}Cs and between 78 and 95% of [239,240]Pu delivered to the open ocean appears to be retained in the water column. [137]Cs/[239,240]Pu inventory ratios in the water column are generally much higher (10-50) than those in the underlying sediments (1-9) confirming beliefs that [239,240]Pu is more « particle » reactive and therefore is more efficiently exported to the deep ocean and into the underlying sediments.

Water column inventories for ^{137}Cs and [239,240]Pu are up to twice fallout estimates between 30 and 40°N and are higher than those in more northern latitudes (Figs. 2.7. and 2.8.). The lower ^{137}Cs inventories north of the Subarctic Convergence zone suggests that water is being redistributed possibility as a result of upwelling. Excess [239,240]Pu inventories have also been observed in the immediate vicinity of the Marshall Islands (data not shown; Noshkin and Wong, 1980). Based on our evaluation of possible sources of fallout radionuclides in the Pacific Ocean, the long term persistence of close-in and/or stratospheric fallout from nuclear weapons testing in the Marshall Islands still appears to be the only plausible explanation for excess radionuclide inventories above those expected from global fallout – this is particularly true of the western North Pacific. Enewetak and Bikini Atolls are located with the North Equatorial Current and close-in fallout would have traveled westward and feed into the Kuroshio Current off the Philippines and turned north flowing along the Japanese islands towards the east. It also appears that localized radionuclide inputs from the Pacific moved

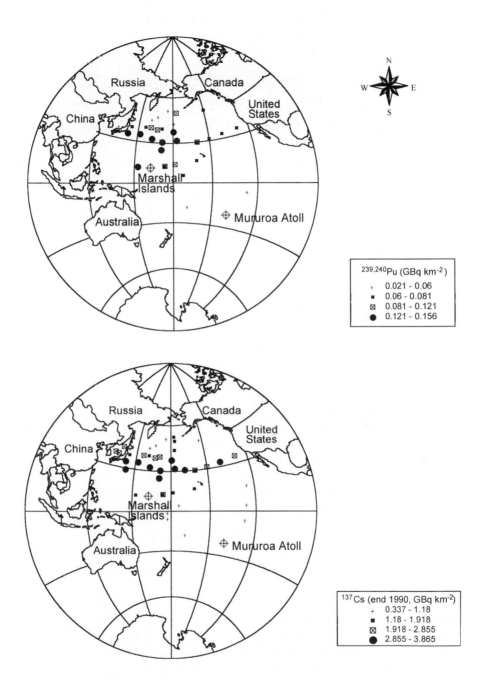

Figure 2.7. ^{137}Cs and ^{239,240}Pu inventories (GBq km^{-2})
in the Pacific Ocean water column (^{137}Cs data has been decay corrected to
a reference data of 31 Dec. 1990).

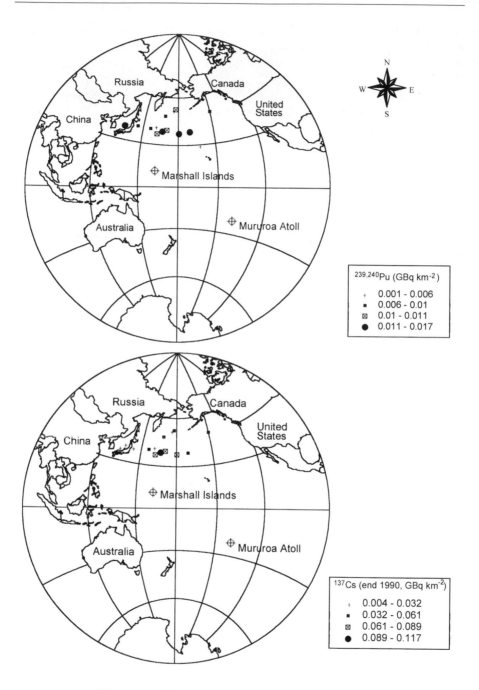

Figure 2.8. ^{137}Cs and ^{239,240}Pu inventories (GBq km^{-2}) in the Pacific Ocean sediment column (^{137}Cs data has been decay corrected to a reference data of 31 Dec. 1990).

south into the Indian Ocean through the Indonesian archipelago. Time histories of fallout radionuclide concentrations in corals appear to support these conclusions and show that close-in and tropospheric fallout from Pacific tests sites elevated ^{90}Sr concentrations in surface waters in both the North Pacific and southern Indian Ocean to values well in excess of those expected from global fallout alone (Toggeiler and Trumbore, 1985). During our presentation we will attempt to provide an overview of the material covered in this paper as well as more detailed discussion on radionuclide distributions and inventories.

Acknowledgments

We thank researchers and scientists from the following institutions for their contribution to the study of artificial radioactivity in the Pacific Ocean: Divisional of Marine Radioecology, Isozaki (Japan); Environmental Measurements Laboratory, New York (USA); Faculty of Science, Kanazawa University (Japan); Geochemistry Research Association, Tokyo (Japan); the International Atomic Energy Agency (IAEA); Japan Marine Science and Technology Center, Yokosuka (Japan); Korea Ocean Research & Development Institute, Ansan (Korea); Lawrence Livermore National Laboratory, Livermore (U.S.A.); Meteorological Research Institute, Tsukuba (Japan); National Institute of Radiological Sciences, Hitachinaka (Japan); Ocean Research Institute, University of Tokyo, Tokyo (Japan); Service Mixte de Sécurité Radiologique, Montlhéry (France); and the Wood Hole Oceanographic Institute, Wood Hole (USA). We also wish to acknowledge the assistance of Mr. Dong-Jin Kang (KORDI) for help with compiling published data, and Ms. Lynn Wilder and Rayla Bradsher (LLNL) for preparing maps and figures. Work performed under the auspices of the U.S. Department of Energy at Lawrence Livermore National Laboratory under contract W-7405-Eng-48.

References

Aoyama M. and Hirose K. (1995) The temporal and spatial variation of ^{137}Cs concentration in the western North Pacific and its marginal seas during the period from 1979 to 1988. *J. Environ. Radioactivity* **29**, 57-74.

Aoyama M., Hirose K., Suzuki Y., Inoue H. and Sugimura Y. (1986) High level radioactive nuclides in Japan in May. *Nature* **321**, 819-820.

Baumgartner A. and Reichel E. (1975) World Water Balance: Mean, Annual Global, Continental and Maritime Precipitation, Evaporation and Runoff, Elsevier, N.Y., 179 pp.

Baxter M.S. (1983) The disposal of high-activity nuclear waste in the oceans. *Mar. Poll. Bull.* **14**, 126-132.

Beasley T.M., Ball L.A. and Blakesley B.A. (1981a) Plutonium and americium export to the North-east Pacific Ocean by Columbia river runoff. *Est. Coastal Shelf Sci.* **13**, 659-669.

Bealsey T.M., Ball L.A, Andrews III J.E. and Halverson J.E. (1981b) Hanford-derived plutonium in Columbia River sediments. *Science* **214**, 913-915.

Bennet B.G. (1978) Environmental aspects of americium. USDOE Report EML-348.

Bertstein R.E. and Betzer P.R. (1991) Labile phases and the ocean's strontium cycle: A method of sediment trap sampling for acantharians, In: *Marine Particle: Analysis and Characterization* (D.C. Hurd and D.W. Spencer, Eds.) pp. 369-374. Geographical Monographs 63, American Geophysical Union.

Bourlat Y., Milliès-LaCroix J.-C. and Nazard R. (1995) Determination of plutonium radioactivity in Mururoa lagoon water. *J. Radioanal. Nucl. Chem.* **197**, 387-408.

Bourlat Y. and Martin G. (1992) Precise determination of the concentration of radiocaesium in the water of Mururoa lagoon. *J. Environ. Radioactivity* **17**, 13-29.

Bowen V.T., Noshkin V.E., Livingston H.D. and Volchok H.L. (1980) Fallout radionuclides in the Pacific Ocean: vertical and horizontal distributions, largely from GEOSECS stations. *Earth Plan. Sci. Lett.* **49**, 411-434.

Burton J.D. (1985) Radioactive nuclides in the marine environment. In: *Chemical Oceanography* Vol. 3 (J.P Riley and G. Skirrow, Eds.) pp. 91-191. Academic Press.

Drake D.E. (1976) Suspended sediment transport and mud deposition continental shelves. In: *Marine Sediment Transport and Environmental Management* (D.J. Stanley and D.J.P. Swif, Eds.) pp. 127-158. John Wiley & Sons, New York.

Eisma D. (1993) *Suspended Matter in the Aquatic Environment*, Springer-Verlag, New York, 315 pp.

Fisher N.S. and Fowler S.W. (1983) The role of biogenic debris in the vertical transport of transuranic wastes in the sea. In: *Oceanic Processes in Marine Pollution*, Vol 2, Chapter 16 (T.P. O'Connor, W.V. Burt and I.W. Duedall, Eds.) pp. 197-207. Robert E. Krieger Publishing Co., Florida.

Fowler S.W., Ballestra S., La Rosa J. and Fukai R. (1983) Vertical transport of particulate-associated plutonium and amercium in the northwest Pacific. *Deep-Sea Res.* **7**, 35-47.

GESAMP (1989) The Atmospheric Input of Trace Species to the World Ocean, IMO/FAO/UNESCO/WMO/WHO/IAEA/UN/UNEP Joint Group of Experts on the Scientific Aspects of Marine Pollution (GESAMP), Reports and Studies No. 38, 111 pp.

Hardy E.P. (1973) Global inventory and distribution of fallout plutonium. *Nature* **241**, 444-445.

Hardy E.P. (1977) Final Tabulation of Monthly [90]Sr Fallout Data, 1954-76. USERDA Report HASL-329.

Harley N., Fisenne I., Ong L.D. and Harley J. (1965) Fission yield and fission product decay. USAEC Health and Safety Laboratory, Fallout Program Quarterly Summary Report, HASL-164, pp. 251-260.

Hirose K., Sugimura Y. and Aoyama M. (1992) Plutonium and ^{137}Cs in the western north Pacific: estimation of residence time of plutonium in surface waters. *Appl. Radiat. Isot.* **43**, 349-359.

Hodge V., Johnson S.R. and Goldberg E. (1978) Influence at atmospherically transported aersols on surface ocean composition. *Geochim.* **12**, 7-20.

Honjo S. (1980) Material fluxes and modes of sedimentation in the mesopelagic and bathypelagic zones. *J. Mar. Res.* **38**, 53-97.

IAEA (1991) Inventory of Radioactive Material Entering the Marine Environment: Sea Disposal of Radioactive Waste. IAEA-TECDOC-588, 54 pp.

Irino T. and Tada R. (1994) Temporal variation of the Kosa flux at ODP site 797, the Japan Sea during last 200Ka. In: *International Symposium on Global Fluxes of Carbon and its Related Substances in Coastal Sea-Ocean-Atmosphere* (Collected abstracts, 1994 Sapporo IGBP Symposium) pp. 98-99, Sapporo.

Iseki K. (1981) Vertical transport of particulate organic matter in deep Bering Sea and Gulf of Alaska. *J. Oceanogr. Soc. Japan* **37**, 101-110.

Joseph A.B., Gustafson P.F., Russel I.R., Schuert E.A., Volchok H.L. and Tamplin A. (1971) Sources of Radioactivity and their Characteristics. In: *Radioactivity in the Marine Environment.* National Academy of Sciences, Washington, pp. 6-41.

Katsuragi M. and Aoyama M. (1986) Seasonal variation of Sr-90 fallout in Japan through the end of 1983. *Pap. Meteorol. Geophys.* **37**, 15-36.

Larsen R.J. (1984) Graphic Presentation of Quarterly [90]Sr Fallout Data, 1954-82. USDOE Report EML-424.

Larsen R.J. (1985) Worldwide deposition of ^{90}Sr through 1982. USDOE Report EML-430.

Larsen R.J., Sanderson C.G. and Kada J. (1995) EML Surface Air Sampling Program, 1990-93 Data, USDOE Report EML-572, 247 pp.

Larsen R.J., Sanderson C.G., Rivera W. and Zamichieli M. (1986) The Characterization of Radionuclides in North America and Hawaiian Surface Air and Deposition Following the Chernobyl Accident. USDOE Report EML-460, 104 pp.

Lee Y.K. (1994) The study on the atmospheric deposition of anthropogenic radionuclides in the Korean Peninsula. MS Thesis, Hanyang University (Seoul) 43 pp. (in Korean).

Livingston H.D. and Bowen V.T. (1979) Pu and ^{137}Cs in coastal sediments. *Earth Planet. Sci. Lett.* **43**, 29-45.

Martin J.H. (1970) The possible transport of trace metals *via* moulted copepod exoskeletons. *Limnol. Oceanogr.* **15**, 756-761.

Matthews K.M. (1995) Measurements of residual traces of ^{137}Cs in the atmosphere in New Zealand. *J. Environ. Radioactivity* **27**, 221-229.

Milliman J.D. and Meade R.H. (1983) World-wide delivery of river sediment to the oceans. *J. Geol.* **91**, 1-21.

Miyake Y., Saruhashi K., Sugimura Y., Kanazawa T. and Hirose K. (1988) Contents of ^{137}Cs, plutonium and americium isotopes in the southern ocean waters. *Papers in Meteorology and Geophysics* **39**, 95-113.

Miyake Y., Sugiura Y. and Kameda K. (1955) On the distribution of radioactivity in the Sea around Bikini Atoll in June 1954. *Pap. Meteor. Geophys.* (Tokyo) **5**, 253-263.

Miyake Y. and Tsubota H. (1963) Radioisotopes in Hydrology, SM-38/21, IAEA.

Monetti A. (1996) Worldwide Deposition of Strontium-90 through 1990. USDOE Report EML-579, 56 pp.

Nakamura K. and Nagaya Y. (1975) Accumulation of radionuclides in coastal sediment of Japan (II). Contents of fission products in some coastal sediments collected in 1966-72. *J. Radiat. Res.* **16**, 184-192.

Nagaya Y. and Nakamura K. (1976) ^{90}Sr and ^{137}Cs contents in the surface waters of the adjacent seas of Japan and the North Pacific during 1969 and 1973. *J. Oceanogr. Soc. Japan* **32**, 228-234.

Nagaya Y. and Nakamura K. (1981) Artificial radionuclides in the western northwest Pacific (I) ^{90}Sr and ^{137}Cs in the deep waters. *J. Oceanogr. Soc. Japan* **37**, 135-144.

Nagaya Y. and Nakamura K. (1984) [239,240]Pu, ^{137}Cs and ^{90}Sr in the central North Pacific. *J. Oceanogr. Soc. Japan* **40**, 416-424.

Nakamura K. and Nagaya Y. (1985) Accumulation of Cs-137 and Pu-239,240 in sediments of the coastal sea and the north Pacific. In: *Marine and Estuarine Geochemistry*, Chapter 12 (A.C. Sigleo and A. Hattori, Eds.) pp. 171-180. Lewis Pub., Chelsea.

Nagaya Y. and Nakamura K. (1987) Artificial radionuclides in the western northwest Pacific (II): [137]Cs and [239,240]Pu inventories in water and sediment columns observed from 1980 to 1986. *J. Oceanogr. Soc. Japan* **43**, 345-355.

Nagaya Y. and Nakamura K. (1992) [239,240]Pu and ^{137}Cs in the East China and Yellow Seas. *J. Oceanogr.* **48**, 23-35.

Nagaya Y. and Nakamura K. (1993) Distributions and mass-balance of [239,240]Pu and ^{137}Cs in the northern North Pacific. In: *Deep Ocean Circulation, Physical and Chemical Aspects* (T. Teramoto, Ed.) pp. 157-167. Elsevier Science Pub.

Nakanishi T., Shiba Y., Muramatsu M. and Azizul Haque M. (1995) Estimation of mineral aerosol fluxes to the Pacific by using environmental plutonium as a tracer. In: *Biogeochemical Processess and Ocean Flux in the Western Pacific*, (H. Sakai and Y. Nozaki, Eds.) pp. 15-30. Terra Scientific (TERRAPUB), Tokoyo.

Nakanishi T., Yajima M., Senaga M., Takei M., Ishikawa A. and Sakamoto K. (1984) Determination of ^{239,240}Pu in sea water. *Nucl. Instru. Meth. Phy. Res.* **223**, 239-242.

Newell R.E. (1971) The global circulation of atmospheric pollutants. *Sci. Am.* **224**, 32-42.

Noshkin V.E. and Bowen V.T. (1973) Concentrations and distributions of long-lived fallout radionuclides in open ocean sediments. In: *Radioactive Contamination of the Marine Environment*, pp. 671-686, IAEA, Vienna.

Noshkin V.E. and Wong K.M. (1980) Plutonium in the North Equatorial Pacific. In: *Processes Determining the Input Behavior and Fate of Radionuclides and Trace Elements in Continental Shelf Environments*, USDOE Conf. Rep., 790382, pp. 11-28.

Noshkin V.E. and Wong K.M. (1979) Plutonium mobilization from sedimentary sources to solution in the marine environment. In: *Proceedings of the Third NEA Seminar on Marine Radioecology*, pp. 165-178, Tokoyo.

Noshkin V.E., Wong K.M., Jokela T.A., Brunk J.L. and Eagle R.J. (1987) Plutonium and Americium Behavior in Coral Atoll Environments. In: *Oceanic Processes in Marine Pollution*, Vol 2, Chapter 14 (T.P. O'Connor, W.V. Burt and I.W. Duedall, Eds.) pp. 159-174, Robert E. Krieger Publishing Co., Florida.

Osterberg C., Cutshall N. and Cronin J. (1965) Chromium-51 as a radioactive tracer of Columbia River water at sea. *Science* **150**, 1585-1587.

Parrington J.R., Zoller W.H. and Aras N.K. (1983) Asian Dust: Seasonal Transport to the Hawaiian Islands. *Science* **220**, 195-197.

Roether W. (1974) The tritium and carbon-14 profiles at the GEOSECS I (1969) and GOGO I (1971) North Pacific stations. *Earth Planet. Sci. Lett.* **23**, 108-115.

Saruhashi K., Katsuragi Y., Kanazawa T., Sugimura Y. and Miyake Y. (1975) ^{90}Sr and ^{137}Cs in the Pacific water. *Rec. Oceanogr. Wks. Japan* **13**, 1-15.

Schell W.R., Lowman F.G. and Marshall R.P. (1980) Geochemistry of Transuranic Elements at Bikini Atoll. In: *Transuranic Elements in the Environment*. (W.C. Hanson, Ed.) pp. 541-577, US Department of Energy.

Simpson H.J., Olsen C.R., Trier R.M. and Williams S.C. (1976) Man-made radionuclides and sedimentation in the Hudson Estuary. *Science* **194**, 179-182.

Toggweiler J.R. and Trumbore S. (1985) Bomb-test ^{90}Sr in Pacific and Indian Ocean surface waters as recorded by banded corals. *Earth Planet. Sci. Lett.* **74**, 306-314.

UNSCEAR (1982) Ionizing Radiation: Sources and Biological Effects. United Nations, New York, 773 pp.

Vdovenko V.M., Kolesnikov A.G., Spitsyn V.I., Bernovskaya R.N., Gedenonov L.I., Gromov V.V., Ivanova L.M., Nelepo V.A., Tikhomirov T.N. and Trusov A.G. (1972) Radioactivity of ocean waters and the behaviour of certain fission products in the ocean, Proceedings of the

4th International Conference on Peaceful Uses of Atomic Energy, **11**, 609-630.

Volchok H.L., Bowen V.T., Folson T.R., Broeker W.S., Schuert E.A. and Bien G.S. (1971) Oceanic distributions of radionuclides form nuclear explosions. Sources of Radioactivity and their Characteristics. In: *Radioactivity in the Marine Environment*, pp. 42-89, National Academy of Sciences, Washington.

Yamagata N., Matsuda S. and Kodaira K. (1963) Run-off of caesium-137 and strontium-90 from rivers. *Nature* **200**, 668-669.

White Book (1993) Yablokov A.V., Karasev V.K., Rumyantsev V.M., Kokeyev M.Ye., Petrov O.I., Lystsov V.N., Yemelyanenkov and Rubrsov P.M. Facts and Problems Related to Radioactive Waste Disposal in Seas Adjacent to the Territory of the Russian Federation, Office of the President of the Russian Federation, Moscow.

Windom H.L. (1975) Eolian contributions to marine sediments. *J. Sediment Petrol.* **45**, 520-529.

3 Radioactivity from the North Pole to the Antarctic

E. Holm, P. Roos,
D. Josefsson and B. Persson

The major scientific expeditions to the Antarctic and the Arctic, such as the Swedish Arctic Expedition (YMER-80), Swedish Antarctic Research Expedition (SWEDARP 88/89), Swedish Arctic Expedition (SWEDARTIC-91 actually a Swedish-German-USA collaboration), the Swedish-Russian Tundra Expedition (TUNDRA-94) covered areas in the North and South Atlantic from 90° N to 72° S and in the Arctic Ocean from 15° W to 160° E.

During these expeditions, in particular, surface water was collected at sampling stations and during steaming between stations and from Sweden to the Antarctic and the Arctic and analysed for radiocaesium and plutonium. In combination with data published from other major expeditions such as for example the GEOSECS expedition 72/73 the distribution of radionuclides in time over 22 years and space can be assessed.

Data show that radiocaesium from nuclear detonation tests carried out in the late 1950's and the early 1960's shows a long residence time in surface waters in the North and South Atlantic. The half-life, corrected for physical decay is in the order of 100 years while plutonium has a half-life of 7-8 years.

Results from the central Arctic ocean and continental shelf along the European-Siberian tundra show that radiocaesium from European reprocessing plants is transported eastwards along the coast to the Laptev Sea and then advected into the central Arctic ocean with the so-called Trans Polar Drift. The origin of plutonium in the Arctic Sea is mainly from nuclear tests, only 5-10% for $^{239+240}$Pu but 20-40% for ^{238}Pu and ^{241}Pu. The work also comprises transfer of radiocaesium in the Antarctic and Arctic food chains. Concentration factors are generally higher in the Antarctic than in the Arctic.

3.1.   Introduction

On a global bases nuclear test fallout constitutes still the most important source for contamination of the oceans with respect to radiocaesium and plutonium although from radiological point of view natural radionuclides such as ^{210}Po is more important. Locally other sources such as releases from nuclear reprocessing plants and the Chernobyl accident are more significant. Most of this activity is present in the oceans may be with the exemption for the Chernobyl accident.

Radionuclides are subject to a number of processes influencing their concentration in sea water including horizontal and vertical advection of large water masses, turbulent diffusion sediments, reversible/irreversible scavenging by suspended particles, etc. The knowledge of source terms and the physical decay of radionuclides provide an excellent tool for tracer studies in time and space. Furthermore long-term studies of low activities in the oceans are necessary for predictions and dose assessment following eventual major accidents/releases. This paper describes the general latitudinal global of plutonium and radiocaesium in the South and North Atlantic from the North Pole to the Antarctic and the longitudinal distribution along the European-Siberian coast following releases from major sources.

3.2.   Materials and Methods

Results are available from several important scientific expeditions such as YMER-80 to the Barents and Greenland Seas, SWEDARP 1988-1989 to the Antarctic Peninsula area, SWEDARCTIC 1991 to the North Pole, and the Swedish-Russian expedition 1994 along the coast of the European-Russian Tundra. The areas covered by these expeditions are shown in Figures 3.1. to 3.4.

At the previous conference, 1991 at Norwich (Holm *et al.*, 1992) results from the expeditions performed before 1991 were put in the perspective of the GEOSECS expedition 1972/1973 to the North and South Atlantic and the Polish expedition 1977/1978 to the Antarctic Peninsula area. The results from these expeditions showed an astonishing agreement of the latitudinal distribution of plutonium and ^{137}Cs after correction for physical decay.

During the expeditions surface water was generally obtained by direct continuous supply to a laboratoy container. Water profiles were either collected by large volume bottles or in shallow waters, such as during the Tundra expedition, pumped from a hose submersed to the desired depth. Radiocaesium was precipitated on copper-ferrocyanide from 200 l water samples using ^{134}Cs as radiochemical yield determinant. The samples were analysed by HPGe gamma spectrometry for 2 days in 60 or 180 ml calibrated geometry. Actinides were preconcentrated on board from 200 l samples by precipitation with sodium hydroxide, at pH 9-10, after acidification, reduction with sodiumdisulfite and equilibration of the radiochemical yield determinant ^{242}Pu. For the assessment of the ^{134}Cs/^{137}Cs activity ratio large volumes, 1 000 l, or more, were pumped through cotton wound cartridge filters impregnated with copper ferrocyanide. Sediment samples were collected with a HAPS or boxcorer during the Tundra expedition or regarding the central Arctic ocean collected by box corers or multicorer devices and obtained from other research groups participating in expeditions not mentioned above. Plutonium was separated by radiochemical methods described previously (IAEA, 1986) and analysed for 7-10 days by solid state alpha spectrometry.

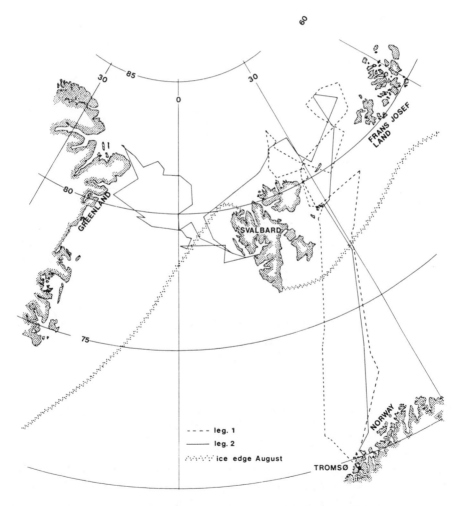

Fig. 3.1. Cruising and sampling route for the expedition to the Barents and Greenland Seas, YMER-80, 1980.

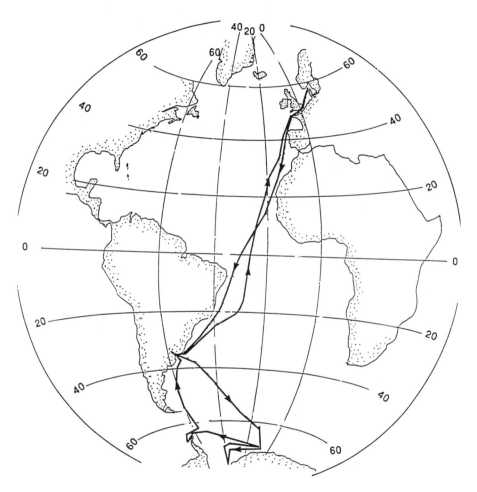

Fig. 3.2. Areas covered by the Swedish Antarctic Research Expedition, SWEDARP, 1988/1989.

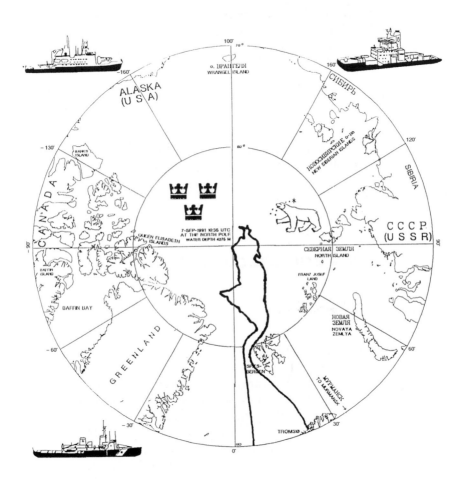

Fig. 3.3. Cruising and sampling route for the Expedition to the North Pole,
SWEDARTIC-1991.

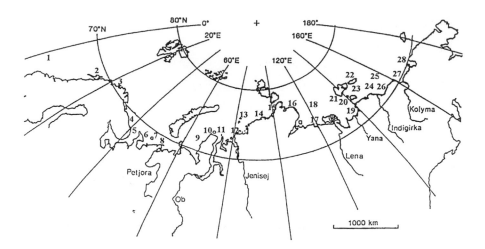

Fig. 3.4. Sampling stations along the coast of the European-Siberian Tundra
during the Swedish-Russian Tundra Expedition, 1994.

3.3.　Results and Discussion

3.3.1.　*Radiocaesium*

Latitudinal Distribution

Caesium-137 is present today in various concentrations in surface sea water,
from a few tenth of mBq l^{-1} such as in the Antarctic area to 100 mBq l^{-1} such
as in the Baltic sea following the Chernobyl accident or even higher locally
close to nuclear facilities. Levels of ^{134}Cs are in the order of 3% of those for
^{137}Cs if water masses are mainly contaminated from the Chernobyl accident
(1986) and in the order of 0.3% if contaminated through the major period of
releases (1974-1979) from European reprocessing facilities (mainly
Sellafield).

　　Figure 3.5. shows the latitudinal distribution of ^{137}Cs in surface water
from the Antarctic Peninsula area to the North Pole. These data were
obtained through the Swedish Expedition to the Antarctic 1988-1989
(SWEDARP, 88/89) and the Swedish expedition to the Arctic and the North
Pole 1991 (SWEDARCTIC, 1991). Activity concentrations are not decay corrected (about 5% in 2.5 years) since the two expeditions cover areas mainly
contaminated from different sources during different periods.

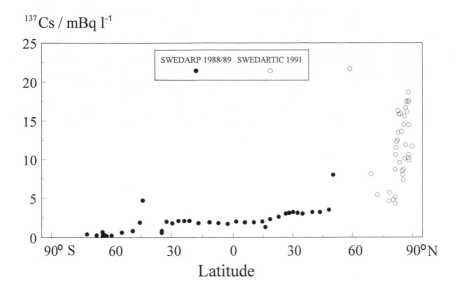

Fig. 3.5. Activity concentration of ^{137}Cs in surface water as a function of latitude from Sweden to the Antarctic Peninsula Area, 1988/1989 (SWEDARP) and from Sweden to the North Pole, 1991 (SWEDARCTIC).

Below 30° S concentrations are low and in the order of 0.5 mBq l^{-1}. Significantly higher concentrations were found at 45° S, which is difficult to explain but also ^{60}Co was detected in these samples. From 30° S to 25° N activity concentrations are significantly higher, around 2 mBq l^{-1}. With a lot of good will one can say that there is an increase in activity concentrations, to 2.5 mBq l^{-1}, between 30° S and 20° S which someone could interpret as a result of nuclear tests in the Pacific at these latitudes, but many other distribution processes might play a role. The effective ecological half-life of radiocaesium in the North and South Atlantic was estimated to be as long as 100 years since the surface water is exchanged with water which is also contaminated.

North of 20° N activity concentrations are about 3 mBq l^{-1} if they are not influenced from European reprocessing facilities or the Chernobyl accident. Above 45° N concentrations are very variable in the North and Norwegian Seas and activity concentrations vary with distance to sources (European reprocessing facilities) and distance from the coast. It has been shown that the activity is transported by the Gulf Stream and there is a very sharp gradient in activity concentrations of radiocaesium with distance from the Norwegian coast due to the coriolis force (Dahlgaard *et al.*, 1986).

We have been collecting surface sea water samples during steaming along the Norwegian coast to and from the Arctic during the expeditions and data are shown in Figure 3.6. In 1980 activity concentrations along the

Norwegian coast reflect the releases from the Sellafield nuclear fuel reprocessing plant where the releases were the highest during 1974-1979 (annual
discharges 3000-5000 TBq). The transit time from Sellafield to west Norway
has been estimated to 3-4 years and the travelling time along the coast of
Norway about 1 year (Dahlgaard *et al.*, 1986; Kershaw and Baxter, 1995).
This resulted in activity concentrations of about 100-200 mBq l^{-1} or about
twice as high as those in the Baltic Sea following the Chernobyl accident.
The activity concentration decreased very little along the coast, less than a
factor 2 (Holm *et al.*, 1983).

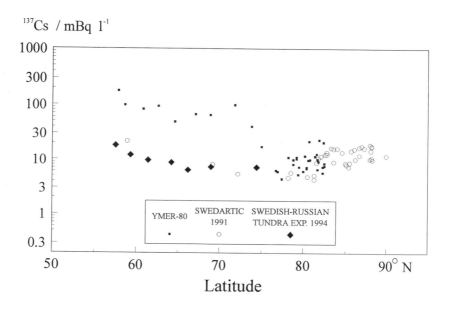

**Fig. 3.6. Activity concentrations of ^{137}Cs in surface water along
the Norwegian coast to the Arctic in 1980 (YMER-80), 1991 (SWEDARCTIC-91)
and 1994 (TUNDRA-94).**

Further north the ^{137}Cs concentration $C(x)$ varied with distance (x) from
70° N for locations east of Svalbard according to the equation:

$$C(x) = 141 \exp(-000122\,x)$$
(half distance 568 km)

and west of Svalbard according to:

$$C(x) = 148 \exp(-0.00164\,x)$$
(half distance 423 km)

This means that more radiocaesium went to the east then to the west of
Svalbard.

As a result of the decrease in releases from the European reprocessing facilities activity concentrations along the Norwegian coast were only 10-30 mBq l^{-1} in 1991. The decrease would have been even more significant without the Chernobyl accident. There is an annual outflow of ^{137}Cs from the Baltic Sea to the North Sea of about 50-60 TBq. The total nuclear test fall-out of ^{137}Cs in the North Atlantic is estimated to 76 000 TBq and the releases from European reprocessing facilities (decay-corrected) 29 000 TBq (Kershaw and Baxter, 1995). These sources are much smaller today. Fallout from nuclear test is almost negligible and releases from reprocessing plants have been reduced in such a way that outflow from the Baltic Sea today constitutes the most significant source for radiocaesium along the Norwegian coast and further into the Arctic.

It can be observed that activity concentrations of ^{137}Cs were higher in the central Arctic ocean than in the region between Norway and Svalbard. The highest concentrations were found around the North Pole, 14-19 mBq l^{-1}, between longitudes 50-180° E and 0-15° E but lower along the 0 meridian and 10-20° W. The activity ratios $^{134}Cs/^{137}Cs$ (0.003-0.006) and the physical half-life of ^{134}Cs ($T_{1/2}$ = 2.4 years) indicate that the origin of radiocaesium is mainly the Sellafield pulse 1974-1979 (ratio about 0.2). This means that it has taken about 14 years for radiocaesium from this source to reach this area.

In 1994 the ^{137}Cs activity concentrations along the Norwegian coast were quite similar to those in 1991. This means that present levels of radiocaesium are maintained by the outflow of Chernobyl related activity from the Baltic Sea.

Longitudinal Distribution

The distribution along the coast of the European Siberian Tundra is shown in Figure 3.7. One could expect that run-off from the tundra is effective and the large rivers drain enormous areas which would result in a significant transfer of fallout deposited radionuclides to the Arctic ocean. West of 150° E concentrations of radiocaesium are quite constant, 6-11 mBq l^{-1} while levels in the East Siberian Sea are in the order of 1-3 mBq l^{-1} where ^{134}Cs is absent which indicates that the only source is nuclear test fallout. The activity ratio $^{134}Cs/^{137}Cs$ west of 150° E was about 0.015 indicating that about 30% of ^{137}Cs in these regions originated from the Chernobyl accident. A third source, tentatively European reprocessing facilities, is also present. The effects are even more pronounced when observing the bottom water, which is less influenced from the river water. The lower salinity coastal river water carries lower concentrations radiocaesium while the opposite is the case for Norwegian Coastal Current, Norwegian Sea and the Barents Sea (Kershaw and Baxter, 1995) where coastal and Baltic water are contaminated from the Chernobyl accident. Radionuclides are not accumulated at the continental shelf of the European-Siberian Tundra coast but washed off and advected together with the continental shelf water from the Laptev Sea along the Lomosov Ridge with the Trans Polar Drift to the central Arctic towards Fram Strait.

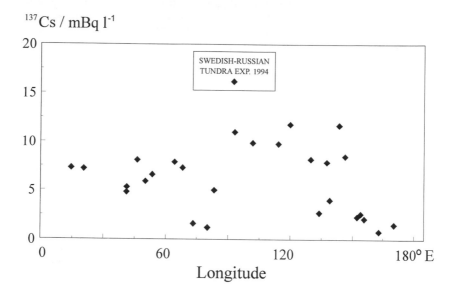

Fig. 3.7. Concentrations of ^{137}Cs in surface water in 1994 as a function of longitude along the continental shelf of the European-Siberian Tundra (TUNDRA-94).

3.3.2. Plutonium

Latitudinal Distribution

Plutonium-239+240 is present in seawater from about less than 1 µBq l^{-1} to a few hundred µBq l^{-1}. A significant difference to radiocaesium is that caesium behaves rather conservatively in most waterbodies while plutonium is particle reactive and redox sensitive. This means that geochemical concentrations processes of plutonium can take place. On the other hand plutonium is not concentrated in food chains like caesium.

Figure 3.8. shows the distribution of plutonium in surface water from the North Pole to the Antarctic Peninsula Area obtained through the Swedish expedition to the Antarctic 1988/1989 and the Swedish Arctic Expedition 1991. As for radiocaesium different symbols have been used for the two expeditions and decay correction would here in any case not be necessary due to the long physical half-life of the plutonium isotopes (5 670 years and 24 100 years, respectively).

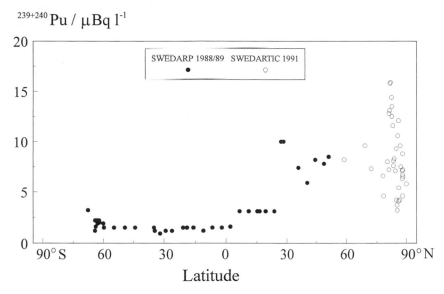

Fig. 3.8. Activity concentration of plutonium in surface water from Sweden to the Antarctic Peninsula Area and from Sweden to the North Pole in 1988/1989 (SWEDARP) and 1991 (SWEDARCTIC) respectively.

In the latitude band $0°$ S – $60°$ S activity concentrations are about 1.5 mBq m^{-3} while concentrations surprisingly are higher, about 2 mBq m^{-3}, below the Antarctic convergence zone. There is no evidence of increased concentrations at latitudes where the Pacific nuclear tests were performed but the relatively short residence time of plutonium in surface water would in any case have erased such signals. In the latitude band 5-25° N we find concentrations about 3 mBq m^{-3} and at 25-50° N around 8 mBq m^{-3}. Along the Norwegian coast from $60°$ N – $75°$ N activity concentrations of plutonium are decreasing while in the central Arctic ocean we find among the highest concentrations of $^{239+240}$Pu. This is rather unexpected since it has been shown that only a fraction (4%) of plutonium released from the Sellafield nuclear fuel reprocessing plant is present as soluble Pu and the remainder is deposited relatively close to the source (Pentreath *et al.*, 1985). Results from the YMER-80 expedition showed that in 1980, 5-10% of $^{239+240}$Pu, 26-49% of ^{238}Pu and 19-45% of ^{241}Pu in the Barents and Greeland Seas originated from European reprocessing facilities (Holm *et al.*, 1986). Again in 1991 as for radiocaesium we find the highest concentrations around the North Pole between longitudes 0-15° E, 9-16 mBq m^{-3}, while concentrations are lower between longitudes 50-80, 3-11 mBq m^{-3} where we actually found the highest ^{137}Cs concentrations. In Figure 3.9. the distributions of plutonium in 1980 and 1991 along the Norwegian coast and in the Arctic Sea are compared. The mean activity concentrations decreased from

13 ± 2 mBq m⁻³ (n = 48, 2 S.E.) to 8.4 ± 1.2 (n = 38, 2 S.E.) which gives an effective apparent ecological half-life of 17 years or twice as high as for other parts of the North and South Atlantic.

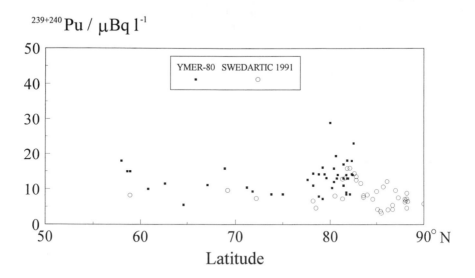

$^{239+240}$Pu / μBq l⁻¹

Fig. 3.9. Activity concentration of $^{239+249}$Pu along the Norwegian coast and in the Arctic in 1980 (YMER-80) and 1991 (SWEDARTIC).

There are several possible explanations for these results. The major pulse from the Sellafield reprocessing plants, 1974-1979, reached the central Arctic Ocean 10 years later and the fraction of the total plutonium from this source increased compared to the figures above. On the other hand already in 1980 plutonium concentrations were much higher than expected above 75° N and the isotopic composition indicated mainly that nuclear test fallout was the major source. A difference in source term behaviour might be possible, but the distribution of plutonium on suspended matter was not different for ^{238}Pu and ^{241}Pu compared to $^{239+240}$Pu. The activity ratio ^{238}Pu/$^{239+240}$Pu in releases from nuclear fuel reprocessing plants is in the order of 0.28 compared to 0.026 in fresh fallout. The corresponding figure for the activity ratio ^{241}Pu/$^{239+240}$Pu are 30 and 16 respectively. A more spectacular explanation is that personal unconfirmed information claim that during the former USSR tests at Novaya Zemlya they looked for that the wind was heading north. In this way activity contaminated Franz Josef land and its glaciers and constitute a continuous source to the Arctic Sea for plutonium and other radioisotopes. Another explanation is that plutonium behaves differently in the polar ice covered regions. The fraction of plutonium associated with suspended material was in 1980 in Barents and

Greenland Seas 30 ± 8% which is higher compared to other regions of the South and North Atlantic in 1989/1990 except for around 30° S and south of 60° S in the Weddell Sea and the Antarctic Peninsula area (Fig. 3.10.). A higher fraction associated with suspended matter would actually normally decrease the residence time. These observations were done during the summer months and for the rest of the year the situation might be different. The composition of suspended material is certainly also different compared to other parts of the Atlantic. The more or less permanent ice cover, melting and freezing processes might also change the behaviour of plutonium and other radionuclides (oxidation state, etc., prevention of vertical mixing, etc.). Radiocaesium and radiostrontium would be expected to freeze out from the ice, but for particle reactive elements, in this particular environment, the behaviour is difficult to predict at this stage.

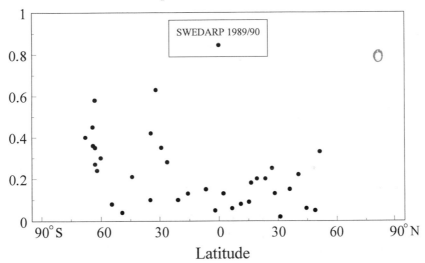

Fig. 3.10. Fraction of plutonium associated with suspended matter as a function of latitude from Sweden to the Antarctic Peninsula Area in 1991 (SWEDARP).

A closer look at the behaviour of plutonium compared to caesium in the South and North Atlantic is done by forming the Pu/Cs ratio (Fig. 3.11.). Nuclear test fallout is the major source and the integrated ratio in 1989 is also indicated in the figure. The figure shows the scavenging of plutonium relative to caesium which results in a shorter residence time for plutonium. The lowest Pu/Cs ratios are found around 30° S indicate relatively higher scavenging of plutonium in this region, and the highest ratios are found in the Antarctic are indicating recirculation of organic material. The corresponding ratio for 1980 and 1991 in the Arctic Ocean were not plotted but were about $(0.5 - 1) \times 10^{-3}$ and $(0.5 - 1.5) \times 10^{-3}$, respectively, which is the same as for the Antarctic area. This is similar to other areas of the North Atlantic where fallout is the major source of contamination but is much higher than expected since Sellafield is the major source for ^{137}Cs and the ratio should decrease with distance. The Pu/Cs ratio would be in the order of 0.2×10^{-3} if plutonium had behaved as expected. This suggests a significant different behaviour of plutonium and possibly other actinides in the polar regions which should be investigated further.

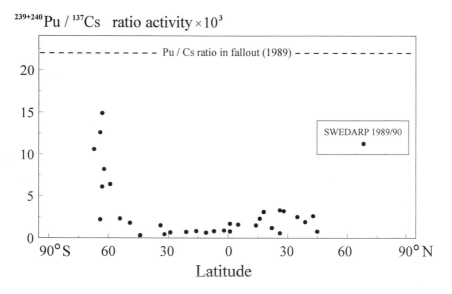

Fig. 3.11. The activity ratio $^{239+240}$Pu/^{137}Cs as a function of latitude from Sweden to the Antarctic Peninsula Area in 1991 (SWEDARP).

3.4. Conclusions

The shorter effective ecological residence time of plutonium (8 years) compared to radiocaesium (100 years) can be demonstrated in the North and South Atlantic. The Pu/Cs ratios in surface waters are therefore well below integrated fallout ratios. The ratios are enhanced as are the fractions on suspended matter of plutonium in the polar regions. The residence time of plutonium in the upper mixed layer is at least twice as high in the Arctic and possibly also in the Antarctic area as in other areas of the South and North Atlantic. This suggests a different behaviour of particle reactive and/or redox-sensitive elements in these region by influence of ice formation and/or the strong seasonal variation.

The releases of ^{137}Cs from the Sellafield reprocessing plant in 1974-1979 have now reached the central Arctic Ocean while Chernobyl related radiocaesium could in 1994 be found along the European-Siberian Tundra coast up to the Laptev Sea from where it will be advected together with shelfwater into the central Arctic ocean with the Trans Polar Drift. Plutonium has mainly nuclear test fallout as origin and is distributed differently compared to radiocaesium in the central Arctic Ocean. Outflow from the Baltic Sea into the North Sea is transported by the Norwegian current and constitutes today a major source for input of radiocaesium into the Arctic.

Acknowledgements

These expeditions were made possible through the logistical assistance of the Swedish Polar Research Secretariat. Assistance from the organisers, supporters and leaders of the expeditions is thereby gratefully acknowledged as is the financial support from the Swedish Radiation Protection Institute, the Swedish Natural Research Council, the CEC Fission and Safety Programme, The Nordic Committee for Nuclear Safety Research (NKS), Crafoordska Stiftelsen, Magn. Bergvalls Stiftelse, Carl Jönssons Understödsfond.

The following companies gave their support to these investigations in form of equipment. AB Tetra Pak, Alfa Laval AB, SAB-NIFE AB, Nordic Camera AB, Esselte Office AB, Nordisk Balzer AB, Arla Ekonomiska Förening, Christian Berner AB, Scanpump AB, Kiviks Musteri AB, AB Ventilationsutveckling, Gambro AB, Vattenteknik AB, Millipore AB, Hitachi Sales Scandinavia, Compac Computer AB, Fuji Film Sweden, Tele Ton Växjö, Barsebäck Kraft AB, Kärcher AB, Fiskars OY AB, Marine Power Sweden AB, Volvo Personvagnar, Siemens.

We also thank Mr K.-Å. Carlsson for his outstanding logistical support and participation in the expeditions. Special thanks also to Mrs G. Johansson, Mrs. B. Amilon, Mrs C. Lingårdh and Mrs M. Wolff for their skilful technical assistance.

References

Dahlgaard H., Aarkrog A., Hallstadius L., Holm E. and Rioseco J. (1986) Radiocaesium transport from the Irish Sea *via* the North Sea and the Norwegian Coastal Current to East Greenland. *Rapp. P-v. reun. Con. int. Explor. Mer* **186**, 70-79.

Holm E., Aarkrog A., Ballestra S. and Dahlgaard H. (1986) Origin and isotopic ratios of plutonium in the Barents and Greenland Seas. *Earth Planet. Sci. Lett.* **79**, 27-32.

Holm E., Persson B.R.R., Hallstadius L., Aarkrog A. and Dahlgaard H. (1983) Radiocaesium and transuranium elements in the Greenland and Barents Seas. *Oceanologica Acta* **6**, 457-462.

Holm E., Roos P., Persson R.B.R., Bojanowski R., Aarkrog A., Nielsen S.P. and Livingston H.D. (1992) Radiocaesium and plutonium in Atlantic surface waters from 73° N to 72° S. In: *Radionuclides in the study of marine processes*. (P.J. Kershaw and D.S. Woodhead Eds.) pp. 3-11. Elsevier Applied Science, London.

IAEA (1986) Methods for radiochemical analysis of plutonium, americium and curium. In: *Measurements of Radionuclides in Food and the Environment*. Technical Report Series No. 295, pp. 105-116.

Kershaw P. and Baxter A. (1995) The transfer of reprocessing wastes from north-west Europe to the Artic. *Deep Sea Res. II* **42**, 1413-1448.

Pentreath R.J., Harvey B.R. and Lovett M.B. (1985) Chemical speciation of transuranium nuclides discharged into the marine environment. In: *Speciation of Fission Products in the Environment*. (R.A. Bulman and J.R. Cooper, Eds.) pp. 212-325. Elsevier Applied Science Publishers, London.

4 ^{90}Sr, ^{137}Cs and $^{239+240}$Pu in World Ocean Water Samples Collected from 1992 to 1994

Y. Bourlat, J.-C. Milliès-Lacroix,
G. Le Petit and J. Bourguignon

At our request, about fifty surface ocean water samples were collected by French Navy ships in Atlantic and Pacific ocean from 1992 to 1993. Some additional samples collected in 1994 in Indian Ocean complete the study on ^{90}Sr, ^{137}Cs and $^{239+240}$Pu concentrations in oceans today in order to draw up current radiological maps.

^{90}Sr measurements were made by β counting on its daughter product ^{90}Y after chemical extraction. ^{137}Cs was analysed by HPGe γ spectrometry after concentration on copper ferrocyanide. Plutonium measurements were made by grid chamber or semiconductor α spectrometry after iron hydroxyde co-precipitation, purification and electrodeposition.

Results show levels generally more higher in the northern hemisphere than in the southern hemisphere. Highest ^{90}Sr and ^{137}Cs concentrations reach respectively 2 and 4 Bq m^{-3}. The lowest concentrations are recorded off Argentina and Chile coasts (below 1 Bq m^{-3} for ^{90}Sr and ^{137}Cs) and near Antarctica (about 0.1 Bq m^{-3} for ^{137}Cs). $^{239+240}$Pu concentrations vary generally from 0.5 to 5 mBq m^{-3}. Punctually in the northern hemisphere, levels up to 20 mBq m^{-3} can be observed.

4.1. Introduction

Man-made radionuclides are excellent ocean water mass tracers. ^{90}Sr and ^{137}Cs, essentially present in soluble form, are effective mainly through dilution, whereas sedimentation and biological transport appear to play a major role in the case of Plutonium.

Nearly 50 years after the first nuclear explosion, five French sampling campaigns have yielded a picture on the current radioactivity status of world surface waters. To investigate the behaviour of the radionuclides of interest through time, concentration data were reviewed and compared with data from the 1988-1989 Swedish Antarctic Research Expedition as regards the Atlantic, and with the Miyake (1977-1978), Livingston (1978-1980) and Hirose (1985-1987) data as regards the Pacific.

4.2. Sampling and Measurements

Ocean surface water samples were taken during 5 campaigns (see Fig. 4.1.).

Participating ships were French naval vessels and research vessels operated by the « Centre National de la Recherche Scientifique » (CNRS):

- « P.H. Jeanne d'Arc » cruise (32 samples in the Atlantic and Pacific from December 12, 1992, through June 4, 1993),
- « BSL Rhin » cruise (10 samples in the Atlantic and Pacific from February 4 through April 13, 1993),
- « AE Balny » cruise (9 samples in the North-Western Pacific, August 28 through October 21, 1993),
- « RV Marion-Dufresne » cruise (2 samples in the Southern Indian Ocean, February 12 through 22, 1994),
- « RV Antarès » cruise (3 samples in the Southern Indian Ocean, March 16 through 22, 1994).

The amount of water sample was usually 300 litres (from 270 to 360 litres). Acidification to a pH of 1.7 (using HCl) was carried out on board immediately after sampling, whereas tracers (Stable Y, ^{134}Cs, ^{236}Pu and ^{242}Pu) were added in the laboratory on receipt of the samples. Following filtration (0.45 micron), ^{137}Cs was fixed on copper ferrocyanide powder, then measured by Gamma spectrometry using HP Ge semiconductor detectors. Plutonium in the filtrate was co-precipitated by iron hydroxide $Fe(OH)_3$ (40 mg with iron per litre of sea water). The precipitate was then dissolved in HCl 6N. Following calcination and dissolving, the filter containing any traces of particulate Plutonium not solubilized by acidification was added to the solution. The Plutonium was then fixed on DOWEX AG1 × 8 resin in a HNO_3 8N medium and eluted in HCl 1 N with hydroxylamine chlorhydrate. The plutonium was then electro-deposited on a stainless steel disc using NH_4 Cl for an electrolyte. $^{239+240}$Pu was measured by alpha spectrometry using grid ionization chambers or semi-conductors detectors. Following separation of its ^{90}Y radioactive daughter product, ^{90}Sr was measured by Beta counting of ^{90}Y using low-noise proportional counters.

4.3. Results and Discussion

Results are summarized in Table 4.I.

^{137}Cs Radioactivity

^{137}Cs distribution through ocean water as a function of latitude (see Fig. 4.2. and 4.3.) shows a fairly regular drop in radioactivity from 30 - 40° N (2.5 to 3 Bq m^{-3}) to 40 - 50° S (0.5 Bq m^{-3}). Radioactivity is lower in Southern

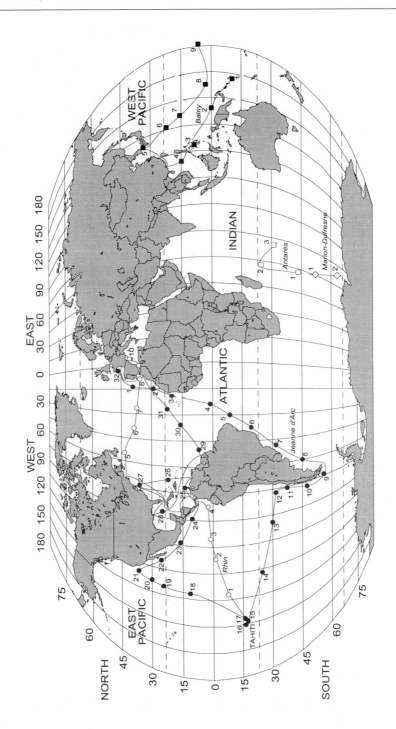

Fig. 4.1. Cruise tracks in the Pacific, Atlantic and Indian oceans in 1992/1994.

Table 4.I. ^{90}Sr, ^{137}Cs, ^{238}Pu and $^{239+240}$Pu concentrations in surface waters collected in Pacific, Atlantic and Indian Oceans.

Date	N°	Lat.	Long.	^{90}Sr (Bq m^{-3})	^{137}Cs (Bq m^{-3})	$\frac{^{137}Cs}{^{90}Sr}$	^{238}Pu (Bq m^{-3})	$^{239+240}$Pu (Bq m^{-3})	$\frac{^{238}Pu}{^{239+240}Pu}$
10/12/92	J1	40°55'N	12°55'W	1.57 ± 0.19	2.58 ± 0.30	1.6	≤ 0.67 × 10^{-3}	(6.9 ± 1.9) × 10^{-3}	–
13/12/92	J2	27°48'N	14°54'W	1.60 ± 0.20	2.53 ± 0.27	1.6	≤ 0.57 × 10^{-3}	(6.6 ± 1.7) × 10^{-3}	–
15/12/92	J3	18°24'N	17°53'W	1.00 ± 0.14	1.60 ± 0.20	1.6	≤ 0.55 × 10^{-3}	(2.44 ± 0.90) × 10^{-3}	–
24/12/92	J4	1°50'N	25°10'W	1.02 ± 0.14	1.60 ± 0.17	1.6	≤ 0.44 × 10^{-3}	(1.93 ± 0.53) × 10^{-3}	–
26/12/92	J5	8°56'S	31°18'W	0.92 ± 0.13	1.82 ± 0.22	2.0	≤ 0.33 × 10^{-3}	(2.10 ± 0.76) × 10^{-3}	–
28/12/92	J6	18°15'S	37°05'W	1.02 ± 0.14	1.56 ± 0.17	1.5	≤ 0.32 × 10^{-3}	(4.20 ± 0.62) × 10^{-3}	–
06/01/93	J7	31°44'S	51°37'W	0.662 ± 0.090	0.79 ± 0.10	1.2	no data	no data	–
21/01/93	J8	45°27'S	59°40'W	0.354 ± 0.059	0.56 ± 0.10	1.6	≤ 0.58 × 10^{-3}	(1.80 ± 0.55) × 10^{-3}	–
24/01/93	J9	54°28'S	73°26'W	0.410 ± 0.061	0.69 ± 0.10	1.7	no data	no data	–
26/01/93	J10	47°27'S	76°06'W	0.454 ± 0.068	0.65 ± 0.10	1.4	≤ 0.45 × 10^{-3}	(0.82 ± 0.50) × 10^{-3}	–
28/01/93	J11	36°25'S	73°38'W	0.405 ± 0.063	0.65 ± 0.14	1.5	≤ 0.30 × 10^{-3}	(1.32 ± 0.52) × 10^{-3}	–
05/02/93	J12	33°24'S	77°05'W	0.500 ± 0.073	0.77 ± 0.10	1.5	≤ 0.95 × 10^{-3}	(2.25 ± 0.69) × 10^{-3}	–
08/02/93	J13	30°17'S	95°08'W	0.81 ± 0.11	1.35 ± 0.14	1.7	≤ 0.20 × 10^{-3}	(0.87 ± 0.36) × 10^{-3}	–
14/02/93	J14	25°15'S	122°10'W	1.30 ± 0.15	2.30 ± 0.26	1.8	≤ 0.45 × 10^{-3}	(1.81 ± 0.40) × 10^{-3}	–
19/02/93	J15	17°34'S	145°30'W	1.31 ± 0.16	2.48 ± 0.30	1.9	≤ 0.30 × 10^{-3}	(2.50 ± 0.58) × 10^{-3}	–
20/02/93	J16	17°27'S	149°15'W	1.17 ± 0.14	2.01 ± 0.23	1.7	≤ 0.47 × 10^{-3}	(2.60 ± 0.59) × 10^{-3}	–
01/03/93	J17	16°21'S	143°50'W	1.22 ± 0.15	2.16 ± 0.23	1.8	≤ 0.36 × 10^{-3}	(1.44 ± 0.35) × 10^{-3}	–
06/03/93	J18	9°25'N	132°34'W	1.13 ± 0.17	2.55 ± 0.26	2.3	≤ 0.36 × 10^{-3}	(1.37 ± 0.38) × 10^{-3}	–
09/03/93	J19	24°45'N	127°40'W	1.15 ± 0.17	3.30 ± 0.35	2.9	≤ 0.35 × 10^{-3}	(1.70 ± 0.41) × 10^{-3}	–
10/03/93	J20	29°01'N	126°09'W	1.66 ± 0.19	3.97 ± 0.46	2.4	≤ 0.30 × 10^{-3}	(0.60 ± 0.29) × 10^{-3}	–
11/03/93	J21	33°58'N	124°22'W	1.58 ± 0.18	2.84 ± 0.30	1.8	≤ 0.22 × 10^{-3}	(0.69 ± 0.45) × 10^{-3}	–
20/03/93	J22	25°34'N	113°56'W	1.74 ± 0.19	2.91 ± 0.30	1.7	≤ 0.59 × 10^{-3}	(0.85 ± 0.32) × 10^{-3}	–
28/03/93	J23	17°56'N	103°33'W	1.35 ± 0.16	2.57 ± 0.29	1.9	≤ 0.20 × 10^{-3}	(0.78 ± 0.29) × 10^{-3}	–
31/03/93	J24	9°54'N	87°43'W	1.43 ± 0.17	2.43 ± 0.28	1.7	≤ 0.50 × 10^{-3}	(2.44 ± 0.60) × 10^{-3}	–
07/04/93	J25	12°46'N	71°13'W	1.07 ± 0.13	1.95 ± 0.25	1.8	≤ 0.39 × 10^{-3}	(4.15 ± 0.68) × 10^{-3}	–
15/04/93	J26	21°09'N	68°32'W	0.99 ± 0.13	2.11 ± 0.28	2.1	≤ 0.44 × 10^{-3}	(3.30 ± 0.63) × 10^{-3}	–
18/04/93	J27	36°22'N	73°38'W	1.41 ± 0.16	2.63 ± 0.32	1.9	no data	no data	–

Date	N°	Latitude	Longitude						
05/05/93	J28	23°50'N	86°26'W	0.92 ± 0.11	1.84 ± 0.31	2.0	$\leq 0.50 \times 10^{-3}$	$(2.48 \pm 0.79) \times 10^{-3}$	–
18/05/93	J29	6°57'N	49°31'W	0.93 ± 0.12	1.45 ± 0.28	1.6	$\leq 0.51 \times 10^{-3}$	$(1.63 \pm 0.54) \times 10^{-3}$	–
21/05/93	J30	16°05'N	36°25'W	0.87 ± 0.11	2.08 ± 0.37	2.4	$\leq 0.59 \times 10^{-3}$	$(3.22 \pm 0.71) \times 10^{-3}$	–
23/05/93	J31	22°55'N	26°05'W	1.14 ± 0.14	2.13 ± 0.41	1.9	$\leq 0.72 \times 10^{-3}$	$(3.92 \pm 0.83) \times 10^{-3}$	–
04/06/93	J32	47°32'N	5°13'W	1.31 ± 0.15	2.42 ± 0.28	1.8	$\leq 0.60 \times 10^{-3}$	$(7.50 \pm 0.93) \times 10^{-3}$	–
04/02/93	R1	7°23'S	130°16'W	0.89 ± 0.11	2.56 ± 0.27	2.9	$(0.66 \pm 0.45) \times 10^{-3}$	$(2.01 \pm 0.62) \times 10^{-3}$	0.33
08/02/93	R2	2°19'S	112°37'W	1.24 ± 0.15	2.12 ± 0.21	1.7	$\leq 0.82 \times 10^{-3}$	$(2.82 \pm 0.97) \times 10^{-3}$	–
11/02/93	R3	1°54'N	99°01'W	1.37 ± 0.15	2.35 ± 0.25	1.7	$\leq 0.30 \times 10^{-3}$	$(2.78 \pm 0.93) \times 10^{-3}$	–
17/02/93	R4	2°34'N	79°29'W	1.11 ± 0.14	2.08 ± 0.21	1.9	$(0.64 \pm 0.32) \times 10^{-3}$	$(2.42 \pm 0.52) \times 10^{-3}$	0.26
31/03/93	R5	43°13'N	53°21'W	1.67 ± 0.18	2.56 ± 0.26	1.5	$(0.52 \pm 0.31) \times 10^{-3}$	$(11.5 \pm 2.3) \times 10^{-3}$	0.05
03/04/93	R6	38°53'N	38°55'W	1.26 ± 0.15	2.47 ± 0.26	2.0	$(0.47 \pm 0.34) \times 10^{-3}$	$(8.7 \pm 1.8) \times 10^{-3}$	0.05
05/04/93	R7	38°08'N	27°49'W	1.42 ± 0.16	2.32 ± 0.24	1.6	$(0.44 \pm 0.28) \times 10^{-3}$	$(7.1 \pm 1.6) \times 10^{-3}$	0.06
11/04/93	R8	36°08'N	9°03'W	1.59 ± 0.18	2.50 ± 0.26	1.6	$(0.42 \pm 0.27) \times 10^{-3}$	$(7.1 \pm 1.5) \times 10^{-3}$	0.06
12/04/93	R9	36°39'N	1°43'W	1.58 ± 0.18	2.82 ± 0.29	1.8	$(0.39 \pm 0.29) \times 10^{-3}$	$(11.9 \pm 2.4) \times 10^{-3}$	0.03
13/04/93	R10	40°30'N	2°40'E	1.69 ± 0.20	2.86 ± 0.31	1.7	$(1.93 \pm 0.51) \times 10^{-3}$	$(20.7 \pm 3.5) \times 10^{-3}$	0.09
28/08/93	B1	11°20'S	162°55'E	1.39 ± 0.16	1.93 ± 0.39	1.4	$\leq 1.3 \times 10^{-3}$	$(3.7 \pm 1.4) \times 10^{-3}$	–
04/09/93	B2	0°18'N	146°46'E	1.66 ± 0.19	2.77 ± 0.55	1.7	$(0.81 \pm 0.58) \times 10^{-3}$	$(7.6 \pm 1.9) \times 10^{-3}$	0.11
08/09/93	B3	11°43'N	126°52'E	2.04 ± 0.23	2.87 ± 0.57	1.4	$\leq 1.1 \times 10^{-3}$	$(5.7 \pm 1.3) \times 10^{-3}$	–
15/09/93	B4	15°16'N	116°25'E	1.74 ± 0.20	no data	–	$\leq 3.2 \times 10^{-3}$	$(7.0 \pm 2.7) \times 10^{-3}$	–
29/09/93	B5	35°21'N	130°40'E	2.11 ± 0.23	2.82 ± 0.70	1.3	$(1.01 \pm 0.54) \times 10^{-3}$	$(17.8 \pm 2.3) \times 10^{-3}$	0.06
10/10/93	B6	23°35'N	136°18'E	2.06 ± 0.23	3.12 ± 0.78	1.5	$\leq 1.8 \times 10^{-3}$	$(4.8 \pm 1.6) \times 10^{-3}$	–
12/10/93	B7	16°30'N	142°15'E	1.65 ± 0.19	3.12 ± 0.78	1.9	$\leq 0.95 \times 10^{-3}$	$(4.3 \pm 1.1) \times 10^{-3}$	–
18/10/93	B8	4°20'N	160°35'E	1.74 ± 0.19	2.59 ± 0.65	1.5	$\leq 0.86 \times 10^{-3}$	$(5.2 \pm 1.1) \times 10^{-3}$	–
21/10/93	B9	7°12'N	179°37'W	1.51 ± 0.18	no data	–	$\leq 1.2 \times 10^{-3}$	$(2.36 \pm 0.95) \times 10^{-3}$	–
12/02/94	M1	52°01'S	61°32'E	≤ 0.12	0.100 ± 0.029	–	$\leq 0.97 \times 10^{-3}$	$(1.77 \pm 0.68) \times 10^{-3}$	–
22/02/94	M2	63°18'S	69°59'E	≤ 0.12	0.072 ± 0.025	–	$\leq 1.3 \times 10^{-3}$	$(1.33 \pm 0.69) \times 10^{-3}$	–
16/03/94	A1	44°29'S	57°29'E	1.09 ± 0.17	1.63 ± 0.19	1.5	$\leq 0.90 \times 10^{-3}$	$(1.00 \pm 0.72) \times 10^{-3}$	–
20/03/94	A2	23°56'S	58°37'E	1.47 ± 0.21	2.33 ± 0.26	1.6	no data	no data	
22/03/94	A3	31°40'S	68°20'E	1.45 ± 0.22	1.96 ± 0.22	1.4	no data	no data	

N° column: J: « P.H. Jeanne d'Arc » cruise; R: B.S.L. Rhin » cruise; B: « A.E. Balny » cruise; M: « R.V. Marion-Dufresne » cruise; A: « R.V. Antarès » cruise. Uncertainty at ± 2 σ.

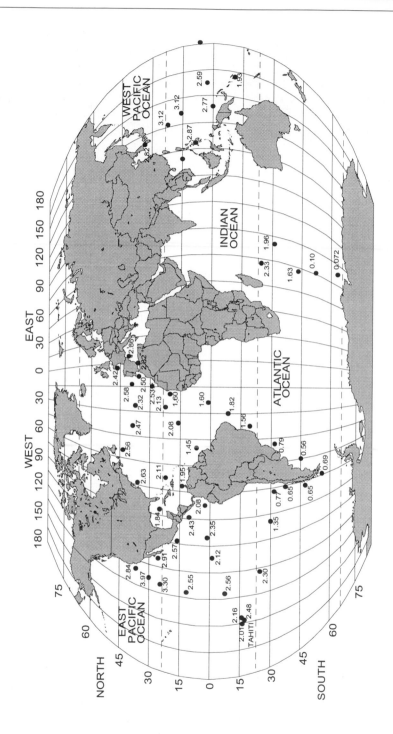

Fig. 4.2. ^{137}Cs radioactivity in the Pacific, Atlantic and Indian oceans (Bq m^{-3}).

Hemisphere waters because there was less fallout from atmospheric testing (approximately 3/4 of fallout affected the Northern Hemisphere, and 1/4 the Southern Hemisphere (Aarkrog, 1994). Increases in concentrations possible consequences of reprocessing plant releases or the Chernobyl accident are not detectable, since the samples were usually collected far away from the coastline and south of the 45° N parallel. Levels are seen to be slightly higher in the Pacific than in the Atlantic from 50° N to 30° S (on the average, 3.0 and 2.5 Bq m^{-3} respectively around 30° N, reaching a maximum of 4 Bq m^{-3} off lower California), then approximately constant and identical between the 30° S and 60° S parallels (0.6 to 0.7 Bq m^{-3}). The lowest concentrations were recorded off coasts of Argentina and Chile (less than 1 Bq m^{-3}), and in the Southern Indian Ocean, near Antarctica (0.10 Bq m^{-3} or less).

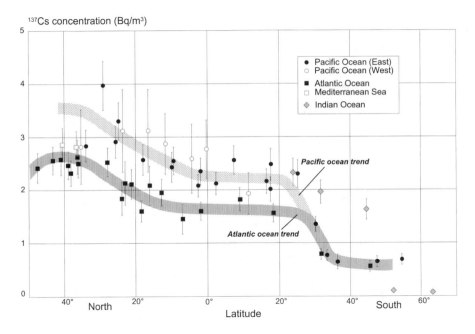

Fig. 4.3. ^{137}Cs radioactivity in the Pacific, Atlantic and Indian oceans.

SMSRB measurements on ocean surface water samples collected since 1979 in French Polynesia point out to a regular decrease of ^{137}Cs radioactivity with an apparent half-life of the order of 14 years (see Fig. 4.4.). Applying that half-life to measurements by Hirose (1992) and Miyake (1988) on Pacific Ocean water, and by Holm (1991) on Atlantic Ocean water, it can be seen that our measurements are in good agreement with theirs (see Figs. 4.5. and 4.6). Due to gradual dilution of ^{137}Cs in the deeper layers, the above apparent half-life is shorter than ^{137}Cs radioactive half-life. Figure 4.7. shows an example of ^{137}Cs vertical distribution, illustrated by samples taken off Tahiti island (17°39′ S, 149°39′ W) in April 1993. Considering the ^{137}Cs radioactive half-life, caesium residence time is thus estimated at 26 years, which fully agrees with the general surface water residence time of 25 years (Holm, 1994).

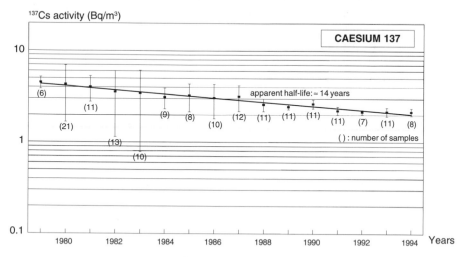

Fig. 4.4. ^{137}Cs radioactivity changes
in French Polynesia ocean surface waters since 1979.

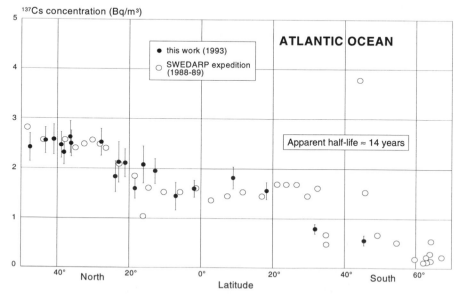

Fig. 4.5. ^{137}Cs radioactivity in Atlantic surface water.
All data are corrected for apparent half-life to July 1993 (uncertainty at ± 2σ).

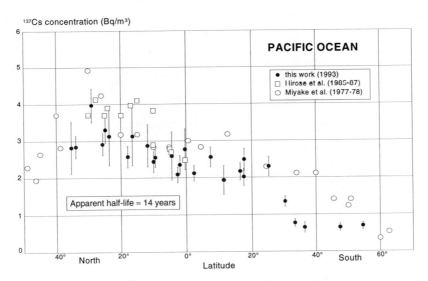

Fig. 4.6. ^{137}Cs radioactivity in Pacific surface water.
All data are corrected for apparent half-life to July 1993 (uncertainty at ± 2σ).

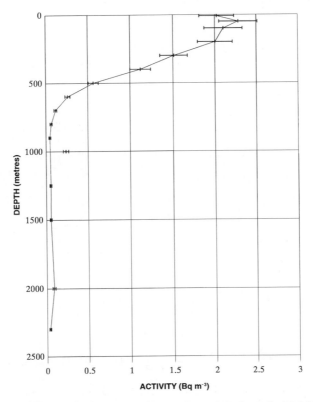

Fig. 4.7. ^{137}Cs radioactivity profile in French Polynesia (Tahiti, 1993).

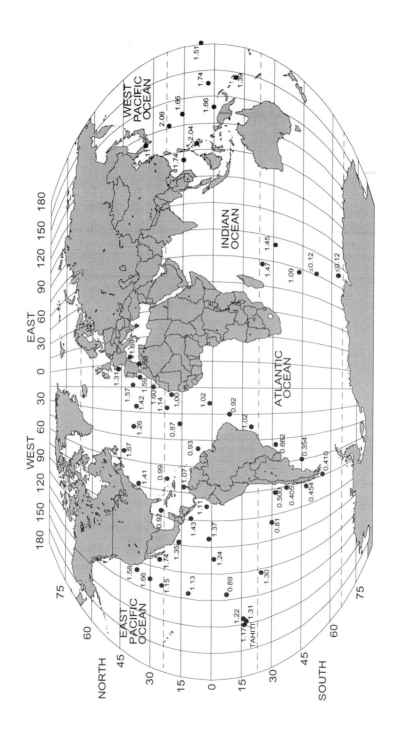

Fig. 4.8. ^{90}Sr radioactivity in the Pacific, Atlantic and Indian oceans (Bq m^{-3}).

^{90}Sr Radioactivity

The distribution of ^{90}Sr radioactivity through ocean water as a function of latitude (see Figs. 4.8. and 4.9.) is similar to that of ^{137}Cs. It shows a fairly regular decrease in radioactivity from 30-40° N (1.5 to 2 Bq m^{-3}) to 40-50° S (0.4 Bq m^{-3}). The higher activity levels were observed in the China Sea, Western Pacific (2.1 Bq m^{-3}).

As in the case of ^{137}Cs, the lower concentrations were found off the coasts of Argentina and Chile (0.5 Bq m^{-3}) and near Antarctica (less than 0.12 Bq m^{-3}).

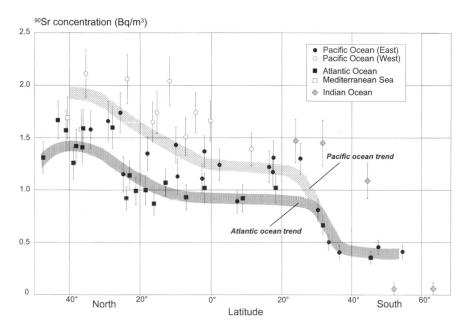

Fig. 4.9. ^{90}**Sr radioactivity in the Pacific, Atlantic and Indian oceans.**

^{90}Sr radioactivity measurements made by SMSRB on ocean surface water samples collected in French Polynesia since 1989 show a radioactivity decrease with an apparent half-life identical to that of ^{137}Cs, *i.e.*, of the order of 14 years (see Fig. 4.10.).

The ^{137}Cs/^{90}Sr activity ratio is noticeably the same in all three oceans investigated (see Fig. 4.11.), *i.e.*, 1.7 on the average. It is independant of latitude. An exceptionally high ratio of 2.9 was registered off lower California and Vanuatu. In these odd cases, we cannot rule out possible error in radio-chemical processing, which might have led to unusually high ratios through an under-estimation of ^{90}Y activity, perhaps due to ^{90}Y-^{90}Sr disequilibrium.

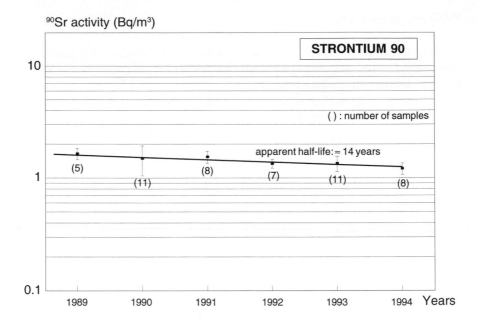

Fig. 4.10. ^{90}Sr radioactivity changes
in French Polynesia ocean surface waters since 1989.

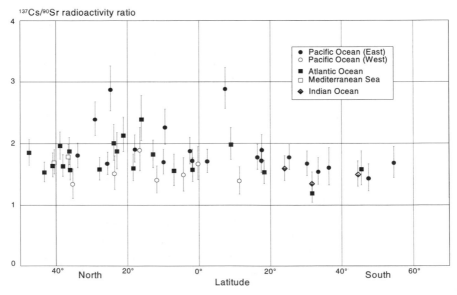

Fig. 4.11. ^{137}Cs/^{90}Sr radioactivity ratio in the Pacific, Atlantic and Indian oceans.

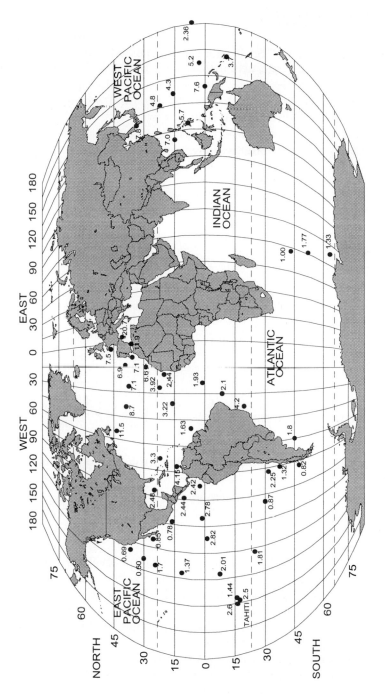

Fig. 4.12. $^{239+240}$Pu radioactivity in the Pacific, Atlantic and Indian oceans (mBq m^{-3}).

239+240Pu Radioactivity

Unlike the ^{137}Cs and ^{90}Sr distributions discussed above, the distribution of [239+240]Pu through ocean water does not exhibit a well-defined pattern with respect to latitude. However, the higher concentration levels are found in the Northern Hemisphere. In the Atlantic and western Pacific, activity varies from 7 to 20 mBq m^{-3} at latitudes from 30° N to 50° N, and from 2 to 10 mBq m^{-3} between 0 and 30° N, whereas concentration is generally from 0.8 to 3 mBq m^{-3} in the Southern Hemisphere.

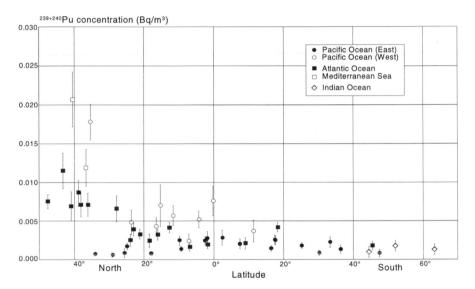

Fig. 4.13. [239+240]Pu radioactivity in the Pacific, Atlantic and Indian oceans.

It can also be noted that activity levels are slightly lower in the Atlantic than in the Pacific, with a peak of 18 mBq m^{-3} in the Yellow Sea, north-western Pacific. Levels are also generally higher in the north-western Pacific than in the north-eastern Pacific.

In the north-eastern Pacific, concentration levels are particularly low, from 0.6 to 3 mBq m^{-3}. In particular, the four samples taken off the California coast, down to southern Mexico (sampling points J20 to J23) show activity levels under 1 mBq m^{-3}. In this zone, affected by the California current, upwelling effects can be observed (Tchernia, 1978). Therefore, higher activity levels might have been expected.

When comparing our data with those obtained by Livingston (1987) in 1978-80 and Hirose (1992) in 1985-87 for the Pacific Ocean, and with Holm's data (1991) for the Atlantic Ocean in 1985-87 (see Figs. 4.14 and 4.15) there is no clear evidence of [239+240]Pu activity decay in surface water. In French Polynesia, no significant change has been observed since 1990, considering

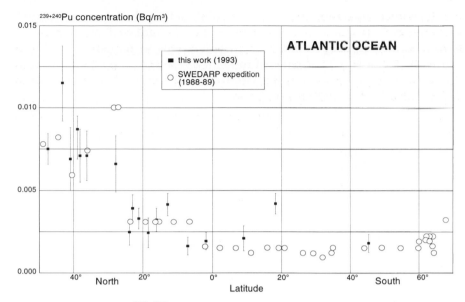

Fig. 4.14. $^{239+240}$Pu radioactivity in Atlantic surface water.
(Uncertainty at ± 2 σ).

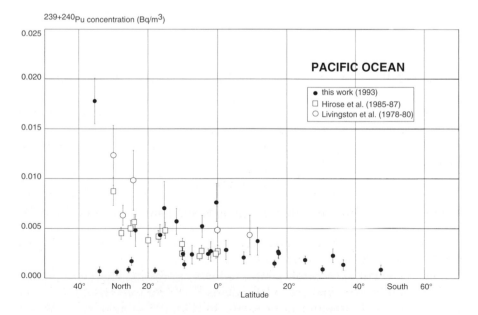

Fig. 4.15. $^{239+240}$Pu radioactivity in Pacific surface water.
(Uncertainty at ± 2 σ).

the fluctuations between one sampling point and another (usually from 0.8 to 3 mBq m^{-3}). It should be noted that most of the radioactivity in seawater is now located in deep water (around 600 metres in the South Pacific as shown by Fig. 4.16.). This makes it difficult to estimate the Plutonium residence time, assessed at 7 or 8 years by Holm for the North and South Atlantic (Holm *et al.*, 1991; Holm, 1994).

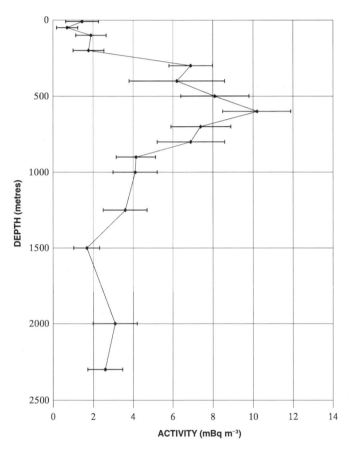

Fig. 4.16. $^{239+240}$Pu radioactivity profile in French Polynesia (Tahiti, 1993).

The $^{239+240}$Pu/^{137}Cs activity ratio follows approximately the same distribution pattern with respect to latitude as $^{239+240}$Pu (see Fig. 4.17), *i.e.*, of the order of 4 x 10^{-3} around 40° N, down to 0.5 x 10^{-3} around 60° S. At any given latitude, the ratio is practically the same in all three oceans investigated. An exceptionally high ratio of 6 x 10^{-3} is observed in the Yellow Sea.

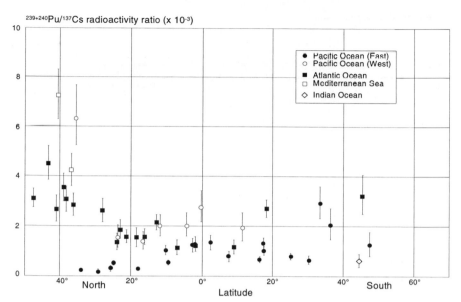

Fig. 4.17. $^{239+240}$Pu/^{137}Cs radioactivity ratio in the Pacific,
Atlantic and Indian oceans.

^{238}Pu Radioactivity

In the Southern Hemisphere, ^{238}Pu originates mainly from the destruction of the SNAP-9A satellite at a high altitude over the Mozambique channel in 1964; the satellite contained 1 kg of ^{238}Pu in metal form (5.1 x 10^{14} Bq) (Aarkrog, 1987). The average ^{238}Pu/$^{239+240}$Pu activity ratio (see Fig. 4.18.) is of the order of 0.18 (Aarkrog, 1987) - 0.25 (Holm, 1994) in the Southern Hemisphere and 0.036 (Aarkrog, 1987) in the Northern Hemisphere (the ratio due to nuclear test fallout is 0.025, Holm, 1994). At any given latitude, the ^{238}Pu/$^{239+240}$Pu activity ratio is approximately the same in all three oceans investigated (Fig. 4.18).

In view of the uncertainty affecting some of the ^{238}Pu/$^{239+240}$Pu activity ratio figures, only orders of magnitude can be derived from our measurements:
- Northern latitudes: 30° N-50° N: ^{238}Pu/$^{239+240}$Pu $\approx 0.06 \pm 0.04$.
- Equatorial latitudes: 10° N-10° S: ^{238}Pu/$^{239+240}$Pu $\approx 0.23 \pm 0.15$.

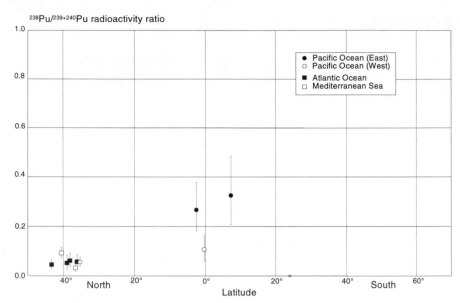

Fig. 4.18. ^{238}Pu/$^{239+240}$Pu radioactivity ratio in the Pacific,
Atlantic and Indian oceans.

4.4. Conclusion

The above investigations have determined the current world-wide levels of ocean
surface water radioactivity, highlighting or confirming the following points:

- ^{90}Sr and ^{137}Cs concentrations generally decrease from North to South and
  the levels in the Pacific Ocean are slightly higher than in the Atlantic
  Ocean between latitudes 50° N and 30° S. The ^{137}Cs/^{90}Sr activity ratio is
  approximately constant, close to 1.7. Strontium and Caesium have residence times of the order of 25 years.
- The distribution of $^{239+240}$Pu radioactivity is rather non-uniform and significant variations, from 0.5 to 20 mBq m^{-3}, can be observed at a given latitude in the Northern Hemisphere; the concentrations vary from 0.5 to
  4 mBq m^{-3} in the Southern Hemisphere.

Some oceanic areas, especially the Indian Ocean and south-eastern
Atlantic, not covered by this study, are worthy of investigation.

Acknowlegments

The authors wish to thank most sincerely the French Navy, the CNRS and the commanding officers and crews of P.H. Jeanne d'Arc, B.S.L. Rhin, A.E. Balny, R.V. Marion-Dufresne and R.V. Antarès for accepting to participate in this study and following the sampling procedures.

We are especially endebted to S. Schmidt of CFR/Gif-sur-Yvette for the sampling in the Southern Indian Ocean, and to D. Abt, B. Girardot, M. Girard and J.S. Le Levier for their radioanalytical work.

References

Aarkrog A. (1987) Worldwide data on Fluxes of [239+240]Pu, [238]Pu to the Oceans. Riso National Laboratory, DK-4000 Roskilde, Denmark.

Aarkrog A. (1994) Source terms and Inventories of Anthropogenic Radionuclides. In *Radioecology. Lectures in environmental radioactivity* (E. Holm, Ed.) pp. 23-38. Lund, Sweden. World Scientific Publishing.

Hirose K., Sugimura Y. and Aoyama M. (1992) Plutonium and ^{137}Cs in the Western North Pacific: Estimation of Residence Time of Plutonium in Surface Waters. *Appl. Radiat. Isot.* **43**, 349-359.

Holm E. (1994) Sources and Distribution of Anthropogenic Radionuclides. In *Radioecology. Lectures in Environmental radioactivity* (E. Holm, Ed.) pp. 65-83. Lund, Sweden. World Scientific Publishing.

Holm E., Roos P., Persson R.B.R., Bojanowski R., Aarkrog A., Nielsen S.P. and Livingston H.D. (1991) Radiocaesium and Plutonium in Atlantic Surface Waters from 73° N to 72° S. (P.J. Kershaw and D.S. Woodhead, Eds.) p. 3-11. Elsevier applied Science, London and New York.

Livingston H.D., Mann D.R., Casso S.A., Sneider D.L., Surprenant L.D. and Bowen V.T. (1987) Particle and Solution Phase Depth Distributions of Transuranics and [55]Fe in the North Pacific. *J. Environmental Radioactivity* **5**, 1-24.

Miyake Y., Saruhashi K. Sugimura Y., Kanazawa T. and Hirose K. (1988) Contents of ^{137}Cs, Plutonium and Americium isotopes in the Southern Ocean Waters. *Papers in Meteorology and Geophysics* **39**, 95-113.

Tchernia P. (1978) Océanographie régionale. Description physique des océans et des mers. École Nationale Supérieure de Techniques Avancées (Centre d'Édition et de Documentation de l'ENSTA, 32 boulevard Victor, 75015 Paris).

5 Radioactive Contamination of the Arctic Marine Environment

P. Strand, M. Sickel, A. Aarkrog,
J.M. Bewers, Y. Tsaturov and S. Magnusson

Lately, considerable attention has been focused on radioactive contamination of the Arctic Marine Environment. This has occurred mainly because of the reported dumping of radioactive wastes in the Barents and Kara Seas. A contributing factor has been reports of problems connected with the management of nuclear waste in the Russian military and civilian fleets. The sources that have made the largest contributions to radionuclides to the arctic marine environment are global fallout from nuclear weapons testing, releases from West European nuclear fuel reprocessing plants and the Chernobyl accident runoff from contaminated land areas. Predominant among these sources is global fallout which has contributed of the order of 28 PBq ^{137}Cs and 19 PBq ^{90}Sr. The fuel reprocessing plant Sellafield in the U.K. has, since the 1960s, discharged ^{137}Cs of which 10 - 15 PBq has probably reached the Arctic Ocean.

5.1. Introduction

Although there are few nuclear industries in the Arctic, the arctic marine environment has been contaminated by global fallout, radionuclides in waste discharges from spent fuel reprocessing plants in Europe, releases from the Chernobyl accident in 1986 and a variety of civil and military vessel operations. Accordingly, the arctic marine environment can be expected to show evidence of radionuclide contamination arising from all these sources.

Radionuclide contamination of the Arctic has become a topic of increased interest during the last five years largely as a result of the revelations of sea dumping of liquid and solid radioactive wastes and nuclear-powered vessels in the Kara and Barents Seas by the former Soviet Union and the Russian Federation. Concerns have also been expressed about the consequences of the sinking of the nuclear-powered submarine *Komsomolets* in the Norwegian Sea in 1989 and reported difficulties in the decommissioning of Russian nuclear-powered military vessels. This has led to international efforts to assess current and potential radiological exposures and associated risks to human health and the environment in the Arctic. The Arctic Monitoring and Assessment Programme, AMAP, is undertaking an overall assessment of the radioactive contamination of the Arctic and associated radiological consequences.

This paper summarizes present knowledge of the various contributions to the arctic marine radionuclide inventory and the distributions and trends of radionuclides derived from anthropogenic sources.

5.2. The Arctic Ocean - Transport and Pathways

The Arctic Ocean is the circumpolar ocean between the American and the Eurasian continent, covering an area of 9.5×10^6 km^2, corresponding closely to the area of the United States and slightly greater than the land area of Europe. Its central and largest part (approx. 70% of the area) is the deep Polar Basin. The Polar Basin is divided into two distinct sub-basins by a submarine rock barrier, the Lomonosov Ridge, which extends across the Arctic Ocean from the Laptev Sea in Siberia to northwest Greenland.

The major connection between the Arctic Ocean and other large seas of the world is Fram Strait between Greenland and Svalbard which provides a 2 600 m deep connection to the Atlantic Ocean. Other connections are the wider but shallower passage between Svalbard and the Norwegian Mainland (*via* the Barents Sea) and the even shallower area of the Canadian Archipelago. The Arctic Ocean is also connected with the Pacific *via* the narrow Bering Strait. Thus, the exchange of water between the Eurasian Basin and the Atlantic is of a much larger scale than the exchange of water between the Canadian Basin and the Pacific Ocean.

The northerly current along the coast of Norway is divided into two parts. One part moves into Fram Strait along the west coast of Svalbard, becomes progressively cooled as it moves northward and eventually sinks beneath arctic surface water of lower salinity. This stream of comparatively warm water from the south results in an ice free bay west of Svalbard throughout the year. The other part of the current enters the shallow Barents Sea, affecting environmental conditions in the waters east of Svalbard, north of Novaya Zemlya and the eastern parts of the Kara Sea.

The Arctic Ocean also receives warm water from the Pacific *via* the Bering Strait. This amount, however, is less than one-tenth of the amount received from the Atlantic.

The flow pattern in the Polar Mixed Layer is closely related to that of the overlying sea-ice. The flow in the Atlantic layer is generally cyclonic. Most of the Atlantic water enters the Arctic Ocean through Fram Strait in the west Spitzbergen Current and the Norwegian Atlantic Current over the Barents and Northern Kara Sea shelves and leaves it through the East Greenland Current. A simplified picture of the water circulation of the Arctic Seas is shown in Figure 5.1. (Rey, 1984).

The Central Arctic is covered by sea-ice over an area twice as large in the early spring as in the late summer. Large areas of the arctic shelf seas, which are covered by sea-ice during the winter, are free of ice during some months of the summer season.

When radioactive material is released to, or transported within, the marine environment, the physical processes of water movement and sedimentation are of major importance in determining the pathways of transport and fate of the constituent radionuclides.

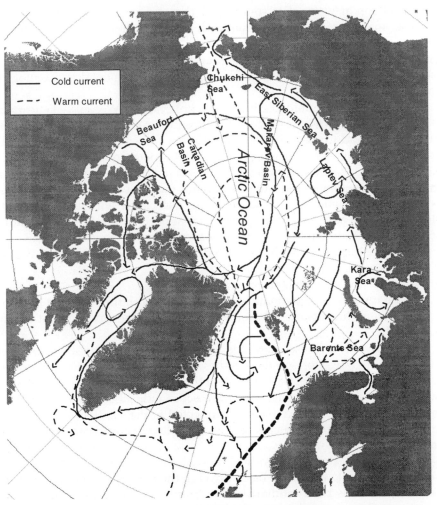

Fig. 5.1. Simplified picture of water circulation in the Arctic Ocean (Rey, 1984).

One of the important geochemical factors affecting the transport of radionuclides is particle-water exchange. In water, radionuclides are partitioned between the dissolved and particulate phases. The partitioning will depend on the chemical form of the radionuclide, the properties of the element and the characteristics of the environment. Radionuclides that bind strongly to particles in sedimentary environments are likely to sediment quickly and may therefore be transported only relatively short distances. When radionuclides are released to the marine environment through river systems, the characteristics of the estuarine system will play an important role in determining the partitioning of radionuclides between the dissolved and particulate phases.

The uptake in aquatic biota generally depends on the levels of dissolved radionuclides in water. For some biota that are in close contact with, or process, marine sediments, radionuclide concentrations in sediments can exert a greater influence on the extent of biological uptake. The bioaccumulation of radionuclides by aquatic biota also depends on the biogeochemistry of the isotope and the specific range of environmental and ecological conditions.

Ice transport is a unique pathway in polar areas (Weeks, 1995; Pfirman *et al.*, 1995). The transport of ice is not directly linked to water mass movement (Rigor and Colony, 1993), and different transport models need to be applied. During ice formation, dissolved contaminants are excluded together with sea salt and the levels of dissolved contaminants are therefore lower in sea ice than in sea water. The main focus on ice transport has been on the transport and fate of radionuclides associated with sediment particles. For impact assessment the questions that need to be addressed include:

- How much sedimentary material is incorporated in the ice?
- Where are the sediments incorporated?
- Where are the transport routes of the ice?
- Where are the sediments released? and
- What happens to the radionuclides associated with the sediment particles when the sediments are reintroduced to the marine environment during ice melt.

The answers to these questions are not yet fully available; however, there is an ongoing work on these issues. Ice may incorporate radionuclides associated with sediment particles when there is contact between the ice and the particles during freezing. This may occur either because of high sediment load or where fast ice (*i.e.*, ice connected to the sea floor or to land) is in direct contact with sediments such as in shallow water areas or river estuaries.

The Ob and Yenesei rivers together discharge about one third of the freshwater input to the Arctic Basin through the Kara Sea (Shiklomanov and Skakalsky). It has been estimated that about 20-30 million tonnes of sediments are transported annually by these rivers (Shiklomanov and Skakalsky). Akvaplan NIVA has processed very high resolution radiometer

(AVHRR) satellite images that give an indication of suspended loads. As shown, for example, in Figure 5.2., there is a considerable amount of suspended material in the Ob Estuary. Most of the Kara Sea has a ice cover from late October to late July. In the late autumn, river-transported suspended material reaches the Kara Sea in an area where drift ice is forming at the time. Many investigations of the routes of the ice transport have been

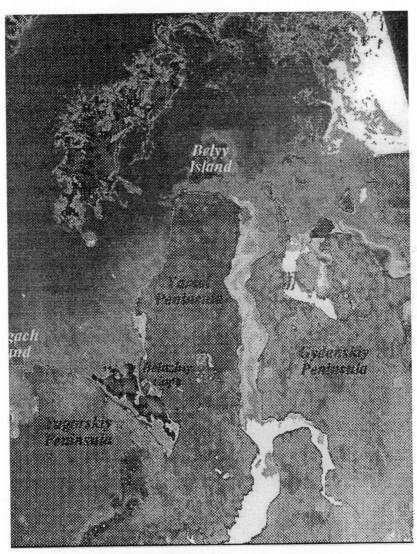

Fig. 5.2. AVHRR satellite image showing
suspended matter distribution.

carried out and these have indicated that drift ice is being transported from the Kara Sea through Fram Strait to the Atlantic or to the Barents Sea (Ecosystem Barents Sea, 1994). There is also an indication that there may be sediment transport from the northern Russian shelves to the North Atlantic. In 1995, Meese *et al.* presented results showing that sea ice is one transport mechanism by which contaminated sediments from rivers such as the Yenisei are redistributed throughout the Arctic Ocean and possibly exported into the North Atlantic and Greenland Sea through Fram Strait.

5.3. Radioactive Contamination of the Arctic Ocean

5.3.1. *Sources of Contamination*

Contemporary levels of radionuclides in the arctic marine environment are mainly attributable to global fallout from nuclear weapons tests and discharges from European fuel reprocessing plants. The Chernobyl accident has also contributed and will probably continue to do so in the future as a result of marine transport of radionuclides from areas of initial deposition, particularly the Baltic Sea. In addition to these sources, local underwater nuclear weapons tests, the nuclear weapons accident at Thule, Greenland, and dumping of reactors and radioactive waste in the Kara Sea have resulted in local peculiarities in the distributions of radionuclides.

Furthermore, there is also most probably some influence of releases from Russian land-based activities, including reprocessing operations in central Russia. However, it has been difficult to quantify the introduction of radionuclides to the Arctic Ocean from these latter activities.

5.3.1.1. *Nuclear Weapons Explosions*

The main input of artificial radioactivity to the Arctic Ocean has come from nuclear weapons testing in the atmosphere during the 1950s and 1960s, particularly from thermonuclear weapons that have contributed most to global fallout. Contamination from civil nuclear explosions, that have been carried out underground is negligible in comparison with that from atmospheric testing. Nevertheless, local contamination has occurred as a result of such explosions. The two major test sites for atmospheric testing of thermonuclear weapons have been Novaya Zemlya in the arctic region of the former USSR and the Bikini and Eniwetok Islands (US) in the Pacific Ocean. In addition, China has carried out tests at Lop Nor in Western China, France at Mururoa in the Pacific Ocean and the UK at Christmas Island in the Pacific.

The USA, UK and USSR discontinued atmospheric testing by 1962 and there has been no atmospheric testing carried out by any country since 1980. A total of 520 atmospheric explosions including 8 underwater tests had occurred up to 1980. The total explosive yield amounts to 545 Mt TNT; 217 Mt from fission weapons and 328 Mt from fusion weapons. Of the total fallout, that deposited close to the test sites accounts for 12%, tropospheric fallout, which is deposited in a latitude band approximating that of the test site, for 10%, and global fallout, which is mainly deposited on the same hemisphere as the test site, for 78% (UNSCEAR, 1993).

As most test explosions have been carried out in the Northern Hemisphere, most of the contamination by radionuclide fallout is found there, as shown in Figure 5.3. This figure further illustrates that the contamination of arctic regions is less than that of temperate latitudes. The total integrated deposition of ^{90}Sr north of 60° N is 41.8 PBq corresponding to 18.8 PBq (decay-corrected) in 1995. Of this activity, 39% was deposited in the ocean and the balance on land. The ratio between ^{137}Cs and ^{90}Sr in global fallout is 1.5; hence the present (decay-corrected) inventory of global fallout ^{137}Cs in the Arctic (latitude range 60°-90°) is 28 PBq. The amount of the local fallout around the Novaya Zemlya test site is not known but local fallout from thermonuclear weapon tests tends to be minor compared with the global contribution because these tests were frequently carried out at high altitude (Zander and Araskog, 1973) in which the fireball created by the explosion does not touch the soil and create radioactive particles that can be deposited locally.

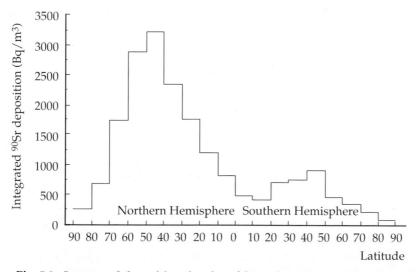

Fig. 5.3. Integrated deposition density of Strontium-90. (UNSCEAR, 1993)
(Due to radioactive decay of ^{90}Sr cumulative deposition is 0.45 x
integrated in 1995).

5.3.1.2   Releases from European Nuclear Fuel Reprocessing Plants

Discharges from European nuclear fuel reprocessing plants constitute the second most significant source of radionuclides in the Arctic. The principal sources are nuclear fuel reprocessing operations at La Hague near Cherbourg, France, at Sellafield in Cumbria on the west coast of England and at Dounreay in the north-east of Scotland (Tab. 5.I.). Releases from these plants, have contributed to the introduction of radionuclides through water transport to the Arctic. While there are also other reprocessing operations in Western Europe, these are of minimal significance to the Arctic.

Discharges from the nuclear fuel reprocessing plant at Sellafield (formerly Windscale) on the eastern side of the Irish Sea, began in 1951 when the facility was initially put into operation. The chronology of releases, both to sea and to the atmosphere, from the Sellafield reprocessing operation has been most recently and comprehensively documented by Gray *et al.* (1995). Maximum releases from Sellafield occurred in about 1975 when approximately 5 PBq (excluding ^{3}H) were discharged to the Irish Sea. Releases have continually been reduced since that time and are now of the order of 0.1 PBq per year (excluding ^{3}H). The nuclide representing the major proportion of the total releases is ^{137}Cs (41 PBq). Total α-emitter releases in the same period were about 1% of the total and are dominated by ^{239}Pu (0.0053%) and ^{241}Am (0.0041%) (CEC, 1990).

The reprocessing facility at Cap de la Hague was brought into operation in 1965. The total discharges from this site were, excluding ^{3}H, about 8 PBq up to 1986 – much less than those from Sellafield. Releases of individual nuclides up to 1982 were given by Calmet and Guéguéniat (1985) and these were cited and extended to 1986 in CEC (1990). In contrast to the contributions made to activity discharges from Sellafield by individual nuclides, for La Hague the dominant contributor to activity releases (55%) is the beta-emitter ^{106}Ru followed by ^{90}Sr. For some radionuclides, *e.g.* ^{129}I, La Hague is currently the dominant contributor accounting for 90% of the total release rate.

Table 5.I. Contributions (%) to total discharges within the European Community made by nuclear fuel reprocessing plants for discharges up to the end of 1984 (CEC, 1990).

Facility	α-emitters	β-emitters	Tritium
Sellafield	95.2	86.9	52.9
La Hague	0.52	5.3	16.4
Dounreay	1.8	6.7	0.33
Total (%)	97.5	98.9	69.6
Total (Bq)	1.4×10^{15}	1.5×10^{17}	4.6×10^{16}

Releases from Dounreay are much smaller than those from Sellafield (Freke *et al.*, 1969). The aggregate activity discharged up to 1986 was about 10 PBq with small amounts being radionuclides transportable to the Arctic. Only relatively small amounts of ^{3}H are discharged from Dounreay. Discharges of β-activity were at their highest during the 1960s and early 1970s with small peaks in 1968 and 1973 resulting from plant washout and decontamination procedures. In 1980, fuel from the Prototype Fast Reactor began to be reprocessed and this gave rise to increased discharges of α-emitters, mainly ^{238}Pu, ^{239}Pu and ^{241}Am.

Sellafield has been the primary contributor to activity releases among the three western European reprocessing plants. The arctic inventory of ^{137}Cs released from Sellafield has been estimated at 10-15 PBq in 1993 (Aarkrog, 1993). In view of the minimal decay since that date, this figure is probably an appropriate measure of the contemporary inventory of Sellafield radiocaesium in the Arctic. The time-trend of ^{137}Cs in the Barents Sea virtually mirrors the pattern of releases from Sellafield with a delay of approximately 5 years (Aarkrog, 1993; Dahlgaard, 1994). The rate of introduction of ^{137}Cs from Sellafield into the Barents Sea in 1994 was estimated at 200-300 TBq a^{-1} (Kershaw and Baxter, 1995). Some evidence of higher ^{137}Cs values in the Kara Sea in 1982 has been used to suggest that the peak Sellafield signal was delayed about 7 years before appearing in the Kara Sea (Dahlgaard, 1994). Recent measurements of the distribution of ^{137}Cs in the Arctic show increased concentrations in waters of east Greenland of polar origin (Kershaw and Baxter 1993; Kershaw *et al.*, 1995). These are attributable to radiocaesium from earlier Sellafield discharges that has entered the arctic circulation and is being transported back into the Atlantic through the East Greenland Current.

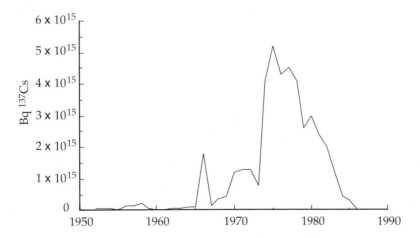

Fig. 5.4. Releases of ^{137}Cs from Sellafield.

5.3.1.3.   River Transport from Russian Land Based Sources

In Russia, fuel reprocessing takes place, or has taken place, at the Mayak Production Association, Chelyabinsk, and at plants in Krasnoyarsk and Tomsk. All these installation are located within the drainage basin of rivers discharging into the Kara Sea.

Until 1956, radioactive waste from the activities at the Mayak PA were discharged directly into the Techa River, one of the tributares of the Ob, which leads to Kara Sea. After 1956, liquid radioactive waste were discharged into Lake Karachai, a lake with no outlet. These releases have contaminated groundwater and rivers and the mobile radionuclides, *e.g.* ^{90}Sr, have been transported into the Kara Sea (Christensen *et al.*, 1995).

Present investigations have confirmed the high activity concentrations in the environment around the Mayak area, especially in the reservoirs of the upper Techa River at the Asanov swamp and in areas contaminated by the Kyshtym accident (Joint Russian Norwegian Expert Group on Radioactive Contamination of the Northern Areas, 1996a).

The Siberian Chemical Combinate, Tomsk-7 and Krasnoyarsk-26 were two of the main nuclear weapons production facilities of the former USSR. The former is located on the River Tom, a tributary of the Ob, the latter is located in the Yenisey drainage basin. At both locations, much of the activity has ceased the last years. Deep underground injection has been used as the main depository for liquid nuclear waste at these two installation although reservoirs at both locations hold large volumes of waste. At Tomsk, low level waste has been discharged into the Tom River. The Russian authorities started monitoring of ^{90}Sr in the major rivers discharging to the Northern Seas in the second half of 1961. However, systematic measurements of ^{137}Cs in river water are not available. The total, non decay corrected, input of ^{90}Sr to the Arctic Seas by the rivers over the period of measurements is estimated to be 2.4 PBq (Tab. 5.II.) (Tsaturov *et al.*, 1995). During recent investigations on the vertical distribution of ^{137}Cs and Pu-isotopes in dated sediment profiles from the Ob estuary, only the signal from global fallout is found. This indicates that the contribution to the Arctic Seas from the land-based Russian sources has been small compared to fallout. (Panteleyev *et al.*, 1995).

Table 5.II. The river discharges of ^{90}Sr to the Eastern shelf seas (1961-1994) (Tsaturov *et al.*, 1995).

Sea area	Integrated amount of ^{90}Sr (TBq)
White and Barents Seas	381
Kara Sea	1355
Laptev Sea	462
East Siberian Sea	170
Total	2368

5.3.1.4. The Chernobyl Accident

On April 26 1986, an explosion and fire occurred at the Chernobyl nuclear power plant (NPP) in the Ukraine, and large amounts of radioactivity were released to the atmosphere. Even though the Chernobyl NPP is located at approximately 52° N, fallout from the accident was detected in northern areas mainly because of atmospheric and subsequent marine transport. Over time the marine transport pathway has become of increasing in importance. Currently, the main amount of Chernobyl-derived ^{137}Cs transported to the Arctic Oceans originates in the Baltic Sea and is transported to northern sea areas *via* the Norwegian coastal current

5.3.2. Levels of Radionuclides

5.3.2.1. Distribution in Surface Sea Water

The levels of ^{137}Cs in the surface water of the Arctic Ocean are presently in the range 0.8 to 15 Bq m^{-3}. In Figure 5.5., data from the Russian – Swedish Tundra Ecology Expedition (Persson *et al.*, 1995; Josefsson *et al.*, 1995), the Canadian 1994 Arctic Ocean Section (Ellis *et al.*, 1995), Danish monitoring data around Greenland (Aarkrog, 1996) and Icelandic monitoring data (Ólafdóttir *et al.*, 1996) are shown. There are presently no comparable data available on the levels of ^{137}Cs in the surface water of the Canadian Basin and the Beaufort Sea. However, in view of current knowledge of sources and currents, such levels cannot be higher than levels measured in the rest of the Arctic Basin.

One special feature of these data are the high levels in the vicinity of the North Pole over the Lomonosov Ridge (Ellis *et al.*, 1995). A slight increase in the ^{137}Cs level can also be seen in the Laptev Sea compared with the Kara and Barents Seas. East of the outlet of the large Siberian rivers, *i.e.*, Ob, Yenisei and Lena, the level of ^{137}Cs decreases. This geographical trend follows a decrease in salinity and probably reflects dilution of ^{137}Cs derived predominantly from riverine sources (Josefsson *et al.*, 1995). This is further confirmed by the increased ^{90}Sr/^{137}Cs ratio in the low-salinity waters of the north-eastern Kara Sea (Joint Russian Norwegian Expert group for Investigation of Radioactive Contamination in the Northern Area, 1996b). In the vicinity of Greenland, the highest levels are found along the east coast. The lowest measured levels are found in the East Siberian Sea and over the southeastern part of the Makarov Basin.

This distribution pattern is consistent with the transport of ^{137}Cs released from Sellafield which indicates that the peak releases in the mid 1970s are now reflected in the peaks found in the North Pole Basin and the Laptev Sea.

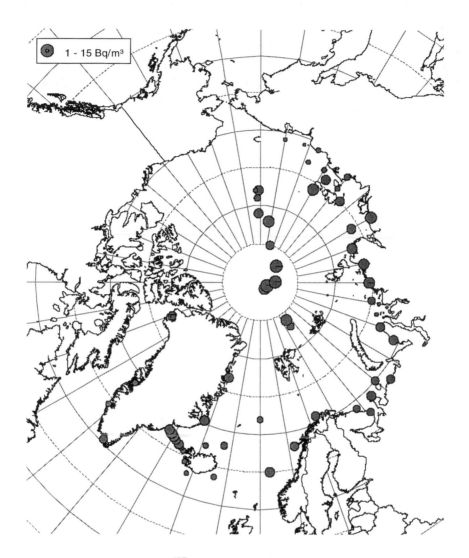

Fig. 5.5. Measurements of ^{137}Cs in surface sea water from 1994 (Persson *et al.*, 1995; Josefsson *et al.*, 1995; Ellis *et al.*, 1995; Aarkrog, 1996; Ólafdóttir, 1996).

5.3.2.2. Trends for Radionuclides in Sea Water

The trends for radionuclides in sea water at different locations correspond to the principal sources of radionuclides. The main source of ^{90}Sr was the atmospheric tests of nuclear weapons during the 1950s and 1960s with an addition from land-based sources, including the Russian reprocessing plants in the areas drained by the rivers Ob and Yenisei. In contrast, the main sources of

^{137}Cs are atmospheric nuclear weapons tests, releases from European reprocessing plants and fallout from the Chernobyl accident. Few data are available on levels of ^{137}Cs in sea water of the Arctic before the beginning of the 1970s. Numerous series of ^{90}Sr measurements are available. In Figure 5.6., time series are shown for ^{137}Cs and ^{90}Sr (Aarkrog, 1996). The decrease of ^{90}Sr following the atmospheric nuclear test ban can be seen clearly.

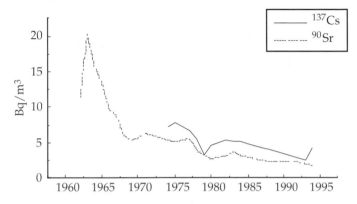

Fig. 5.6. Time trend for levels of ^{137}Cs and ^{90}Sr at Southeast Greenland.

5.3.2.3. Levels in Sediments

The vertical distributions of radionuclides in sediments often provide a record of previous levels in water. However, contaminated sediments can become sources of some radionuclides to water when levels in water change and the partitioning equilibrium between sediments and water is modified as a result. Contaminated surface sediments can therefore be regarded as a potential source of water contamination.

In Figure 5.7., an overview of the average levels of ^{137}Cs in sediments from 1992 to 1995 is presented (Aarkrog *et al.*, 1986; Joint Russian Norwegian Expert Group for Investigation of Radioactive Contamination in the Northern Areas, 1996b; Strand *et al.*, 1994; Sickel *et al.*, 1996; Brungot *et al.*, 1996). For most locations, the ^{137}Cs levels are on average below 10 Bq kg^{-1}. In the Norwegian Sea and in the open Kara Sea, some locations with levels of up to 100 Bq kg^{-1} are found. This may be caused by peculiarities in the sedimentation rate or sediment characteristics. The only locations with concentration levels over 100 Bq kg^{-1} is in Chernaya Bay on the southern coast of Novaya Zemlya and at some locations close to the dumped nuclear wastes along the coast of Novaya Zemlya, where levels of up to several thousand Bq kg^{-1} are found (Joint Russian Norvegian Expert group for Investigation of Radioactive Contamination in the northen areas, 1996b; Smith *et al.*, 1995).

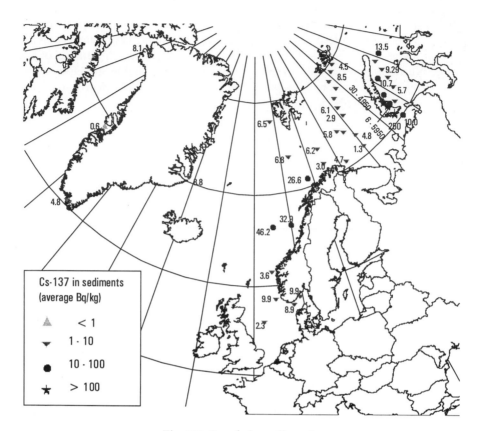

Fig. 5.7. Levels in sediments.

5.3.3. Local Contamination

5.3.3.1. Underwater Nuclear Explosions at Novaya Zemlya

In the vicinity of the Novaya Zemlya archipelago, the former USSR detonated three nuclear weapons underwater. All these weapons were fairly
small (< 20 kT) and have contributed in only a minor way to the total inventory of radionuclides in the arctic marine environment (Tsaturov and
Polikarpov, 1993). These three underwater detonations were performed in
(or in the vicinity of) Chernaya Bay on the southwestern coast of Novaya
Zemlya.

Chernaya Bay is a 15 km long fjordic inlet on the south-western coast of Novaya Zemlya. It has a variable width of 1 to 6 km and is connected to the Pechora Sea in the south-eastern extremity of the Barents Sea. Chernaya Bay contains finer, organic rich sediments. With the exception of the deeper sedimentation basins containing large proportions of fine sediment, the sediments of the Pechora Sea are coarser than those in Chernaya Bay. Chernaya Bay sediments contain anomalous concentrations of radionuclides largely due to underwater nuclear explosions that reportedly took place within the Bay in September 1955, and October 1957, and in the vicinity of the Bay in 1961. The distribution of several radionuclides in the sediments of the Pechora Sea, including Chernaya Bay, has been examined in some detail by Smith et $al.$ (1995). Within the surficial sediments of Chernaya Bay the levels of ^{239,240}Pu, (~ 8500 Bq kg^{-1}), ^{241}Am (~ 430 Bq kg^{-1}) and ^{137}Cs (~ 160 Bq kg^{-1}) are elevated compared to external areas. The activation product, ^{60}Co also occurs in these sediments in measurable amounts (~ 90 Bq kg^{-1}). Smith et $al.$ (1995) examined the ratios among the plutonium and americium isotopes and made comparisons with ratios in global fallout and in areas contaminated by nuclear explosions elsewhere, including underwater tests. While some contribution from radionuclides contained in wastes dumped in Chernaya Bay in 1991 (Yablokov et $al.$, 1993) cannot be ruled out, the distribution and relationships among the transuranic isotopes suggest that the underwater explosions were the primary source of the augmented levels of radionuclides in the sediments.

The ^{239,240}Pu/^{137}Cs activity ratios (> 50) in the sediments of Chernaya Bay and Enewetak Lagoon, which was the site of several nuclear tests in the 1950s, are much greater than those in sediments predominantly contaminated by global fallout, which lie in the range 0.02 to 0.50, and atmospheric fallout itself, which has ratios in the range 0.0012-0.018. The ^{60}Co concentration (91.5 Bq kg^{-1}) was also in the range of those measured at Enewetak (20-200 Bq kg^{-1}) while the relationships between ^{60}Co and ^{137}Cs and between ^{60}Co and ^{239,240}Pu were variable and exhibited low correlations.

The ^{239,240}Pu inventory in Chernaya Bay at a single station is approximately 300 000 Bq m^{-2}, similar to other sites of major plutonium contamination such as in the vicinity of the test explosion sites at Enewetak Lagoon (Nelson and Noshkin, 1973), in the most contaminated area of Bylot Sound (Aarkrog et $al.$, 1987) and in the Irish Sea in the vicinity ($i.e.$, within an adjacent 100 km^2 area) of the Sellafield nuclear fuel reprocessing plant (Pentreath et $al.$, 1986) where sediment inventories are comparable but exceed 300 000 Bq m^2. Interestingly, the integrated Chernaya Bay sediment inventory of 3 TBq estimated by Smith et $al.$ (1995) is larger than that of Bylot Sound (~ 1 TBq) resulting from the weapons plutonium spill at Thule (Aarkrog et $al.$, 1987), of the same order as that of Enewetak Lagoon inventory of 8.5 TBq, but dwarfed by the inventory of the upper 30 cm of Irish Sea sediments of 280 TBq.

5.3.3.2. The Nuclear Weapons Accident at Thule

In January 1968, an American B-52 aircraft carrying four nuclear weapons crashed on the ice in Bylot Sound near Thule, Greenland. The impact triggered the conventional explosive, fragmenting the weapons, resulting in the release of plutonium onto the ice. Debris and the upper layer of contaminated snow was removed, but the ice had been broken around the point of impact and some Pu was deposited on the underlying sediments. From measurements of plutonium in marine sediments collected at expeditions to Thule in 1968, 1970, 1974, 1979 and 1984 (Aarkrog *et al.*, 1971; 1984; 1987; Smith *et al.*, 1994), it was calculated that about 1 TBq, or half a kilogram, of plutonium was deposited on the bottom of Bylot Sound from the Thule accident. As the amount of Pu left on the ice after the decontamination effort in 1968 was estimated to be 1 TBq (± 50%), it seems likely that a substantial part of the plutonium in the sediments comes from the melting of sea-ice. On the other hand, it is evident that the highest levels are found beneath the point of impact and, as some of the contaminated ice drifted away before it melted, it seems likely that some debris entered the sea directly through the impact hole in the ice.

Plutonium in Thule Sea Water

In the summer of 1968, the sea water in Bylot Sound contained about 0.2 Bq m^{-3} of ^{239,240}Pu. This was nearly a factor of two higher than seen at other locations along the Greenland coast which were assumed to be contaminated by global fallout only. As the total volume of water in Bylot Sound is 50 km^3, the estimated amount of ^{239,240}Pu in sea water in 1968 was estimated to be 10^{10} Bq. Of this amount, half (*i.e.*, 5 GBq or 2 g plutonium) was due to the Thule nuclear weapons accident.

In 1970, sea water levels (0.02-0.1 Bq m^{-3}) of Pu did not differ significantly from the fallout background. This has also been verified by later sampling. The only subsequent anomaly found in sea water was in particle-bound Pu in near-bottom water at the point of impact. This is probably due to resuspension of contaminated sediments.

Plutonium in Thule Sediments

The low solubility of PuO$_2$ (high K_d value) makes it likely that most of the plutonium that entered the sea from the Thule accident was to be found in the marine sediments on the bottom of Bylot Sound. Extensive sampling has been performed (Aarkrog *et al.*, 1984; 1987; Aarkrog, 1971; Smith *et al.*, 1994) showing that the Pu from the accident has only been minimally dispersed from the crash site and is being vertically mixed into the sediments. Thus, the site is currently no significant source of plutonium contamination to the proximal environment (Smith *et al.*, 1994).

5.3.3.3. Dumped Radioactive Material

Between 1960 and 1991, the former USSR carried out dumping of radioactive waste in the Kara and Barents Seas. The dumping sites are shown in Figure 5.8. The wastes dumped at sea included liquid and solid waste, the latter including reactor compartments and entire submarines. Some of the reactors contained spent nuclear fuel (Yablokov *et al.*, 1993). In addition to the official information provided by the Government of the Russian Federation, the International Arctic Sea Assessment project (IASAP) of the International Atomic Energy Agency (IAEA), has produced revised inventories. These revised estimates are shown in Table 5.III. (Rubtsov *et al.*, 1995; Sivintsev *et al.*, 1995).

**Table 5.III. Inventories of the main dumping area
in the Kara Sea decay corrected to 1993 - 1995, all numbers in TBq.**

	$^{137}\mathrm{Cs}$	$^{90}\mathrm{Sr}$	$^{238+239+240}\mathrm{Pu}$
Tsivolky Fjord (Rubtsov *et al.*, 1995)	493	447	11
Abrosimov Fjord (Sivintsev, 1994)	352	319	1.6
Stepovogo Fjord (Rubtsov *et al.*, 1995)	189	185	< 0.1
Novaya Zemlya Trough (Sivintsev, 1994)	68.5	74	0.4

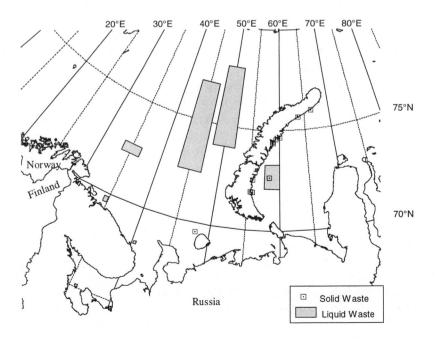

Fig. 5.8. Dumping sites for radioactive waste in the Kara and Barents Seas.

Contamination Levels at the Sea Dumpsites

During the joint Norwegian-Russian oceanographic expeditions that took place between 1990 and 1994, the dumpsites were visually surveyed and samples were collected near to, and further away from, the dumped objects. On the east coast of Nova Zemlya, in Abrosimov and Stepovogo Fjords, enhanced levels of ^{137}Cs, ^{90}Sr, ^{60}Co and Pu-isotopes were observed in sediments collected in the close vicinity of the dumped waste (Tab. 5.IV.) (Joint Russian Norwegian Expert group for Investigation of Radioactive Contamination in the Northern Areas, 1996b). In Abrosimov Fjord, the contamination was significant in the upper 5 cm (^{90}Sr) and upper 10 cm (^{137}Cs, ^{60}Co) of the sediments. In Stepovogo Fjord, enhanced levels of ^{137}Cs, ^{90}Sr, ^{60}Co and Pu-isotopes were observed in the upper 5 cm of the sediments similarly collected in the close vicinity of the dumped containers. Significantly lower levels of ^{137}Cs and ^{90}Sr were observed in sediments at some distance from the localised objects. These levels were similar to those in the open Kara Sea. In Tsivolky Fjord, traces of ^{60}Co in sediments close to the dumped vessel could indicate leakage from dumped waste. No indication of leakage from the waste dumped in the Novaya Zemlya Trough was observed.

The general levels in sea water did not show any increased concentrations of radionuclides. The only exception was an increase of ^{90}Sr in bottom water in the inner Stepovogo Bay (Tab. 5.V.). Concentration levels in biota, *i.e.*, fish, showed no enhanced levels. The levels from Polar Cod and Arctic Char ranged from 0.5 to 2.2 Bq kg^{-1} ^{137}Cs and 0.99-1.6 Bq kg^{-1} ^{90}Sr, respectively. The levels of ^{238}Pu and $^{239, 240}$Pu were below detection limits (0.01 Bq kg^{-1} and 0.008 Bq kg^{-1} respectively).

The concentrations of radionuclides in the open Kara Sea are low and significantly lower than in other marine systems such as the Irish and Baltic Seas. Global fallout is the primary source for radionuclides in the arctic region. However, there remain significant signals of previous discharges from Sellafield and fallout from the Chernobyl accident. Radionuclide signals from river transport can also be observed such as the enhanced ^{90}Sr/^{137}Cs ratio in the low salinity waters in the north-eastern part of the Kara Sea (Strand *et al.*, 1994). A fairly constant ^{134}Cs/^{137}Cs ratio of approximately 0.02 has been found throughout the Kara Sea. Taking account of the known releases and the transport time from Sellafield, the only known source of ^{134}Cs that could contribute to Kara Sea levels is the Chernobyl accident. If no other source has contributed significant amounts of ^{134}Cs, it can be estimated that approximately 30% of the ^{137}Cs in the surface water of the Kara Sea originates from the Chernobyl accident (Joint Russian Norwegian Expert group for Investigation of Radioactive Contamination in the Northern Areas, 1996b).

Table 5.IV. Range of levels in sediments near to the dumped objects (Bq kg^{-1} d.w.) (Joint Russian Norwegian Expert group for Investigation of Radioactive Contamination in the Northern Areas, 1996b).

	^{137}Cs	^{90}Sr	^{60}Co	^{239,240}Pu
Abrosimov Fjord	23-31 000	0.3-3800	0.4-172	0.7-18
Stepovogo Fjord	1-109 000	0.4-310	< 0.1-3150	< 0.1-15

Table 5.V. Ranges of levels in Sea Water (Bq m^{-3}) (Joint Russian Norwegian Expert group for Investigation of Radioactive Contamination in the Northern Areas, 1996b).

	Abrosimov Fjord		Stepovogo Fjord		Tsivolky Fjord		Open Kara Sea	
	^{137}Cs	^{90}Sr	^{137}Cs	^{90}Sr	^{137}Cs	^{90}Sr	^{137}Cs	^{90}Sr
Surface	4-7	2-4	3-9	2-7	4-6	4-6	3-8	3-11
Near bottom	4-9	2-4	6-31	3-26	6-14	3-4	8-20	4-6

5.3.3.4. Sunker Komsomolets Submarine

On April 7th 1989, the Soviet nuclear submarine *Komsomolets* caught fire and sank south west of Bear Island in the Norwegian Sea. This submarine contains two torpedoes with nuclear warheads and a nuclear reactor. The reactor was shut down in an orderly manner prior to sinking. An estimate of the main long-lived radionuclide constituents of the reactor and nuclear weapons of the Komsomolets is given in Table 5.VI. (Høibråten and Thoresen, 1995).

Table 5.VI. Amounts of selected radionuclides (TBq) in Komsomolets decay corrected to January 1, 1995.

^{137}Cs	2 700
^{90}Sr	2 400
^{239}Pu	22

Scientific studies in the vicinity of the site indicate that only minor contamination can be attributed to the submarine (Tab. 5.VII.; Sickel *et al.*, 1996; Kolstad, 1995). Releases from the submarine wreckage are likely to depend on the rate of loss of structural integrity of the hull and reactor components while the plutonium in the nuclear warheads is likely to be released slowly and, because of the high particle reactivity of plutonium, be confined to sediments in the vicinity of the wreck.

Table 5.VII. Levels of radionuclides in sediments near to and approximately 1 nautical mile from Komsomolets compared to average values for the North European Seas in 1995 (Bq kg^{-1} d.w) (Sickel *et al.*, 1996; Kolstad, 1995).

	$^{239+240}$Pu	^{238}Pu	^{241}Am	^{137}Cs	^{137}Cs
Close to Komsomolets, 1995	1.16 ± 0.08	0.04 ± 0.01	0.86 ± 0.06	7.1 ± 0.4	0.6 ± 0.3
Close to Komsomolets, 1993[*]	0.3 ± 0.2	0.090[**]	0.2 ± 0.1	7 ± 4	1.4 ± 0.8
Close to Komsomolets, 1994[*]	0.4 ± 0.4	n.m	n.m	8 ± 4	0.5 ± 0.3
South	0.85 ± 0.06	0.04 ± 0.01	< 0.7	5.1 ± 0.3	n.d
West	n.m.	n.m	0.65 ± 0.05	6.6 ± 0.6	n.d
North	0.95 ± 0.07	0.03 ± 0.01	< 0.96	5.4 ± 0.2	0.3 ± 0.06
East	0.96 ± 0.08	0.13 ± 0.02	0.57 ± 0.05	9.7 ± 0.5	n.d
Other North European Seas[*]	1.4 ± 0.8	0.1 ± 0.1	0.8 ± 0.5		

[*] These numbers are averages of many measurements, the uncertainty given is the standard deviation of the measurements. For the other measurements, the standard deviation is the measurement uncertainty.

[**] Plutonium 238 was detectable in only one sample during this sampling.

n.m. Not measured.

5.4. Conclusions

Current levels of radioactive contamination in the Arctic Ocean are comparable with, or lower than, those in the North Atlantic and European marginal seas. Contemporary large scale contamination can be attributed to four main sources:

- Global fallout from the nuclear weapons testing,
- Releases from Western European nuclear fuel reprocessing,
- Transport through river systems of releases from nuclear installations or runoff from contaminated land,
- Fallout from the Chernobyl accident.

On local scales, higher levels of contamination may occur, *e.g.* close to the dumped nuclear waste in some of the fjords of Novaya Zemlya dose to the Komsomolets submarine wreck, at the site of the Thule nuclear weapons accident and at the sites of underwater nuclear explosions. Estimates of the input from different sources are given in Table 5.VIII.

A number of other sources exist that have the potential to contaminate this area. These include potential accidents involving nuclear materials at the bases of the Russian Northern Fleet along the northern coast of the Kola Peninsula, accidents at nuclear power plants, *e.g.* the Kola and Bilibino nuclear power plants in Northern Russia and possible transport of radionuclides from other contaminated areas such as transport through the Ob river system of radionuclides released from Mayak. All of these sources and the potential for accidental releases requires attention, specifically assessments of the probabilities and consequences of various accident scenarios. Finally, it should be stressed that an understanding of radionuclide behaviour and transport and exposure pathways to man is essential for the preparation of reliable dose and risk assessments.

Table 5.VIII. Estimated inventories or amounts released and transported to the Arctic Oceans from selected sources.

Source	^{137}Cs PBq	^{90}Sr PBq	$^{238+239+240}Pu$ PBq
Global fallout[*] (UNSCEAR, 1993)	28	18.8	0.3
Sellafield[**] (Aarkrog, 1993)	10 - 15	1 - 2	n.d (low)
Komsomolets[***] (Høibråten and Thoresen, 1995)	3	2.7	0.02
River Transport (Tsaturov et al., 1995)	n.d	2.4	n.d (low)
Dumped Nuclear waste[***] (Rubtsov and Ruzhansky, 1995; Sivintsev, 1994)	1.1	1.0	0.013
Chernaya Bay (Smith et al., 1995)	<< 0.001	n.d	0.003
Thule (Aarkog et al., 1984)	n.d (low)	n.d (low)	0.001

n.d: No data available,
n.d (low): No data available, but probably small amounts due to transport or source properties.
[*] Fallout north of 60° N
[**] Estimated amount transported to the Arctic Oceans
[***] These amounts have not been released into the open environment but are currently mostly contained in submerged objects

Acknowledgements

We want to thank Jos Kögeler at Aquaplan NIVA for making sattelite images available and for helpful comments.

References

Aarkrog A. (1971) Radioecological investigations of plutonium in an arctic marine environment. *Health Phys.* **20**, 31-47.
Aarkrog A. (1977) Environmental behaviour of plutonium accidentally released at Thule, Greenland. *Health Phys.* **32**, 271-284.

Aarkrog A. (1993) Radioactivity in Polar Regions – Main Sources. Environmental Radioactivity in the Arctic and Antarctic, (P. Strand and E. Holm, Eds.) pp. 15-34. Norwegian Radiation Protection Authority, Østerås, Norway, 1994.

Aarkrog A. (1996) Radionuclides in the Greenland Marine Environment, National Assessment Report. Risø National Laboratory, Risø 1995, in press.

Aarkrog A., Boelskifte S., Dahlgaard H., Duniec S., Holm E. and Smith J.N. (1987) Studies of transuranics in an Arctic marine environment. *J. Radioanal. and Nuclear Chem.* **115**, 39-50.

Aarkrog A., Dahlgaard H., Nilsson K. and Holm E. (1984) Further Studies of Plutonium and Americium at Thule, Greenland. *Health Phys.* **46**, 29-44.

Brungot A.L. *et al.* (1996) Radioactivity in the Marine Environment, National Survelliance Report, NRPA, Østerås, in prep.

Calmet D. and Guéguéniat P. (1985) Les rejets d'effluents liquides radioactifs du centre de traitement des combustibles irradiés de La Hague (France) et l'évolution radiologique du domain marin. «Behaviour of Radionuclides Released into Coastal Waters», TECDOC-329, International Atomic Energy Agency, Vienna, 183 pp.

CEC (1990) The radiological exposure of the population of the European Community from radioactivity in North European marine waters: Project 'Marina'. Radiation Protection Report 47, Directorate of Nuclear Safety, Impact of Industry on the Environment and Waste Management, Directorate General Environment, Consumer Protection and Nuclear Safety, EUR 12483 EN, 571 pp.

Christensen G.C., Malyshev S.V., Strand P., Salbu B., Romanov G.N., Selnæa T.D., Ougthon D., Glagolenko Y.U., Amundsen I., Rudjord A.L., Bjerk T.O. and Lind B. (1995) Radioactive contamination in the environment of the nuclear enterprice Mayak PA. Results from the joint Russian-Norwegian field work in 1994. Environmental Radioactivity in the Arctic (Per Strand and Andrew Cooke, Eds.) pp. 29-35. Norwegian Radiation Protection Authority, Østerås, Norway.

Dahlgaard H. (1994) Sources of ^{137}Cs, ^{90}Sr and ^{99}Tc in the East Greeland Current. *J. Environ. Radioactivity* **25**, 37-55.

Ecosystem Barents Sea (1994) Universitetsforlaget, Oslo, pp. 43-53 (In Norwegian).

Ellis K.M., Smith J.N., Nelson R.P., Kilius L., Macdonald R., Carmack E. and Moran S.B. (1995) «Distribution of Artificial Radionuclides in the Arctic Ocean from the 1994 Arctic Ocean Section» Environmental Radioactivity in the Arctic, (Per Strand and Andrew Cooke, Eds.) pp. 204-207. Norwegian Radiation Protection Authority, Østerås, Norway.

Freke A.M., Morley F. and Tyler G.R. (1969) A review of the liquid effluent discharges and marine monitoring programme at Dounreay: 1958-1968. Authority Health and Safety Branch Report AHSB(RP) R 88, United Kingdom Atomic Energy Authority, 38 pp., Harwell, Berks.

Gray J., Jones S.R and Smith A.D. (1995) Discharges to the environment from the Sellafield Site, 1951-1992. *J. Radiol. Prot.* **15**, 99-131.

Høibråten S. and Thoresen P.E. (1995) The sunken submarine Komsomolets and its effect on the environment. Environmental Radioactivity in the Arctic (Per Strand and Andrew Cooke, Eds.) pp. 350-355. Norwegian Radiation Protection Authority, Østerås, Norway.

Joint Russian Norwegian Expert Group on Radioactive Contamination of the Northern Areas (1996a) Identification of sources of radioactive contamination entering the drainage and hydrologic system of the River Techa in the area where the « Mayak » P.A. is located, NRPA, Østerås 1996, to be published.

Joint Russian Norwegian Expert Group for Investigation of Radioactive Contamination in the Northern Areas (1996b) Dumping of Radioactive Waste and Radioactive Contamination in the Kara Sea, NRPA, Østerås 1996.

Josefsson D., Holm E., Persson B. R., Roos P., Smith J.N. and Kilius L. (1995) Radiocaesium and ^{129}I along the Russian Coast. Preliminary results from the Swedish Russian Tundra Ecology expedition 1994, Environmental Radioactivity in the Arctic, (Per Strand and Andrew Cooke, Eds.) pp. 273-275. Norwegian Radiation Protection Authority, Østerås, Norway.

Kershaw P.J. and Baxter A.J. (1993) Transfer of reprocessing wastes from NW Europe to the Arctic. In: *Environmetal Radioactivity in the Arctic and Antarctic* (P. Strand and E. Holm, Eds.) pp. 103-106. Norwegian Radiation Protection Authority, Østerås, Norway.

Kershaw P.J. and Baxter A. (1995) The transfer of reprocessing wastes from N.W. Europe to the Arctic. *Deep Sea Research* p. II **42**, 1413-1448.

Kershaw P.J., Gurbutt P.A., Woodhead D.S., Leonard K.S. and Rees J.M. (1995) Estimates of fluxes of caesium-137 in northern waters from recent measurements. In: *Environmental Radioactivity in the Arctic* (Per Strand and Andrew Cooke, Eds.) pp. 95-101. Norwegian radiation Protection Authority, Østerås, Norway.

Kolstad A.K. (1995) Expedition to Komsomolets in 1993 and 1994, StrålevernRapport 1995:7, NRPA, Østerås (In Norwegian).

Meese D., Cooper L., Larsen I.L., Tucker W., Reimnitz E. and Grebmeier J. (1995) Caesium-137 contamination in Arctic Sea ice, Environmental Radioactivity in the Arctic (Per Strand and Andrew Cooke, Eds.) pp. 195-198. Norwegian Radiation Protection Authority, Østerås, Norway.

Nelson V. and Noshkin V.E. (1973) Enewetak Survey Report. USAEC Nevada Operations Office, pp. 131-224, Las Vegas, Nevada, NVO-140.

Ólafdóttir E.D., Pálsson S.E. and Magnusson S.M. (1996) ^{137}Cs i vistkerfisjávar og stöctuvatna 1993-1995. IRPI Reykjavik (in Icelandic).

Panteleyev G.P., Livingston H.D., Sayles F.L. and Medkova O.N. (1995) Deposition of Plutonium Isotopes and Cs-137 in Sediments of the Ob Delta from the Beginning of the Nuclear Age. Environmental

Radioactivity in the Arctic (Per Strand and Andrew Cooke, Eds.) pp. 57-64. Norwegian Radiation Protection Authority, Østerås, Norway.

Pentreath R.J., Woodhead D.S., Kershaw P.J., Jeffries D.F. and Lovett M.B. (1986) The behaviour of plutonium and americium in the Irish Sea. Rapports P.-v. pp. 60-69, Reunion Conseil International de l'Exploration de la Mer, 186.

Persson B.R.R., Holm E., Carlsson K.Å., Josefsson D. and Roos P. (1995) The Russian-Swedish Tundra Radioecology Expedition 1994. Environmental Radioactivity in the Arctic (Per Strand and Andrew Cooke, Eds.) pp. 266-272. Norwegian Radiation Protection Authority, Østerås, Norway.

Pfirman S.L., Eicken H., Bauch D. and Weeks W.F. (1995) The potential transport of pollutants by Arctic Sea Ice. *Sci. Total Environ.* **159**, 129-146.

L. Rey, Ed. (1984) The Arctic Ocean. The hydrographic environment and the fate of polluants, Macmillian, London.

Rigor I. and Colony R. (1993) Production of Drift Ice in the Laptev Sea 1979-1993.

Rubtsov P. and Ruzhansky P. (1995) Radiation Characteristics Estimates of Irradiated Nuclear Fuel in Reactors of Nuclear Submarine and Icebreaker Lenin Dumped Near Novaya Zemlya Archipelago, Moscow.

Shiklomanov I.A. and Skakalsky B.G., Studying Water, Sediment and Contaminant Runoff of Siberian Rivers, Modern Status and Prospects. *Arctic Research.*

Sickel M., Grøttheim S. *et al.* (1996) Report from the German Northern Seas Expedition 1995, NRPA, Østerås, in prep.

Sivintsev Y. (1994) Study of Nuclides composition and Characteristics of Fuel in Dumped Submarine and Atomic Icebreaker « Lenin », Part 2, Nuclear Submarines, Working material of the IASAP, IAEA, Vienna.

Smith J.N., Ellis K.M., Forman S., Polyak L., Ovanov G., Matishov D., Kilius L. and Dahle S. (1995) Radionuclide Sources in the Barents and Kara Seas, Environmental Radioactivity in the Arctic (Per Strand and Andrew Cooke, Eds.) pp. 179-185. Norwegian Radiation Protection Authority, Østerås, Norway.

Smith J.N., Ellis K.M., Naes K., Dahle S. and Matishov D. (1995) Sedimentation and mixing rates of radionuclides in Barents Sea sediments off Novaya Zemlya. *Deep Sea Research II* **42**, 1471-1493.

Smith J.N., Ellis K.M., Aarkrog A., Dahlgaard H. and Holm A. (1994) Sediment Mixing and Burial of the ^{239,240}Pu Pulse from the 1968 Thule, Greenland Nuclear Weapons Accident. *J. Environ. Radioactivity* **25**, 135-159.

Strand P., Nikitin A, Rudjord A.L., Salbu B, Christensen G., Føyn L., Kryshev I.I., Chumichev V.B, Dahlgaard H. and Holm E. (1994) Survey of Artificial Radionuclides in the Barents Sea and the Kara Sea. *J. Environ. Radioactivity* **25**, 99-112.

Tsaturov Y.S., Chelukanov V.V., Vakulovsky S.M., Maokhon'ko K.P., Nikitin A.I. and Chumichev V.B. (1995) A report of the specialists from the Roshydromet for the AMAP international programme, Section « Radionuclides » Roshydromet, Obninsk 1995.

Tsaturov Y. and Polikarpov G.G. (1993) Sources to Environmental Contamination in the Former USSR. Risø National Laboratory (A. Aarkrog, Ed.)

UNSCEAR (1993) Sources and effects of ionizing radiation. The United Nations Scientific Committee on the Effects of Atomic Radiation. United Nations, New York.

Weeks W.F. (1995) Possible Roles of Sea Ice in the Transport of Hazardous Material. *Arctic Research*.

Yablokov A.V., Karasev V.K. Rumyanstev V.M., Kokeev M.E., Petrov O.J., Lystsov V.N., Emelyanenkov A.F. and Rubtsov P.M. (1993) Facts and problems Related to Radioactive waste Disposal in Seas Adjacent to the Territory of the Russian Federation. Small World Publishers Inc. Moscow.

Zander I. and Araskog R. (1973) Nuclear Explosions 1945-1972, Basic Data. FOA 4 Report A4505-A.1. 56 pp., Stockholm.

6 Artificial Radioactivity in the English Channel and the North Sea

P. Guéguéniat, J. Hermann, P. Kershaw,
P. Bailly du Bois and Y. Baron

The artificial radioactivity in the English Channel and North Sea has dropped sharply (250-500 to 10 Bq m^{-3} in the most contaminated area) between 1975-1985 to 1990-1995. The dispersal of dissolved conservative artificial radionuclides released by fuel reprocessing plants is now well understood. So a release of 10,000 Gbq/month at la Hague in the centre of the English Channel gives rise to activities (Bq m^{-3}) of 68-89 near the point of release, 50-70 in Cherbourg Harbour, 21-45 in the Straits of Dover, estimations around 5 and 2.2 at the entrance of Norwegian Channel and Barents Sea. However, a number of uncertainties remain; they include the transit time and the rate of dilution taking place along the Norwegian Channel.

Paradoxically it is now more difficult to explain the artificial radioactivity in some waters of N.W. Europe because certain diffuse sources of negligible impact in the past (long term northerly and southerly components of Sellafield discharges in the Irish Sea) may now become relatively important.

Introduction

A good knowledge of hydrodynamics is essential in order to assess the dispersal of releases from nuclear fuel reprocessing plants such as La Hague and Sellafield. Artificial radionuclide tracers are of particular interest in this context, particularly for the study of long-term currents in the seas around north-western Europe. This is because the sources of such tracers are relatively few in number and the discharges are well quantified. It is also possible to analyse these radionuclides at extremely low levels of concentration in solution, with certain gamma-emitters being currently detected at activities 40,000 times lower than the natural radioactivity of seawater. Furthermore, some radionuclide species exhibit a conservative behaviour, remaining largely in solution throughout their transit in the water masses (since they are only slightly absorbed onto suspended particulate matter and living organisms).

Use was chiefly made of two radionuclides to follow the movement of water masses in the English Channel and North Sea: antimony-125 and caesium-137. The ratios between the concentrations of these radionuclides as measured in seawater are characteristic of the sources of artificial radioactivity in the seas of northwestern Europe.

This study is a synthesis of research work (Livingston *et al.*, 1982; Kautsky, 1988; Nies and Wedekind, 1988; Nies *et al.*, 1991; Fraizier *et al.*, 1992; Guéguéniat *et al.*, 1993a; 1993b; 1994; 1995; Bailly du Bois *et al.*, 1993; 1995; Hermann *et al.*, 1995; Nies, 1998) carried out on the distribution of [125]Sb and ^{137}Cs within English Channel and North Sea, the source-terms being located at Sellafield in the Irish Sea and La Hague in the central English Channel. Otherwise, new results on the distribution of ^{137}Cs in waters adjoining the North Sea are also discussed. On the western boundary of the studied system, these results concern the Celtic Sea and Western approaches to the English Channel, while to the north, they cover the outlet of the North Sea towards the Norwegian Sea. In this context, the main body of the discussion is supported by data on the radioactivity in north - west Europe and Arctic waters (Livingston *et al.*, 1984; Holm *et al.*, 1991; Dahlgaard *et al.*, 1991; 1995; Strand *et al.*, 1993; Kershaw and Baxter, 1995).

One of the main objectives of this study is to quantify the variations in artificial radioactivity of waters as they travel over a distance of 2,000 km from the central English Channel towards the Barents Sea. The study presented here is resulting from a collaboration between France, Germany and the United Kingdom.

6.1. General Pattern of Water Mass Circulation in the North Sea: Present State of Knowledge

The general circulation of water masses in the North Sea (Fig. 6.1.) results from the contributions of four main sources and their outflow towards the north into the Norwegian Sea.

Waters coming from the Atlantic pass round the northern tip of Great Britain (flux of *ca.* 3,400 km^3 per month) and penetrate into the North Sea between the Shetland Islands and the Norwegian Channel. They show little influence from industrial nuclear releases or the Chernobyl fallout. Waters originating from the Irish Sea (*ca.* 850 km^3 per month) penetrate to the north of Great Britain between Scotland and the Shetland Islands. They carry a large part of the releases discharged by the Sellafield plant into the Irish Sea.

Waters entering the North Sea from the English Channel *via* the Straits of Dover (320 km^3 per month) are labelled chiefly by releases from the reprocessing plant at La Hague.

After April 1986, waters from the Baltic (*ca.* 50 km^3 per month) show radiolabelling from the Chernobyl accident. They are characterized by a marked drop in salinity and follow a direct route towards the north along the Norwegian coast.

All four inputs to the North Sea find their outlet through the Norwegian Channel, with a flux of 4,700 km³ per month.

After their passage through the North Sea, radionuclides released by Sellafield and La Hague are transported northward by the Norwegian coastal current before branching off northern Norway. One branch, corresponding to the Nordkapp Current, flows eastwards into the Barents and Kara Seas, while the other becomes the West Spitzbergen Current. The transit time between the Irish Sea and the Barents Sea is about five years (Livingston *et al.*, 1984; Dahlgaard *et al.*, 1995; Kershaw and Baxter, 1995).

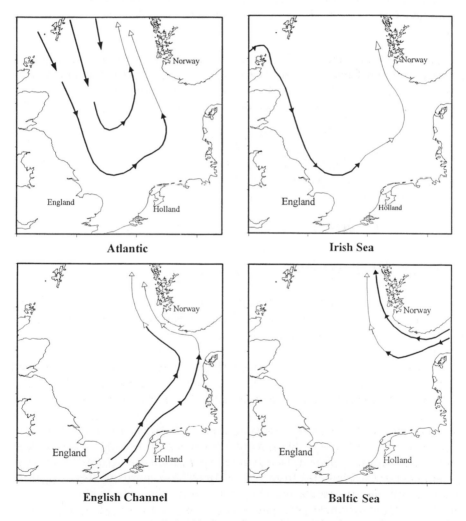

Figure 6.1. General circulation of water masses in the North sea.

6.2. Sampling and Methods

6.2.1. *Radioactive Tracers*

A comparison of the releases from La Hague and Sellafield involving measurements of ^{137}Cs, ^{90}Sr, ^{99}Tc, [125]Sb and [239]Pu, is given in Figure 6.2. The contribution of La Hague to the marine inventory of artificial radionuclides discharged from reprocessing facilities, expressed as a percentage of the Sellafield releases, amounts to 2.3, 12.2, 12.6 and 0.4% for ^{137}Cs, ^{90}Sr, ^{99}Tc, and [239]Pu, respectively (Kershaw and Baxter, 1995). For [125]Sb, [129]I and ^{3}H, the cumulated releases from La Hague showed higher levels compared with Sellafield (by a factor of 2-4 in the case of [125]Sb). The two radionuclides monitored in this study are conservative: [125]Sb and [137]Cs.

Antimony-125 (half-life: 2.7 years) is characteristic of releases from La Hague; English Channel waters labelled by such releases can thus be followed through the North Sea. This radionuclide is practically absent from atmospheric fallout occurring both before and after the Chernobyl accident.

Caesium-137 (half-life: 30 years) is chosen as a tracer to study the dispersion within the North Sea of Irish Sea waters labelled by releases from Sellafield. This is made possible by its relatively high abundance in the Sellafield releases compared with La Hague. [137]Cs is also present in atmospheric fallout from nuclear tests as well as in material derived from the Chernobyl accident.

6.2.2. *Studied Zones*

The following main zones are included in this study:
- The port of Goury situated 5 km from the waste outlet (see Fig. 6.3.).
- Cherbourg harbour 30 km from the same outlet.
- The Straits of Dover.
- North Sea entrance to the Norwegian Channel between lats. 58° and 59° N.
- Outflow of the Norwegian Channel (lats 70° - 72° N, long. 25 - 30° E).

Repeated analyses were carried out from both Goury and Cherbourg waters (one sample every week from 1984 to 1993), as well as on samples from the Straits of Dover (on average, one transect across the English Channel every two months from 1987 to 1992). As regards the investigations in the North Sea and in the Norwegian Channel, the present study is based on the results of major campaigns with research vessels from France (CRYOS in July 1988, NOROIT in June 1989, SUROIT in September 1990 and

NOROIT in July 1991), England (CIROLANA in July 1981 and July-August 1989), and from Germany (GAUSS in November 1989 and November 1994).

Some additional results given here were obtained from cruises of the PLUTEUS (CNRS) and DAHLIA (French National Navy) undertaken in the vicinity of the outlet pipe from La Hague.

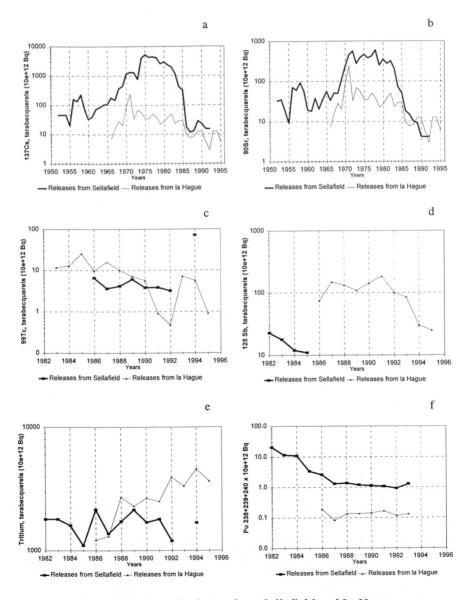

Figure 6.2. Annual releases from Sellafield and La Hague.

6.2.3. Measurement Techniques

In France, radioactivity counting measurements were performed by the IPSN Marine Radioecology Laboratory and the French Navy Atomic Studies Group at Cherbourg, who also arranged the collection and treatment of water samples from Cherbourg harbour. In the United Kingdom, analyses were carried out by the MAFF (Ministry of Agriculture, Fisheries and Food) laboratory at Lowestoft. In Germany, the analyses were carried out by the BSH (Bundesamt für Seeschiffahrt und Hydrographie) in Hamburg.

The techniques used to analyse radionuclides in water samples are described elsewere (Hermann *et al.*, 1995; Gandon and Guéguéniat, 1992).

Numerous measurements of ^{137}Cs activity have been performed on samples that were collected from June to December 1989 in the waters off north-eastern Europe (one campaign with a British vessel, one with a French vessel and one with a German vessel). Advantage is taken of the repeated very closed spaced sampling in the North Sea as a function of time to draw up intercomparisons of the results obtained. Moreover, this enables the mapping of ^{137}Cs distribution over the period concerned in an area comprising the English Channel, the North Sea, the Irish Sea and part of the Arctic Ocean (see Fig. 6.3.). To serve as a comparison, but on a more limited scale, a distribution map of the ^{125}Sb activity will be also presented for June 1989.

6.3. Results

6.3.1. Intercomparison of Results Obtained

The results of the three campaigns carried out in June, July and August 1989 are compared in Figure 6.4a. ^{137}Cs activities are in the range 6-30 Bq m^{-3}, while the configuration of zones delimited by iso-activity contours 5, 10, 20 and 30 are closely similar in all three campaigns (see Fig. 6.4b.).

6.3.2. Distribution of ^{137}Cs and ^{125}Sb on the Mesoscale

The mesoscale mapping of ^{137}Cs distribution in the period June-August 1989 is given in Figures 6.4a., 6.5a., 6.5b., 6.6.and 6.7. for the North Sea, the vicinity of the La Hague outlet, the English Channel, the Irish Sea and Arctic waters, respectively. The activities (Bq m^{-3}) measured near the point sources are 100-400 in the Irish Sea and 10-30 in waters off La Hague.

Figure 6.8. is a ^{125}Sb distribution map for June 1989 covering the area of the English Channel and North Sea. The measured activities (in Bq m^{-3}) are 25-50 for waters off La Hague, 5-10 in Danish waters and 2-4 in Norwegian waters.

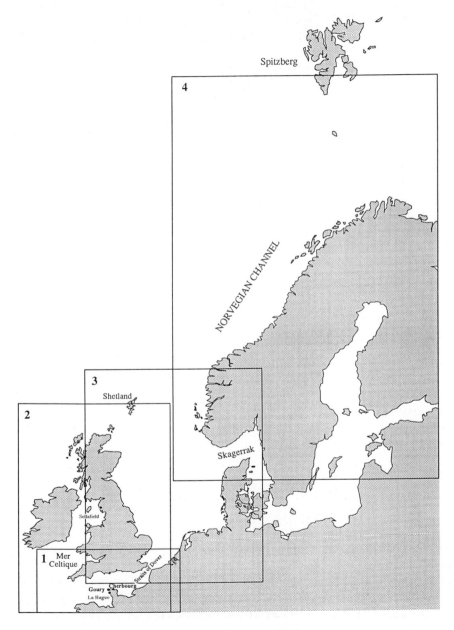

Figure 6.3. Zones studied.

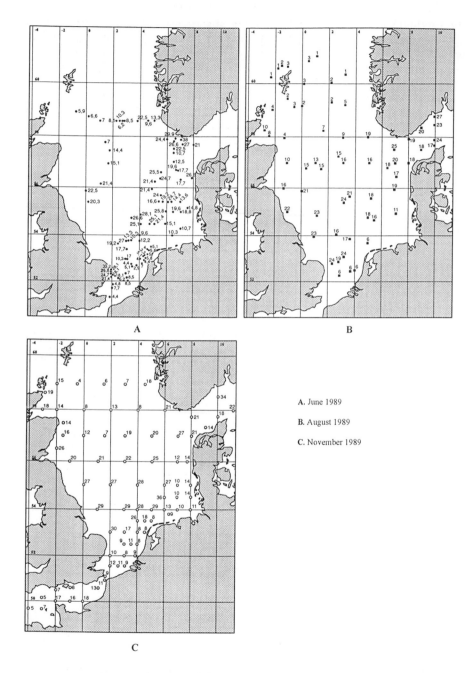

A. June 1989

B. August 1989

C. November 1989

Figure 6.4a. Cartography of activities of ^{137}Cs (Bq m^{-3}) in North Sea.

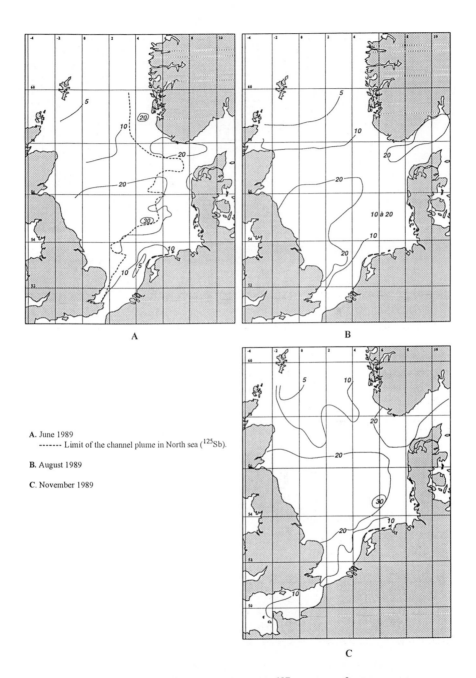

A. June 1989
------- Limit of the channel plume in North sea (^{125}Sb).

B. August 1989

C. November 1989

Figure 6.4b. Cartography of activities of ^{137}Cs (Bq m^{-3}) in North Sea.

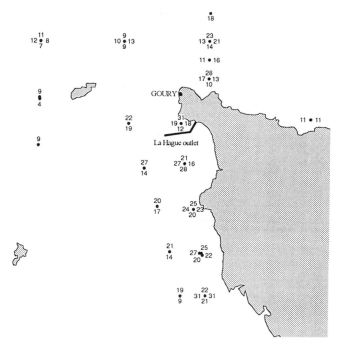

Figure 6.5a. Distribution of ^{137}Cs in the vicinity of La Hague outlet

in September 1989 (z $\overset{x}{\underset{y}{\bullet}}$ w) different analysis at different moments.

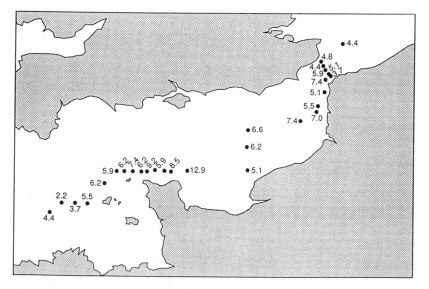

Figure 6.5b. Distribution of ^{137}Cs in the English Channel in June 1989 (Bq m^{-3}).

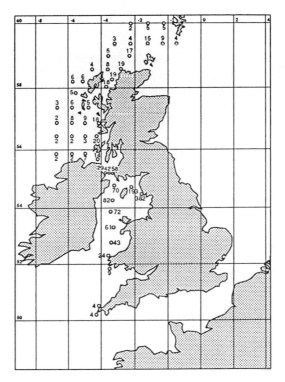

Figure 6.6. Cartography of activities of ^{137}Cs in Irish Sea (Bq m^{-3}).

6.3.3. English Channel Zone

6.3.3.1. Goury - Cherbourg

The dilution of the radiolabelled effluent in waters sampled at Goury and Cherbourg harbour is expressed in terms of the average activities (Bq m^{-3}) measured during the year normalized to the monthly releases from La Hague (Bq/month) for each year from 1984 to 1993. The average values of the untreated and normalized activities are brought together in Table 6.I. Activities were of the order of 100 Bq m^{-3} during the period 1984 - 1989, but declined in 1990-1991 (26-33 Bq m^{-3}). This may be explained by the higher levels of release-normalized activities during 1990-1991 arising from residual effects or due to the fact that, after 1990, releases were spread out over the 12-hours tidal cycle (Fraizier *et al.*, 1992).

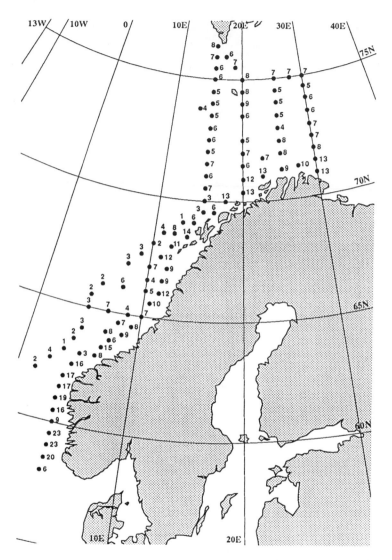

Figure 6.7. ^{137}Cs Distribution in August 1989 in Arctic waters (Bq m^{-3}).

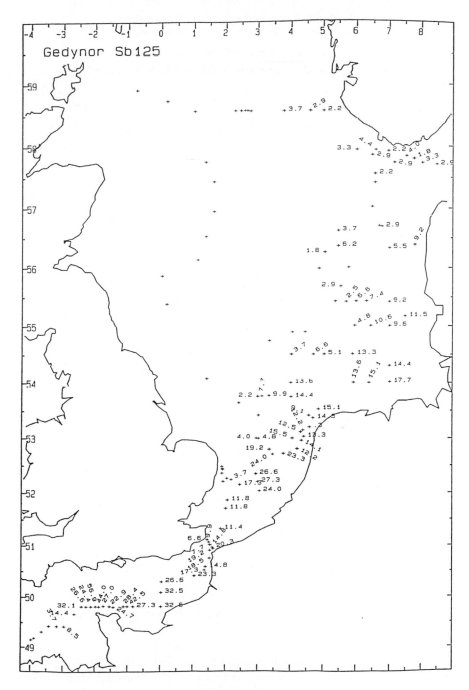

Figure 6.8. Distribution of ^{125}Sb in the English Channel and North Sea in June 1989 (Bq m^{-3}). (+) Below detection limit (1-1.5 Bq m^{-3}).

**Table 6.I. Untreated and normalized values
of ^{125}Sb in waters of Goury and Cherbourg.**

$$Q = \frac{\text{Water radioactivity in Bq m}^{-3}\text{ (annual average)}}{\text{Released radioactivity in Bq (monthly average)}}$$

	GOURY		CHERBOURG
Year	^{125}Sb (Bq m^{-3})	^{125}Sb Normalized values $\times 10^{-11}$	^{125}Sb Normalized values $\times 10^{-11}$
1984	125	Q = 0.89	Q = 0.58
1985	98	Q = 0.89	Q = 0.70
1986	103	Q = 0.68	Q = 0.61
1987	129	Q = 0.68	Q = 0.50
1988	79	Q = 0.77	Q = 0.64
1989	72	Q = 0.84	Q = 0.61
1990	33	Q = 1.08	Q = 0.78
1991	26	Q = 1.20	Q = 0.72
1992	14	Q = 1.32	

By discounting the results for 1990-1992, it would appear that a release of 10,000 GBq/month from La Hague gives rise to activities in the range 68-89 Bq m^{-3} at the Goury sampling site. For waters sampled in Cherbourg Harbour, the residual effect for the period 1990-1991 is less marked; as a general rule, a release of 10,000 GBq/month will produce activities of 50-70 Bq m^{-3} in Cherbourg Harbour. The transit time between the outlet point and Cherbourg is estimated at 3-5 weeks.

6.3.3.2. English Channel

Figures 6.9a. and 6.9b. show the distribution of ^{125}Sb over the entire English Channel in June 1986 and September 1994, bringing together the data from 200 stations. The measured activities are comprised between 0 and 300 Bq m^{-3} in 1986, but are less than 10 Bq m^{-3} in 1994. Under the influence of residual tidal currents, the discharged radionuclides are transported mostly to the east and undergo a certain amount of dispersion.

In 1986, a banded structure is apparent – parallel to the current direction – which displays strongly decreasing activities away from the French coast. To a certain extent, the southern coast of England is protected by this drift effect; as a result, the measured activities near the English coast (0-12 mBq l^{-1}) are lower than those obtained in the Baie de Seine and off the

Pays de Caux – Nord Pas-de-Calais coast (30-80 mBq l⁻¹). Despite the prox-imity of the reprocessing plant of La Hague, the levels of radioactivity in waters around the Channel Islands (Jersey and Guernsey) are lower than those measured 200 km farther east (Cap Gris Nez), being equivalent to the results obtained near Alderney. However, the activities in waters sampled off the Channel Islands can be enhanced during prolonged periods of east-erly winds.

It is shown that soluble radionuclides introduced into the central English Channel by the nuclear fuel reprocessing plant at La Hague are transferred towards the Straits of Dover in 4-7 months, the actual transit time depending on the route taken (Guéguéniat *et al.*, 1993b; 1995). The shortest transit time corresponds to a rapid pathway through the central Channel and the longest to an indirect route *via* inshore waters, both routes (see Fig. 6.10.) being derived from hydrodynamic modelling (Salomon and Breton, 1993; Salomon *et al.*, 1993).

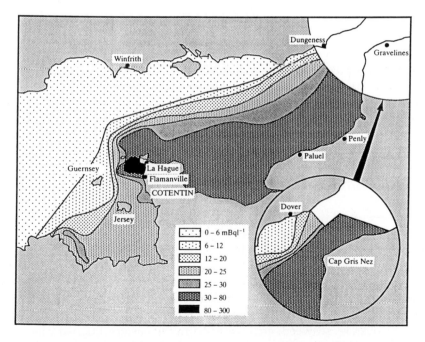

Figure 6.9a. Distribution of ¹²⁵Sb activity in the central and
eastern Channel during June 1986.

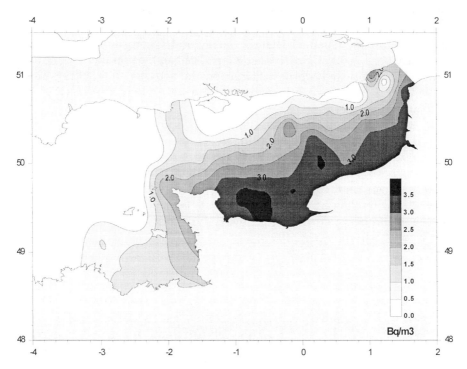

Figure 6.9b. Distribution of ^{125}Sb activity in the central and
eastern Channel during September 1994.

6.3.3.3.   Straits of Dover

Measurements of radioactivity in the Straits of Dover were carried out regularly along a cross-Channel transect between November 1990 and April 1992 (see Fig. 6.11.). Activities in English coastal waters (station 1) are in general ten times lower than values obtained from French coastal waters (station 6). Although the amount of radioactivity passing through this latter zone is very low in terms of flux, it is nevertheless important in conditioning the mechanisms of radiotracer uptake by numerous coastal marine species (*e.g.* mussels, oysters, seaweed, etc.) collected in the eastern English Channel. In fact, the water flux at station 6 corresponds to only a small fraction of the total flux through the Straits, while the same applies to station 1 near the English coast. On the basis of radioactivity measurements, the mean transit time for the rapid route (*i.e.* waters passing through stations 2, 3, 4 and 5) is estimated at 110-152 days (Bailly du Bois *et al.*, 1993).

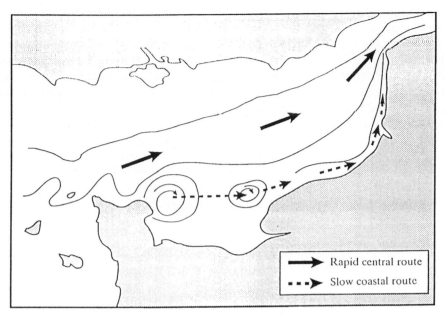

Figure 6.10. Sketch map showing different transfer mechanisms for radiolabelled water discharged from the nuclear fuel reprocessing plant at La Hague. Bold arrows indicate the rapid central route and dashed arrows indicate the slow coastal route towards the entry to the North Sea.

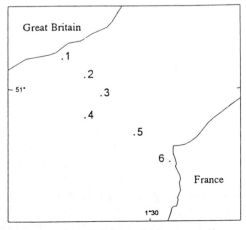

Figure 6.11. Positions of the six standard FLUXMANCHE sites.

During the period from January 1990 to September 1991, the releases of [125]Sb showed relatively little variation, being comprised between 2,000 and 4,000 GBq per month. However, the release for April 1991 was significantly higher, at 5,400 GBq per month. Nine collecting campaigns were carried out during the period in question. In order to calculate the dilution occurring between Goury and the Straits of Dover, the mean activity levels measured (see Fig. 6.12.) at a given time at stations (N° 2, 3, 4 and 5) within the rapid transit zone are associated with the releases taking place 4-5 months previously from La Hague. For the campaigns considered here, a unit release of 10,000 GBq per month will produce activities in the range 21-45 Bq m^{-3}. The scattering of these estimates is linked to the variability of transit time, which itself depends mainly on meteorological conditions that are discussed in more detail elsewhere (Guéguéniat *et al.*, 1995). The most probable mean concentration (*i.e.* most frequently reported value, in 80% of measurements) falls in the class 34-36 Bq m^{-3}. This estimate of the impact of releases from La Hague in the Straits of Dover appears realistic in view of the water fluxes. Assuming an activity of 35 Bq m^{-3} arises from a monthly release of 10,000 GBq, this yields a water flux of 286 km^3 per month through the Straits, a value which is very close to the flux of 296 km^3 calculated from modelling (Salomon *et al.*, 1993) for this period.

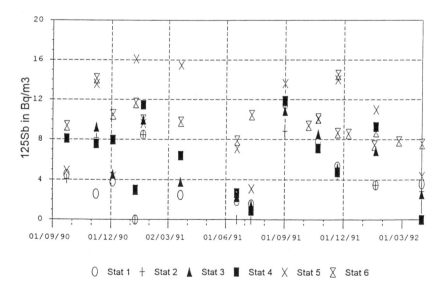

Figure 6.12. Variations of the concentrations of [125]Sb in the Straits of over measured at the six standard FLUXMANCHE sites.

6.3.4.   North Sea

The main source of radioactivity in the North Sea corresponds to the releases of ^{137}Cs from Sellafield, with the maximum impact being observed between 1975 and 1985. Maps of the distribution of ^{137}Cs for this period (*e.g.* 1978, see Fig. 6.13.) show that the zone influenced by Sellafield extends over most of the North Sea; the measured levels of activity were comprised between 100 and 500 Bq m^{-3}. In the remaining parts of the North Sea, corresponding to inshore waters between Holland and Denmark, the activities were clearly lower (10-30 Bq m^{-3}). The plume of English Channel waters labelled by releases from La Hague is known to run along this coastal belt. It is noteworthy that for water sampled at Goury, a few kilometres from the outlet pipe of La Hague, the ^{137}Cs activities for the year 1978 were in the range 15-25 Bq m^{-3}. The same mapping operation carried out in 1994 showed a sharp fall in ^{137}Cs activities for the whole of the North Sea, with values lying between 4 and 14 Bq m^{-3} (see Fig. 6.14.).

As regards the plume of English Channel waters in the North Sea, radiotracer studies carried out with ^{125}Sb have led to a better characterization of the outline and changes in position of the labelled water masses (Guéguéniat *et al.*, 1993b) from one collection campaign to another. The studies undertaken in this context were designed to specify the transit times of radiotracers in the North Sea as well as the dilution of waters coming from the English Channel (Bailly du Bois *et al.*, 1993; 1995), thus making it possible to associate the activity measured at any given moment in the investigated area with a particular level of release from the source. Some of the more detailed studies have been concerned with estimating the impact of releases from La Hague at the outlet of the North Sea, in the Norwegian Channel.

6.3.5.   Entrance to the Norwegian Channel

6.3.5.1. ^{125}Sb

Preliminary studies have shown that, on the basis of the four campaigns carried out between 1988 and 1991, the transit time between the central English Channel and the entrance to the Norwegian Channel attains an average value of 17 months (Guéguéniat *et al.*, 1994). The relations between the average activities measured in this zone and the levels of release are indicated in Figure 6.15. It can be seen that a release of 10,000 GBq/month from the establishment of La Hague will, on average, produce a ^{125}Sb activity of 3.2 Bq m^{-3} at the entrance to the Norwegian Channel. For radionuclides with longer half-lives, it is necessary to correct this activity in proportion to the decay constant; on average, a release of 10,000 GBq will produce an activity of 5 Bq m^{-3} for a long-period radionuclide.

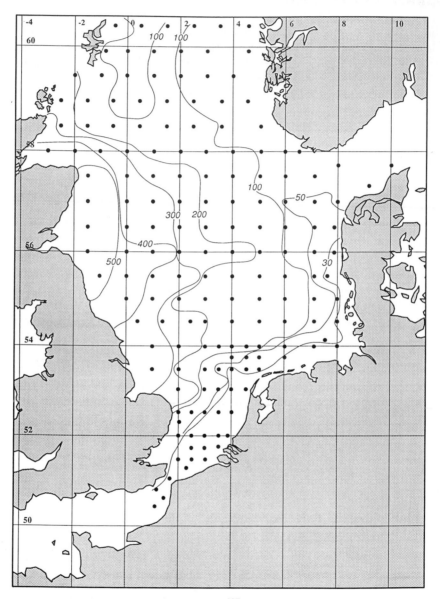

Figure 6.13. Distribution of ^{137}Cs activity in North Sea
in 1978 (Bq m^{-3}).

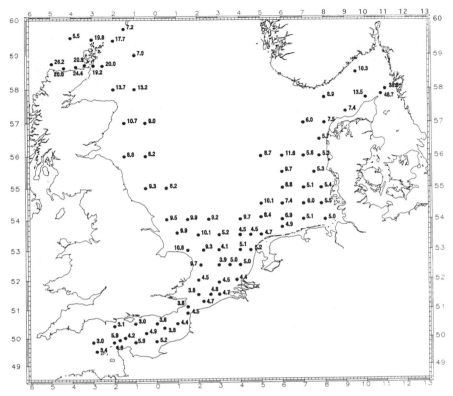

Figure 6.14. Distribution of ^{137}Cs activity in English Channel
and North Sea in February 1994 (Bq m^{-3}).

6.3.5.2. ^{137}Cs

Analyses of ^{125}Sb activity were not carried out in areas beyond latitudes 59°-63° N. ^{137}Cs was used as a basis for evaluating the transfer factors beyond this sector, incorporating data from three campaigns at the entrance to the Norwegian Channel (1988, 1989 and 1991) and two campaigns along the length of the channel (1985 and 1989). The activities measured in this zone show a decrease from 40 to 12 Bq m^{-3} over the period 1988-1991 (see Fig. 6.16.). These levels are attributable to releases from Sellafield and fallout from Chernobyl, while the contribution from La Hague in 1988, according to the release inventory and the transfer factors, only accounts for 0.5 Bq m^{-3}. The contribution from Sellafield is around 17-18 Bq m^{-3} at this time (see Fig. 6.17. showing variation of ^{137}Cs as a function of salinity), taking into account a background of 2.5 Bq m^{-3}.

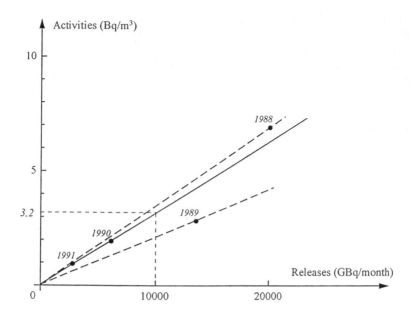

Figure 6.15. Link between ^{125}Sb activities in Norwegian Channel (58°-59° N) during the period 1988-1991 and La Hague releases.

6.3.6. Norwegian Channel

It is possible for Sellafield releases to estimate that waters entering and leaving the Norwegian Channel at given moment are « spiked » by releases that have taken place 3.5 ± 0.5 and 5 ± 0.5 years previously; the approximate transit time along the Norwegian Channel is 1.5 ± 0.5 years. Under these conditions, the approximate transit time between La Hague and the entrance of the Barents Sea is three years. As a consequence the water samples analysed in June 1981 and August 1989 are representative of releases carried out during the periods 1977-1978 and 1985-1986, respectively, and the approximate transit time along the Norwegian Channel is 1.5 ± 0.5 years.

- For the 1981 campaign, it may be assumed that equilibrium is achieved between the releases recorded from July 1976 to July 1978 and the radioactivity of waters in the Norwegian Channel. There is a low degree of dilution (factor of 1.7) between the entry and the outflow of the studied zone (see Fig. 6.18.).

- For the campaign in August 1989, the effects of Chernobyl are superimposed onto the Sellafield releases and a state of equilibrium is no longer achieved. The cumulative effect of these two sources, as measured at the entrance to the Norwegian Channel, shows a marked decrease from June 1988 (40 Bq m^{-3}) to June 1989 (15 Bq m^{-3}). The combined effects of dilution and the presence of two source-terms acts in such a way that activities are evened out; because of this, relatively constant levels of activity (Bq m^{-3}) are observed (see Fig. 6.7.) along the length of the channel (9-19 between lat. 60° and 65° N, 9-13 between lat. 70-71° N long. 20-30° E). Waters entering the channel in June 1988 are characterized by an activity of 26 Bq m^{-3}, but applying a dilution factor of 1.7 does not account for the activities observed in August 1989. The transit time between latitudes 58°-59° N and 70°-71° N should be less than one year, otherwise the dilution factor would need to be increased from 1.7 to 3. Considering the uncertainty associated with the estimation of transit time, a dilution factor of 2.3 ± 0.7 is adopted for the path between the entry and the outflow of the studied zone.

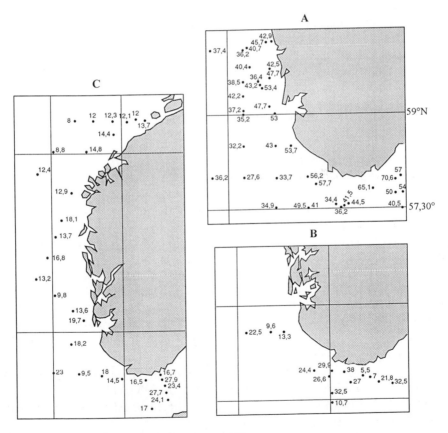

Figure 6.16. Evolution of distribution of ^{137}Cs activity in the Norwegian Channel during 1988 (A), 1989 (B) and 1991 (C) (Bq m^{-3}).

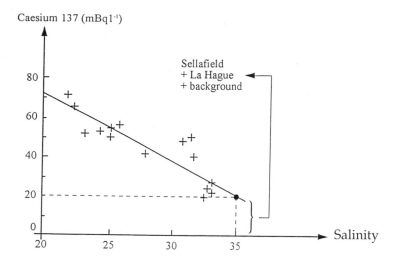

Figure 6.17. Diagram of ^{137}Cs activities salinity for samples collected in the Norwegian Channel during 1988.

6.3.7. Studies of Peripheral Areas

6.3.7.1. Celtic Sea and Western Approaches to the English Channel

Before being labelled by releases from the establishment of La Hague, waters entering the western Channel already exhibit a certain level of artificial radioactivity derived from a number of possible source-terms:

• Fallout resulting from atmospheric nuclear tests.
• A long-term northerly component, due to Sellafield releases being carried out of the North Sea through the Norwegian Channel and towards Spitzbergen, eventually flowing down along the coast of Greenland and back into the North Atlantic Drift (Dahlgaard *et al.*, 1995).
• A component of Sellafield releases coming out of the southern end of the Irish Sea.
• Leakage from radioactive waste dumped in the central Channel trough (« Fosse des Casquets » or « Fosse centrale de la Manche »), or from disposal sites in nearby areas of the Atlantic, even though their significance is negligible for the moment.

Radionuclide activities were measured in 1992 in the North Atlantic near the Azores (Dahlgaard *et al.*, 1995). Although the samples cover a wide

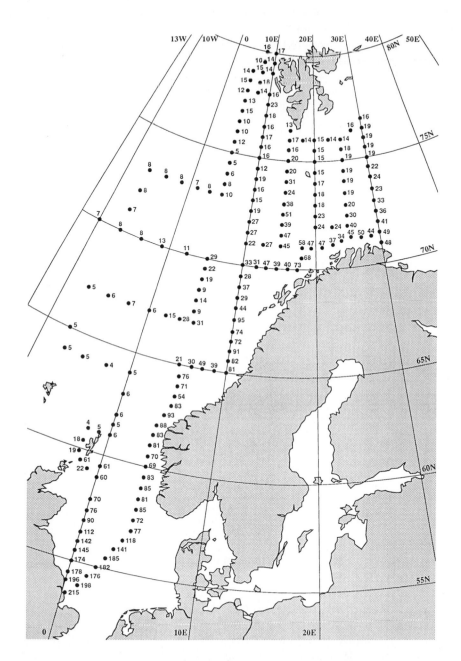

Figure 6.18. ^{137}Cs Distribution in July 1981 (Bq m^{-3}).

area, there appear to be no significant differences between them. The observed average levels for ^{99}Tc, ^{90}Sr and ^{137}Cs (0.005, 1.5 and 2.5 Bq m^{-3}, respectively) were considered as being representative of north-east Atlantic surface waters in the open ocean.

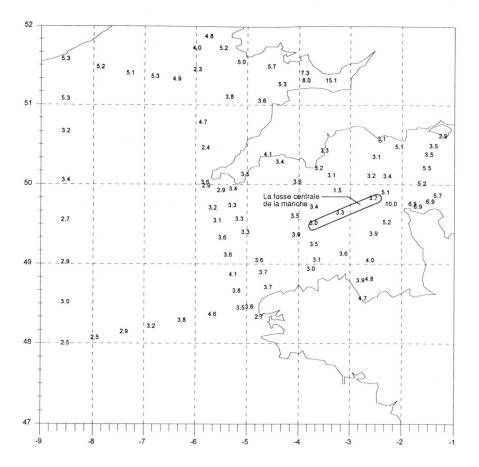

Figure 6.19. Diagram of ^{137}Cs in 1994.

^{137}Cs was analysed in September 1994 (Fig. 6.19) in a series of surface seawater samples collected from the R.V. Noroit in the Celtic Sea and western English Channel, in a zone unaffected by releases from La Hague situated between lat. 48° and 51° N and longs. 3° and 9° W. With the exception of samples from the south-western part of this zone (having 2.5-3 Bq m^{-3} ^{137}Cs), an excess of ^{137}Cs activity is recorded in these waters (*i.e.*, 3-4.6 Bq m^{-3}). This suggests the influence of an additional source-term which could correspond to a contribution of releases coming from Sellafield that have taken a southerly route. In fact, a very small fraction of Sellafield releases are carried towards the southern coast of Ireland (see Fig. 6.18.); ^{137}Cs activities of 5-6 Bq m[-3] were measured in September 1994. Some of these waters could then be injected into the Western approaches of the English Channel after circulating within the Celtic Sea as suggested by the current patterns proposed by Pingree and Le Cann (1989), (see Fig. 6.20.).

Radioactive wastes (notably containing ^{137}Cs) have been dumped in the western part of the English Channel (see Fig. 6.20.) (in a area known as the « fosse centrale de la Manche ») at a water depth of 160 m. The ^{137}Cs activities measured at or near this disposal site are comprised between 3 and 3.5 Bq m[-3] (see Fig. 6.19.); these levels are higher than the seawater background but remain within the range measured in the western approaches to the English Channel.

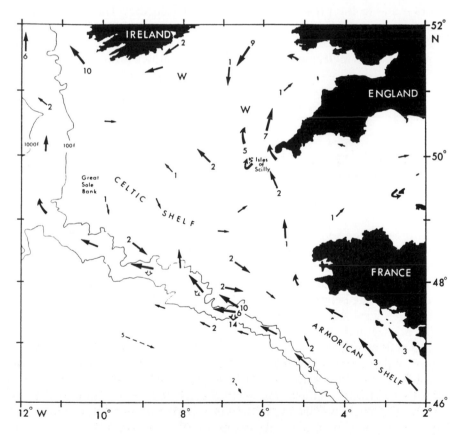

Figure 6.20. An idealized summary diagram of the residual currents on the celtic and Armorican slopes and shelf regions (Pingree and Le Cann, 1989).

6.3.7.2. *Norwegian Channel, Barents and Kara Seas*

The waters now (1995) entering and leaving the Norwegian Channel are labelled by releases from La Hague that took place during the periods from September 1993 to September 1994 and from January 1992 to December 1992. On this basis, and taking account of the amounts of releases from La Hague, it may be assumed that the contribution of this source to the artificial radioactivity (average values, in Bq m^{-3}) of these waters will be as follows:

^{125}Sb:	0.32	in the Norwegian Channel	0.33	in the Barents Sea
^{90}Sr:	0.67	" " " " "	0.33	" " " "
^{137}Cs:	0.22	" " " " "	0.06	" " " "
^{99}Tc:	0.015	" " " " "	0.002	" " " "

As a comparison, the natural background radioactivity of Atlantic waters – due to the presence of ^{40}K – is 12,000 Bq m^{-3}. The artificial background levels in Atlantic waters (a) due to atmospheric fallout (Dahlgaard *et al.*, 1995), as well as the measured artificial radioactivity levels in the Barents (b) and Kara seas (c) (Strand *et al.*, 1993), are as follows (units: Bq m^{-3}):

	a	b	c
^{125}Sb	0	nm(*)	nm(*)
^{90}Sr	1.6	4.2	3/11
^{137}Cs	2.5	5.1	4/12
^{99}Tc	0.005		0.08/0.2

(*) nm = not measured

At present, the level of concentration of radionuclides in the Barents and Kara seas is low and may be attributed to global fallout as well as releases from the Sellafield plant, input from the Ob and Yenesei rivers in the Kara Sea and Chernobyl fallout (Strand *et al.*, 1993), the influence of dumped radioactive waste being currently insignificant for the moment (Strand *et al.*, 1993). The very low ^{99}Tc activity measured in 1992 in Barents Sea: 0.2 Bq m^{-3} (Strand *et al.*, 1993), which is absent both in the seawater background and in Arctic rivers, could be mainly due to releases from La Hague in view of the transit times from Sellafield (5 years) and La Hague (3 years) as well as the amounts discharged from these two plants (see Fig. 6.2.) in 1987 (3.7 TBq from Sellafield) and in 1989 (7.2 TBq from La Hague). If this is the case, the levels of ^{99}Tc in Arctic waters will continue to fall after 1993. Table 6.II. reports the estimated variation with time of La Hague contribution (^{90}Sr, ^{125}Sb, ^{137}Cs, and ^{99}Tc) from 1992 to 1995 in the Norwegian Channel and from 1992 to 1997 in the Barents Sea.

Table 6.II. Estimation of La Hague contribution to the artificial radioactivity (Bq m^{-3}) of waters in the Norwegian Channel (A) and entrance of Barents Sea (B). Hypothesis for transit time: 17 and 36 months for Norwegian Channel and entrance to the Barents Sea. Hypothesis for dilution factor: 10 000 GBq $\rightarrow$ 5 Bq m^{-3} in Norwegian Channel, 2.2 at the entrance of Barents Sea. Error for transit time: one month for Norwegian Channel, 6 months for entrance of Barents Sea. Error for dilution factor: 10 000 GBq $\rightarrow$ activities comprised between 3 and 5.5 in Norwegian Channel. 10 000 GBq $\rightarrow$ activities comprised between 1 and 3.5 at the entrance of Barents Sea.

	^{90}Sr		^{125}Sb		^{137}Cs		^{99}Tc	
	A	B	A	B	A	B	A	B
92	1.33	0.51	1.38	1.55	0.36	0.24	0.10	0.13
93	0.83	0.29	0.63	0.55	1.0	0.24		0.11
94	1.08	0.55	0.42	0.46	0.18	0.10	0.03	0.015
95	0.67	0.33	0.32	0.33	0.22	0.06	0.015	0.012
96		0.46		0.12		0.08		0.011
97		0.29		0.13		0.08		0.006

6.4. Discussion

Considering the evolution of activity levels, it can be seen that the artificial radioactivity in the English Channel and North Sea has dropped sharply during the 1990s, except with regard to ^{129}I and tritium. The dispersal of artificial radionuclides conservative in seawater released by Sellafield and La Hague plants is now well understood on the scale of the English Channel and North Sea.

So, a release of 10,000 GBq/month into the central part of the English Channel gives rise to activities (Bq m^{-3}) of 68-89 at Goury, 50-70 in Cherbourg harbour, 21-45 in the Straits of Dover, around 5 at the entrance to the Norwegian Channel and around 2.2 at the entrance to the Barents Sea. As a consequence, the radioactivity diminishes by a factor of 35 between the central Channel waters and the Barents Sea

However, number of uncertainties remain in the estimation of the impact of releases from La Hague and Sellafield on levels of radioactivity in the Barents Sea. These include the transit time and the amount of dilution taking place along the Norwegian Channel. The predictions so obtained can be tested with ^{99}Tc for example. The data obtained in 1992 (Strand et al., 1993), in Barents Sea yield activities of the order of 0.2 Bq m^{-3} (Guéguéniat et al., 1995) whereas the predicted contribution from La Hague given here is

0.13 Bq m^{-3}. Hence the calculated estimate would appear realistic – at least in 1992 – since the contribution from Sellafield (3.7 TBq in 1987) was less than that coming from La Hague (7.2 TBq in 1989). In this context, it will be interesting to continue measurements of ^{99}Tc in the Barents Sea in order to refine the parameter values used in the forecast. As regards the impact of releases from La Hague, we predict radioactivity levels (units: Bq m^{-3}) of 0.11 for 1993, 0.015 for 1994, 0.012 for 1995, 0.011 for 1996 and 0.006 for 1997. If the transit time for waters between the entrance of the Norwegian Channel and the Barents Sea is longer than 1.5 years, the effect of decreasing releases from the La Hague establishment – which should detected in the Barents Sea between 1993 and 1994 – will be delayed accordingly. Assuming a shorter transit time, the consequences of these decreased discharges will be felt earlier.

Paradoxically, it is now more difficult to explain the analyses of artificial radioactivity in seawater (Celtic Sea, entrance of the English Channel for example) because certain diffuse sources of negligible impact in the past may now become relatively important. In this context, an excess ^{137}Cs activity of the order of 1 Bq m^{-3} was observed in 1994 in waters from the western approaches to the English Channel.

This level may appear negligible in comparison to the natural radioactivity background of seawater (12,000 Bq m^{-3}), but it nevertheless represents a flux of 3,000 Gbq/year taking into account of water fluxes and assuming a constant input of ^{137}Cs into the zone. It is now important to elucidate the source of this input and establish its variation in time and space, in order to be able to assess the consequences of possible radioactive waste leakage from the central English Channel. Moreover, such an investigation would be of interest for studying currents in the North Atlantic.

Obtaining the most accurate possible estimate of artificial radioactivity present in the seawater background proves just as valuable for the study of conservative as for non-conservative radionuclides. The results obtained in the North Atlantic are very constant from 1972 to 1992 (Holm et al., 1991; Dahlgaard et al., 1995) for ^{137}Cs (i.e. 2.5 Bq m^{-3}). In the case of non-conservative radionuclides, such as ^{239}Pu, activity levels have fallen sharply between 1970 and 1989 due to the fixation of radionuclide species onto particulate matter that is free to settle. Thus, the background level of ^{239}Pu in Atlantic waters collected from temperate latitudes was 20-60 mBq m^{-3} in 1970, dropping to 8 mBq m^{-3} in 1989 (Holm et al., 1991). Although this radioactivity background is even lower at present, its actual value remains to be determined. To serve as a comparison, the ^{239}Pu activities measured in the English Channel are of the order of 10-30 mBq m^{-3} (Boust et al., 1996). The slightly higher values in Mediterranean surface waters (20-40 mBq m^{-3}) reflect the decreased importance of particulate matter fluxes towards the seabed in this area.

6.5. Conclusion

In the study of conservative radionuclides as tracers for seawater transport, a number of questions remain to be resolved concerning the transfer mechanisms at the boundaries of this system at the western approaches to the English Channel and at the outflow of the North Sea towards the Barents and Kara seas. Radioactive waste disposal at shallow depth (less than 200 m) also remains to be taken into account, but leakage from submerged material at these sites is currently very slight or non-existent in both of the studied areas adjoining the North Sea. In order to assess the importance of such sources, it is firstly necessary to characterize the artificial radioactivity of waters upstream from the disposal zones.

Up to the present, a number of campaigns have been undertaken in the framework of close collaborations (CCE program: MAST) between France, Denmark, the United Kingdom, Germany and the Netherlands. Radiotracer studies have been organized by various participants in this programme, covering the English Channel and the North Sea and involving the analysis of ^{137}Cs, ^{99}Tc, ^{125}Sb, ^{90}Sr and ^{129}I at different times of the year. The advantage of monitoring ^{129}I have been pointed out by Yiou and Raisbeck (1995), using the technique of Accelerator Mass Spectrometry (AMS), capable of measuring 10^6 atoms of ^{129}I, thus offering an extremely sensitive method of tracing this isotope in the ocean; researches are in progress in order to complete theses first measurements.

The analysis of transuranic radionuclides has been carried out in the framework of another research programme (DG), based on a collaboration between the Irish Republic, U.K., Spain, Italy, Finland, England, Denmark and Sweden. It is now a good opportunity to set up the largest possible coverage in order to study the movement of waters at any given moment between Europe and Greenland. This would require the participation of several oceanographic research vessels to ensure measurement of the fluctuations in seawater background and to characterize for the first time the medium- and long-term components of Sellafield releases in the oceanic environment. It will only be possible to achieve a synthesis of elemental fluxes and draw up an exhaustive inventory of the radionuclides present by implementing a rapid coverage of the entire zone in question.

Acknowledgements

This work was carried out in the framework of the MAST 0052 and 0053 European programme and GDR manche.

References

Bailly du Bois P., Guéguéniat P., Gandon R., Léon R. and Baron Y. (1993) Percentage contribution of inputs from the Atlantic, Irish Sea, English Channel and Baltic into the North Sea during 1988: a tracer-based evaluation using artificial radionuclides. *Neth. J. Sea Res.* **31**, 1-17.

Bailly du Bois P., Salomon J.C., Gandon R. and Guéguéniat P. (1995) A quantitative estimate of English Channel water fluxes into the North Sea from 1987 to 1992 based on radiotracer distribution. *J. Marine Systems* **6**, 457-481.

Boust D., Mitchell P.I., Garcia K., Codren O., León Vintró L. and Leclerc G. (1996) A Comparative Study of the Speciation and Behaviour of Plutonium in the Marine Environment of two Reprocessing Plants. *Radiochimica Acta* **M49**, 1-8.

Dahlgaard H., Nies H., Van Weers A.W., Guéguéniat P. and Kershaw P. (1991) Studies on the transport of coastal water from the English Channel to the Baltic Sea using radioactive tracers (MAST project), Radionuclides in the Study of Marine Processes, Norwich, UK, 10-13 september 1991. (J.P. Kershaw and D.S. Woodhead, Eds.) p.365. Elsevier Applied Science.

Dahlgaard H., Chen Q., Herrmann J., Nies H., Ibett R.D. and Kershaw P.J. (1995) On the background level of ^{99}Tc, ^{90}Sr, and ^{137}Cs in the North Atlantic. *J. Marine Systems* **6**, 571-578.

Fraizier A., Guéguéniat P. and Salomon J.C. (1992) Aspects temporels de l'impact de rejets radioactifs effectués en mer, sur les eaux d'une station littorale de la Manche, *Oceanolog. Acta* **1**, 75-85.

Gandon R. and Guéguéniat P. (1992) Preconcentration of ^{125}Sb onto MnO_2 from seawater samples for gamma-ray spectrometric analysis. *Radiochim. Acta* **57**,159-164.

Guéguéniat P., Bailly du Bois P. and Gandon R. (1995) Estimation of la Hague contribution to the artificial radioactivity of Norwegian waters (1992-1996) and Barents Sea (1992-1997), Second International Conference on Environmental Radioactivity in the Arctic and Antarctic, Norwegian Radiation Protection Authority. (Per Strand and Andrew Cooke, Eds.) pp. 53-65.

Guéguéniat P., Bailly du Bois P., Gandon R., Salomon J.C., Baron Y. and Léon R. (1994) Spatial and Temporal distribution (1987-1991) of ^{125}Sb used to trace pathways and transit times of waters entering the North Sea from the English Channel. *Estuarine Coastal Shelf Sci.* **39**, 59-74.

Guéguéniat P., Gandon R. and Bailly du Bois P. (1993a) Les traceurs radioactifs artificiels: un outil pour l'océanographie, *La Technique Moderne* **5-6-7**, 7-15.

Guéguéniat P., Salomon J.C., Wartel M., Cabioch L. and Fraizier A. (1993b) Transfer pathway and transit time of dissolved matter in the eastern English Channel indicated by space-time radiotracers measurement and hydrodynamic modelling. *Estuarine Coastal Shelf Sci.* **36**, 477-494.

Hermann J., Kershaw P.J., Bailly du Bois P. and Guéguéniat P. (1995) The distribution of artificial radionuclides in the English Channel, southern North Sea, Skagerrak and Kattegat, 1990-93. *J. Marine Systems* **6**, 427-456.

Holm E., Roos P., Persson P.B.R., Bojanowski R., Aarkrog A., Nielsen S.P. and Livingston H.D. (1991) Radiocaesium and plutonium in Atlantic surface waters from 73° N to 72° S, Radionuclides in the study of marine processes, Norwich UK, 10-13 September 1991. (J.P. Kershaw and D.S. Woodhead, Eds.) pp. 3-11. Elsevier Applied Science.

Kautsky H. (1988) Determination of distribution processes, transport routes and transport times in the North Sea and the northern north Atlantic using atificial radionuclides as tracers, Radionuclides: a tool for oceanography, Cherbourg 1-5 juin 1987. (J.C. Guary, P. Guéguéniat and R.J. Pentreath Eds.) pp. 271-280. Elsevier Applied Science Publishers, London-New York.

Kershaw P. J. and Baxter A. (1995) The transfer of reprocessing wastes from north-west Europe to the Arctic, Topical studies in oceanography: Arctic Radioactivity and Related Transport Processes. *Deep Sea Res. II* **42**, 1413-1448.

Livingston H.D., Bowen V.T. and Kupferman S.L. (1982) Radionuclides from Windscale discharges II: Their dispersion in Scottish and Norwegian coastal circulation. *J. Marine Res.* **40**, 1227-1258.

Livingston H.D., Kupferman S.L., Bowen V.T. and Moore R.M. (1984) Vertical profile of artificial radionuclides concentrations in the central Arctic Ocean. *Geochim. et Cosmochim. Acta* **48**, 2195-2203.

Mitchell P.I., Vives i Battle J., Downes A.B., Sanchez-Cabeza J.A., Merino Pareja J., Delfanti R. and Papucci C. (1994) Chemical speciation and colloidal association of plutonium in the western Mediterranean water column and the Palomares area, Marina-Med Seminar on The Radiological Exposure of the Population of the European Community from Radioactivity in the Mediterranean Sea, 17-19 May 1994, Roma, Italy.

Nies H. (1988) Artificial radioactivity in the northeast Alantic, Radionuclides: a tool for oceanography 1988, Cherbourg 1-5 juin 1987. (J.C. Guary, P. Guéguéniat and R.J. Pentreath, Eds.) pp. 250-259. Elsevier Applied Science Publishers, London-New York.

Nies H., Albrecht H. and Herrmann J. (1991) Radionuclides in water and suspended particulate matter from the North Sea, Radionuclides in the study of marine processes, Norwich UK, 10-13 September 1991. (J.P. Kershaw and D.S.Woodhead, Eds.) pp. 24-36. Elsevier Applied Science.

Nies H. and Wedekind Ch. (1988) The contamination of the North Sea and Baltic Sea by the Chernobyl fallout, Radionuclides: a tool for oceanography, Cherbourg 1-5 juin 1987. (J.C. Guary, P. Guéguéniat and R.J. Pentreath, Eds.) pp. 227-239. Elsevier Applied Science Publishers, London-New York.

Pingree R.D. and Le Cann B. (1989) Celtic and Armorican slope and shelf residual currents. *Prog. Oceanog.* **23**, 303-338.

Salomon J.C. and Breton M. (1993) An atlas of long-term currents in the Channel. *Oceanol. Acta* **16**, 439-448.

Salomon J.C., Breton M. and Guéguéniat P. (1993) Computed residual flow through the Dover Strait. *Oceanol. Acta* **16**, 449-455.

Strand P., Rudjord A. L., Salbu B., Christensen G., Foyn L., Lind B., Bjornstad H. and Bjerk T. (1993) Survey of artificial radionuclides in the Kara Sea, International Conference on Environmental Radioactivity in the Arctic and Antarctic, Norwegian Radiation Protection Authority. (Per Strand and Elis Holm, Eds.) pp. 53-65.

Yiou F., Raisbeck J.M., Zhou Z.Q., Kilius L.R. and Kershaw P.J. (1995) Improved estimates of oceanic discharges of ^{129}I from Sellafield and La Hague, Second International Conference on Environmental Radioactivity in the Arctic and Antarctic, Norwegian Radiation Protection Authority. (Per Strand and Andrew Cooke, Eds.) pp. 113-116.

7 Radioactivity in the Irish Sea: Past Practices, Present Status and Future Perspectives

P.I. Mitchell, P.J. Kershaw and L. León Vintró

For over four decades radioactive waste discharges into the north-eastern Irish Sea have been dominated by those from the nuclear facilities sited at Sellafield, in Cumbria, England. These discharges have provided a unique opportunity to study the processes controlling the dispersion of various radio-contaminants throughout the Irish Sea and beyond, as well as their uptake and accumulation in aquatic compartments such as seabed sediments and biota. There is, thus, a considerable body of literature on the behaviour of artificial radionuclides in the Irish Sea and the transfer processes responsible for their redistribution. In this overview, liquid waste discharges from Sellafield are reviewed with emphasis on levels and radionuclide composition, chemical form, chemical form upon dilution into seawater, subsequent spatial and temporal distributions in various key compartments, dispersion processes and environmental inventories.

7.1. Introduction

The issue of artificial radioactivity in the Irish Sea has been one of considerable debate and controversy for almost two decades. It has also been the subject of a number of scientific reviews and reports (IAEA, 1985; Mitchell, 1989; Kershaw *et al.*, 1992). All have confirmed that radioactive waste discharges to the Irish Sea are dominated by those from the Sellafield nuclear fuel reprocessing plant in Cumbria, U.K., discharges from other establishments (*e.g.*, the nuclear power stations at Heysham and Wylfa, hospitals, non-nuclear industries and research centres) being comparatively small. Further, the impact of the Sellafield discharge throughout much of the Irish Sea has been such as to mask the effects of global fallout due to nuclear weapons testing in the atmosphere prior to the limited test ban treaty of 1963 and fallout from the Chernobyl accident in 1986.

Low-level liquid wastes from the Sellafield site are discharged, under authorization, into the north-eastern Irish Sea through a pipe-line which extends some 2.1 km seaward of the low water mark. The discharges are subject to controls under the Radioactive Substances Act 1993 (United Kingdom Parliament, 1993). The most important low-level wastes arise both in water used to purge the cooling/storage ponds in which spent fuel elements are kept, and from the reprocessing plant whose liquid wastes are neutralized in « seatanks » before being discharged at high tide. Significant reductions in releases from the former were achieved following the commissioning of the Site Ion-Exchange Plant (SIXEP) in 1985 (Kershaw *et al.*, 1992).

7.2. Liquid Waste Discharges from Sellafield

7.2.1. *Annual Discharge Levels*

The first discharges from Sellafield took place in 1952 when a total of some 370 TBq of radioactivity was discharged to the north-eastern Irish Sea (Howells, 1966). A breakdown of the principal radioactive components of the effluent has been available since 1960 with more comprehensive data from 1978 onwards. Annual discharge figures have been published by the operator (BNFL) since 1979 and, in recent years, by the responsible Government Departments. Overall, the discharges of most radionuclides peaked in the mid- to late-1970s. As these discharges have been reviewed fully elsewhere (Kershaw *et al.*, 1992; Gray *et al.*, 1995) they will not be discussed in detail here. Suffice that their magnitude and composition have changed markedly in time, with the quantities of shorter-lived fission product nuclides such as ^{95}Zr, ^{106}Ru and ^{144}Ce declining steadily since the early 1970s, longer-lived nuclides such as ^{137}Cs peaking in the mid- to late-1970s and declining thereafter, and the major transuranics, ^{241}Am and ^{239,240}Pu, peaking in the early- to mid-1970s and also declining thereafter (Fig. 7.1). Factors responsible for such variations include the nature of the fuel, its burn-up time, the nature and duration of storage prior to reprocessing, the method of reprocessing and the nature of the effluent treatment plants, all of which have varied throughout the history of the Sellafield plant. Generally, by 1992, discharges were roughly two orders of magnitude or more lower than they were at their peak. Of the longer-lived radionuclides, estimated total activities of 39 PBq of ^{3}H, 6 PBq of ^{90}Sr, 6 PBq of ^{134}Cs, 41 PBq of ^{137}Cs, 120 TBq of ^{238}Pu, 610 TBq of ^{239,240}Pu, 22 PBq of ^{241}Pu, 540 TBq of ^{241}Am and smaller quantities of other transuranium nuclides have been discharged to the Irish Sea during the period 1952-94 (Gray *et al.*, 1995; BNFL, 1980-1995).

Since 1992, with the commissioning of the Enhanced Actinide Removal Plant (EARP), discharges of Pu and Am have been further reduced. However, as a result of the processing of medium-level radioactive liquors previously stored on site and the commissioning of the new Thermal Oxide Reprocessing Plant (THORP) in 1994, there have been modest though measurable increases in the quantities of ^{99}Tc, ^{129}I, ^{60}Co and ^{14}C released.

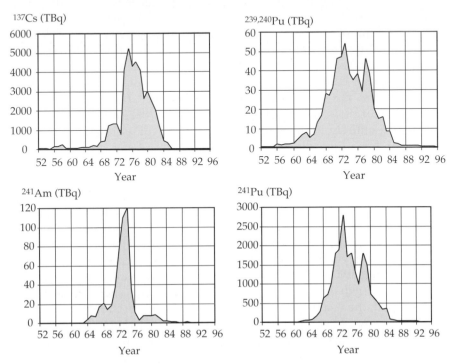

Fig. 7.1. Sellafield pipeline discharges in the period 1952-1994 for some radiologically important radionuclides.

7.2.2. Chemical Form of the Effluent

The chemical composition of the effluent from Sellafield has not been studied extensively, though some useful data exist for the transuranics and other radionuclides (Pentreath *et al.*, 1984; Leonard *et al.*, 1995). Analyses carried out in 1982 (and assumed to be typical of routine releases) showed that some 99% of the Pu(alpha), ^{241}Am and $^{243,244}Cm$ in the seatanks, and about 60% of the ^{237}Np, were associated with particulate (> 0.2 µm) material. In pond water effluents, the corresponding percentages were found to be somewhat lower.

Differences in chemical speciation were also noted, with reduced Pu(alpha) predominating in the filtrate of the effluent from the seatanks and oxidized Pu(alpha) predominating in the filtrate of the effluent from the cooling ponds. However, as the bulk of the effluent came from the seatanks, only about 1% of the total would appear to have been in an oxidized form upon discharge. The nuclides of Am and Cm were present only in the Am(III) and Cm(III) forms (*i.e.,* chemically reduced), while almost 50% of the combined ^{237}Np discharges was in the oxidized, Np(V), form.

These observations have been supported by a more recent study carried out in 1991 on seatank and SIXEP effluent streams (Leonard *et al.,* 1995). In the case of seatank effluent, almost all of the total activity of ^{239,240}Pu and ^{241}Am present was found to be associated with the iron floc material formed upon the neutralization of acid liquors containing ferrous sulphamate – a chemical used to control the valency of Pu during fuel reprocessing. What little Pu was in the solution phase was determined to be in the reduced (tetravalent) form. Further, nuclides such as ^{137}Cs, ^{90}Sr and ^{99}Tc were found to be almost entirely in the solution phase. In SIXEP effluent, on the other hand, all of the radionuclides considered were almost entirely in a dissolved form, presumably as a result of the absence of particulate material in this waste stream.

« Hot particles » have also been identified in the effluent (Pentreath *et al.,* 1984) and have been shown to persist in the marine environment close to Sellafield for at least several months before dissolving, with some being preserved in accreting estuarine sediments (Hamilton, 1981; Hamilton *et al.,* 1991).

Laboratory experiments to determine the colloidal size distribution of a suite of radionuclides in each of the effluent streams (SIXEP and seatank) have been carried out using the ultrafiltration technique (Leonard *et al.,* 1995). Overall, the results suggest that colloidal forms of individual radionuclides, originating from the solution phase, are more likely to occur in SIXEP rather than in seatank effluent. Some typical data are given in Figure 7.2. and show clearly that in SIXEP effluent significant fractions of the ^{90}Sr, ^{137}Cs, ^{239,240}Pu(V), ^{239,240}Pu(IV) and ^{241}Am are in a colloidally-bound form, as evidenced by the level of retention upon ultrafiltration (< 3 kDa). In contrast, almost all of the ^{99}Tc in both waste streams is in a « truly » dissolved form.

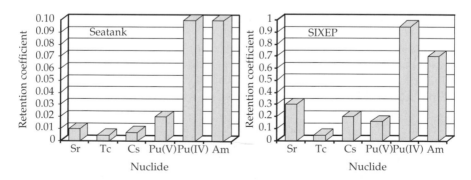

Fig. 7.2. Radionuclide fractionation of Seatank and SIXEP effluent samples upon ultrafiltration (Leonard *et al.,* 1995). Note the order of magnitude difference in scale.

7.2.3.   Chemical Form upon Dilution
with Sea Water

7.2.3.1.   Colloids

Although, as discussed, small amounts of ^{137}Cs, ^{90}Sr and ^{239,240}Pu(V) in colloidal form were identified in SIXEP effluent, further experiments by Leonard et al. (1995), following the dilution of effluent into seawater under laboratory conditions, indicated that these forms did not persist in seawater. On the other hand, the same researchers did find evidence to suggest that colloidal forms of ^{239,240}Pu(IV) and ^{241}Am do persist in seawater. The latter observation is supported by chemical speciation and enhanced sorption analyses carried out under field conditions by Mitchell et al. (1995) on samples of ultrafiltered water from the north-eastern Irish Sea. These confirmed that a significant proportion of the Pu(IV) present in seawater is in a colloidal form and that the size of the colloidal particles or aggregates involved is considerably smaller than that observed in non-saline waters.

7.2.3.2.   Physico-Chemical Speciation

Studies on the physico-chemical speciation of the transuranics in open waters throughout the Irish Sea have shown that a significant proportion of the total Pu and even more of the Am are associated with the particulate phase (Mitchell et al., 1991a; 1995; Pentreath et al., 1986; Kershaw et al., 1986). This contrasts with ^{90}Sr, ^{137}Cs and ^{99}Tc, which show comparatively little affinity for suspended particulate or, indeed, seabed sediment. Measurements of the oxidation state distribution of ^{239,240}Pu (and ^{238}Pu) in filtered water sampled throughout the Irish Sea show relatively little variation, spatially or temporally, with the bulk of the Pu being in the oxidized, Pu(V), state (Mitchell et al., 1991a; 1995; Pentreath et al., 1986; Nelson and Lovett, 1978; Lovett and Nelson, 1981).

7.3. Monitoring in the Irish Sea

Since the mid-1960s, the Ministry of Agriculture, Fisheries and Food (MAFF) Directorate of Fisheries Research Laboratory in the U.K. has conducted extensive monitoring programmes in the Irish Sea and other coastal waters of the British Isles with the twin objectives of verifying the satisfactory control of liquid radioactive waste discharges to the aquatic environment and ensuring that the resulting public radiation exposure is within nationally-accepted limits. This monitoring is independent of similar programmes carried out by nuclear site operators as a condition of their authorizations to discharge radioactive wastes. Particular attention has been given to assessing the levels of artificial radioactivity in a wide range of marine environmental materials taken from the vicinity of Sellafield and other nuclear installations discharging to the Irish Sea, in addition to the general environs of these waters. The results of these programmes have been published in a series of comprehensive annual reports titled « Radioactivity in Surface and Coastal Waters of the British Isles » (MAFF, 1967-1995). The statutory Irish authority charged with the responsibility to monitor radioactivity levels in the marine environment of the Republic of Ireland is the Radiological Protection Institute who publish reports biennially on the results of their marine monitoring (Cunningham and O'Grady, 1986; Cunnigham et al., 1988; O'Grady and Currivan, 1989; McGarry et al., 1994).

In addition to the actual discharges, « compartments » subject to regular monitoring have included seawater, fish, shellfish, seaweed (edible and inedible) and sediments. Beaches close to discharge outlets and fishing gear are also monitored for external dosimetry purposes. Samples are collected from the shoreline and coastal waters as well as from the open waters of the Irish Sea. Research vessel support is an essential prerequisite for such sampling and regular cruises are undertaken by both authorities. The results of this monitoring, together with data from research on the environmental behaviour of important radionuclides, their budgets in environmental compartments and their residence times in particular zones, enable the statutory authorities to assess the impact of waste discharges to these waters, determine realistic dose commitments to critical groups, check the monitoring done by site operators and reassure the public at large.

7.4. Artificial Radionuclide Distributions and Dispersion Processes

The initial dispersion of radionuclides from Sellafield is influenced by a number of factors including variations in the discharge rate, the chemical form of the radionuclides in the effluent, local hydrographic conditions and the distribution and composition of bottom sediments. Data collected over two decades show that those radionuclides which are relatively soluble in seawater (e.g., ^{99}Tc, ^{137}Cs, ^{90}Sr, ^{3}H) are advected principally to the north and west, leaving the Irish Sea via the North Channel, with a mean transit time of about one year (a much smaller proportion is carried south via St. Georges Channel). To illustrate, the influx of fresh seawater pushing up through the Irish Sea from the south is clearly evident from the shape of the concentration isopleths of ^{137}Cs in seawater depicted in Figure 7.3. Indeed, it is well established that Cs discharged from Sellafield mixes with seawater transported through the Irish Sea in a northerly direction, exits through the

North Channel and follows a well-defined path around the west and north coasts of Scotland, where it enters the North Sea (Baxter *et al.*, 1979; Mauchline, 1980; McKinley *et al.*, 1981).

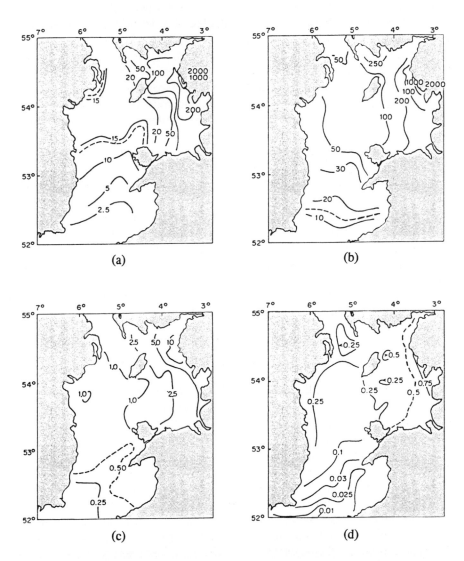

Fig. 7.3 ^{137}Cs distribution in filtered surface seawater in the Irish Sea (MAFF, 1967-1995): (a) July 1974, pCi l^{-1}; (b) January 1976, pCi kg^{-1}; (c) March 1981, Bq kg^{-1}; (d) April 1986, Bq kg^{-1}. The broken line represents the approximate position of the 0.5 Bq kg^{-1} concentration isopleth in each case.

In contrast, non-conservative nuclides, such as Pu and Am, are quickly removed from the water column by direct precipitation or by adsorption on (suspended) particulate matter. Thus, the behaviour and distribution of these nuclides is closely linked to that of the finer-grained seabed sediments. In the Irish Sea, muddy sediments are confined to two main areas: an extensive belt of muds and muddy sands parallel to the Cumbrian coast, and a large and relatively deep (~ 100 m) basin lying between the Isle of Man and the coast of Ireland. Studies have confirmed that these muddy areas are a significant (temporary) sink for many of the radionuclides discharged from Sellafield, with by far the largest repository being the first mentioned (Pentreath *et al.*, 1986; Hetherington, 1978). These sediments are subject to tidal and wave resuspension and extensive reworking by benthic organisms. They are also disturbed by episodic storms. Although the accretion rate of the offshore muds in the vicinity of Sellafield appears to be low (Kershaw *et al.*, 1988), it has been shown that bioturbation gives rise to contamination of the sediments, by artificial radionuclides, to depths in excess of a metre (Kershaw *et al.*, 1984; Pentreath, 1987).

Cores taken from the merse/saltmarsh at locations such as Southwick Water and Skyreburn Bay along the Scottish coast have, upon analysis, yielded an historical record of the Sellafield discharges (MacKenzie and Scott, 1982; MacKenzie *et al.*, 1994). The core profiles were found to match the integrated environmental « signal » rather than the annual discharge « signal », further demonstrating that the offshore sediments are subject to considerable mixing and reworking and cannot be regarded as a final « sink » for Sellafield-sourced radionuclides. Cores retrieved in 1988 from undisturbed sediments in Senhouse Dock, Maryport also provided a record of the Sellafield discharge and enabled a reconstruction of the Pu isotope composition of the releases (Kershaw *et al.*, 1990). In this regard, a near steady increase has been reported in the ^{238}Pu/^{239,240}Pu activity ratio in discharges, from a value of ~ 0.03 in the 1960s to > 0.3 at the present time (Gray *et al.*, 1995; Hetherington, 1976). Measurements of the ^{240}Pu/^{239}Pu atom ratio in dated sediment cores show a similar tendency, with values increasing from ~ 0.05 in the 1960s to ~ 0.22 in recent discharges (Kershaw *et al.*, 1995a; 1995b).

The mechanisms by which sediment-bound nuclides are subsequently dispersed are complex and not yet fully understood. However, it is clear that nuclides associated with sediments can be transported by the sediment flow near the seabed. In the north-eastern Irish Sea, this flow is predominantly northward (Kershaw *et al.*, 1992; Howarth, 1984) and results in the accumulation of transuranics in estuaries along the Cumbrian coast and the south-west coast of Scotland (Aston and Stanners, 1981; McDonald *et al.*, 1990). Indeed, it has been shown that by the mid-1980s, the movement of contaminated silt was the dominant mechanism of supply of Sellafield-discharged Pu to the south-west coast of Scotland (McDonald *et al.*, 1990). Resuspension of contaminated sediments can also result in transport within the water column as suspended particulate (Kershaw *et al.*, 1983). Moreover, resolubilization and subsequent solution transport can play a significant role in the dispersion of previously sediment-bound radionuclides (Hunt and Kershaw, 1990). As a result of these processes, small fractions of the discharged Pu and Am have been transported over considerable distances, *e.g.*, to the Norwegian Sea (Kershaw and Baxter, 1995). Their concentrations in seawater, however, are reported to decrease exponentially with distance from the discharge outlet (McKay and Pattenden, 1993; Boust *et al.*, 1996).

Studies of the distributions of ^{99}Tc, ^{134}Cs, ^{137}Cs, ^{238}Pu, ^{239,240}Pu and ^{241}Am in inshore waters around Ireland carried out in 1985-1986 (Mitchell *et al.*, 1987; 1989) have shown that, in each case, the distribution is strongly asymmetric with highest concentrations being recorded in the general vicinity of the north-east coast where they approached their maxima just south of Bangor. The contrast between the sharp fall-off near Malin Head on the north coast and the much more gradual decrease down the east coast to Hook Head, is quite pronounced and is consistent with the pattern of water circulation in these sea areas. No significant geographical trend is evident in the data from the north-west, west and south-west coasts of Ireland, though the concentrations appear to be slightly higher than representative fallout levels.

Studies, conducted on soil samples taken in West Cumbria, U.K. since the late 1970s, have shown that a small fraction of the Pu and Am discharged into the Irish Sea from Sellafield has been transferred into the atmosphere and returned to land (Peirson *et al.*, 1982). Bubble scavenging in the water column, together with droplet ejection from bubbles bursting at the surface, has been suggested as the mechanism responsible (Walker *et al.*, 1986). A similar phenomenon has been reported for heavy metals. Preliminary estimates have been made which suggest that 40-80 GBq of excess Pu had been deposited in a coastal strip approximately 5 km wide and 40 km long by the year 1980. Such a deposit represents 1/10,000th of the quantity reportedly discharged to sea from Sellafield by the same year. An identical effect, though very much weaker, has been observed along the north-east coast of Ireland (Garland *et al.*, 1989; Mitchell *et al.*, 1991b).

7.5. Time-Trend Analyses of Radionuclide Concentrations in Key Marine Compartments

7.5.1. Sea Water

Surveys of the concentration of radiocaesium in filtered water from throughout the Irish Sea have been conducted on a regular basis for many years (MAFF, 1967-1995). The extensive data available show that general levels reached a peak in the years between 1975 and 1978 and have been declining more or less steadily ever since in line with the reduction in annual discharges. At their peak, ^{137}Cs concentrations attained 5-50 Bq l^{-1} and were more than three orders of magnitude higher than representative fallout levels at similar latitudes. By 1994, concentrations in the north-eastern Irish Sea had declined to between 0.1 and 1.0 Bq l^{-1}. Presently, the distribution pattern is governed by recent discharges from Sellafield and the effects of activities previously discharged which had become associated with seabed sediments but are now being remobilized into the water column.

Data on the distribution of other radionuclides in the waters of the Irish Sea are more limited, though surveys carried out in 1979 and 1985 on the distributions of ^{239,240}Pu and ^{241}Am in filtered seawater showed that the concentrations of both radionuclides in the coastal region of Cumbria had fallen by about a factor of three in the interval between the two surveys. The overall pattern of distribution, however, was similar (Kershaw et $al.$, 1992).

Measurements on seawater in the western Irish Sea reveal comparatively little change in transuranic concentrations in recent years (Vives i Batlle, 1993). This would suggest that for the transuranics near-equilibrium conditions may presently prevail in these waters, in contrast to radiocaesium, the concentrations of which have been declining steadily, to the point where they are now little more than an order of magnitude above global fallout levels, being in the range 30-70 mBq l^{-1} (RPII, private communication).

7.5.2. Seabed Sediments

The sediments of the Irish Sea are uniquely labelled with a variety of radionuclides released over several decades by the reprocessing plant at Sellafield. Both the spatial and temporal variations of these radionuclides in the surface sediments of the Irish Sea have been determined from a large number of samples collected over the period 1968-1988 (McCartney et $al.$, 1994). The most noticeable feature of the trends in the concentrations of these radionuclides in sediments sampled close to the outfall in this period is a general reflection of the reduction of discharges since 1978, the effect being more pronounced for sites closer to the source. Presently, concentrations of radionuclides such as ^{137}Cs, ^{239,240}Pu and ^{241}Am in muddy sediments near the outfall are in the ranges 500-1,500 Bq kg^{-1}, 500-600 Bq kg^{-1} and 700-900 Bq kg^{-1}, respectively (MAFF, 1967-1995). Time-series analyses in surface sediment samples collected in this zone show mean availability times of 2-5 years for radiocaesium and 5-8 years for Pu (MacKenzie et $al.$, 1994; Nicholson and Hunt, 1995; Hunt, 1985). As an illustration, the evolution of measured ^{137}Cs and ^{241}Am concentrations in sediments from

Newbiggin in the Ravenglass Estuary near Sellafield is shown in Figure 7.4., together with the predictions of a simple, semi-empirical model (Nicholson and Hunt, 1995). As expected, the rate of reduction is least for nuclides which exhibit strong sediment-seeking properties. Further afield, this (temporal) reduction in transuranium concentrations is not always evident. Another feature of interest is that the most recent data set of ^{239,240}Pu concentrations in surface sediments shows the Pu concentration isopleths to have been displaced northwards, with a sharp decrease in activity being observed on the landward side of the discharge point (McCartney *et al.*, 1994). Similar behaviour was previously observed in the case of ^{137}Cs (McCartney *et al.*, 1994).

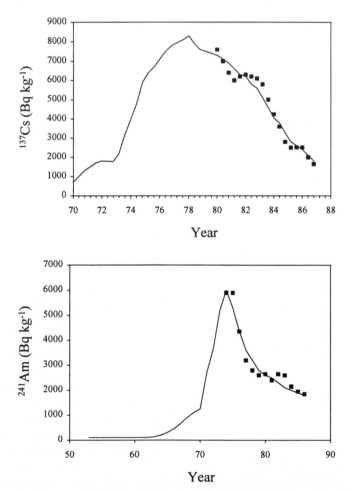

Fig. 7.4. Temporal evolution of measured (■) and model-predicted (——) concentrations of ^{137}Cs and ^{241}Am in surficial sediments sampled at Newbiggin in the Ravenglass Estuary (Nicholson and Hunt, 1995).

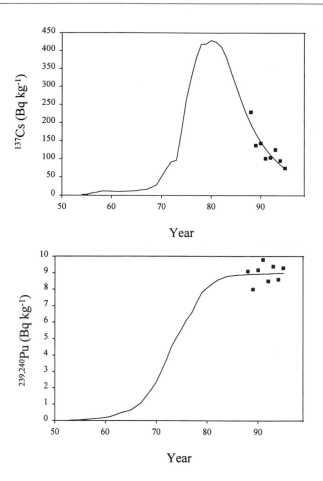

Fig. 7.5. Temporal evolution of measured (■) and model-predicted (—)
concentrations of ^{137}Cs and ^{239,240}Pu in surficial sediments sampled
in the western Irish Sea (Condren *et al.*, 1996).

Time-series analyses of western Irish Sea surface sediments have shown
that, while ^{137}Cs concentrations have fallen by a factor of between 2 and 5
since their peak in 1980-1981, ^{239,240}Pu concentrations have remained relatively constant (Fig. 7.5.). Model predictions (preliminary) for the western
Irish Sea mud basin indicate that, were discharges to remain at their present
levels, ^{137}Cs concentrations will continue to decrease with mean availability
times in the range of 7-17 years, while little or no reduction in ^{239,240}Pu concentrations is likely to occur for some decades to come (Condren *et al.*, 1996).
At the present time, general transuranic concentrations in western Irish Sea
muddy sediments are almost two orders of magnitude lower than the corresponding concentrations in the north-eastern Irish Sea, while ^{137}Cs concentrations are little more than an order of magnitude lower.

7.5.3. Biota

Progressive reductions in the concentrations of a number of radiologically important radionuclides in algae, fish and shellfish sampled in the north-eastern Irish Sea has been observed since the mid-1970s (Kershaw *et al.*, 1992). In general, the reductions in the concentrations of major fission and activation products have been greater than those of the transuranium nuclides due to the apparently longer lag period between the decrease in transuranic discharges and its reflection in environmental materials (Hunt, 1985). Concentrations in both fish and shellfish diminish with distance from Sellafield, the rate of reduction being least for nuclides which are relatively mobile in seawater. A similar pattern is observed for algae. Variations in concentrations between fish species sampled in a given area are compara-tively small and can be explained in terms of residence time in the area as well as feeding habits (MAFF, 1967-1995). On the other hand, substantial variations are observed between shellfish species. For example, molluscs tend to concentrate the transuranics to a considerably greater extent than do crustaceans, which in turn accumulate them more than fish. At the present time, typical fresh weight concentrations of ^{137}Cs in white fish and shellfish sampled in the Sellafield coastal area are 10-20 Bq kg^{-1} and 2-12 Bq kg^{-1}, respectively, while the corresponding ^{239,240}Pu concentrations are 0.01-0.02 Bq kg^{-1} and 2-10 Bq kg^{-1}, respectively (MAFF, 1967-1995).

Surveys carried out in the period 1979-1995 have shown that radiocae-sium concentrations in the main species of fish and shellfish taken mainly in the western reaches of the Irish Sea and landed at Irish east coast ports have declined from a mean of approximately 70 Bq kg^{-1} (fresh wt.) in 1979 to a mean of less than 2 Bq kg^{-1} (fresh wt.) by 1995 (Fig. 7.6.).

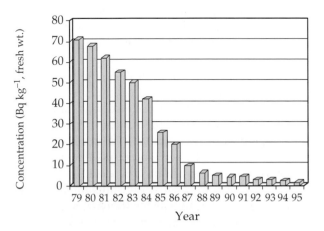

Fig. 7.6. Mean ^{137}Cs concentrations in fish and prawns landed at Irish east-coast ports in the period 1979-1995 (RPII, private communication).

Availability times in biota are generally less than those for sediments, reflecting the relative contributions of recent and historic discharges to present activity concentrations (Nicholson and Hunt, 1995). Further reductions in transuranium and other radionuclide concentrations in biota may be anticipated in the coming years, particularly in the north-eastern Irish Sea.

7.5.4.   The Impact of Chernobyl

The overall decline in ^{137}Cs concentrations in the Irish Sea (and other U.K. waters) was interrupted in April 1986 following the Chernobyl reactor accident. The signal could be detected readily both as an overall increase in radionuclide concentrations of ^{134}Cs, ^{137}Cs, ^{110m}Ag, ^{131}I, ^{129m}Te and ^{103}Ru, and a significant increase in the ^{134}Cs/^{137}Cs ratio. At its peak in the northern Irish Sea in early May, the ^{137}Cs signal did not exceed a few Bq l^{-1} (Camplin *et al.*, 1986). In a matter of days, concentrations in shoreline waters had fallen substantially, levelling off at about 1 Bq l^{-1}, with a ^{137}Cs/^{134}Cs ratio that suggests there was some Chernobyl activity remaining. Levels in seaweeds and molluscs also decreased rapidly throughout the Irish Sea (Camplin *et al.*, 1986).

7.6.   Radionuclide Inventories in the Irish Sea

7.6.1.   Artificial Radionuclides

It is important to consider the total radionuclide inventory now residing in the environs of the Irish Sea and further afield. For shorter-lived radionuclides (*i.e.* half-life $\leq$ 30 y) the total environmental inventory has decreased in line with the reductions in the annual discharges. Moreover, the decrease in radiocaesium concentrations in surface sediments appears to have been accelerated throughout the 1980s due to the desorption of radiocaesium from the sediments into the now relatively clean seawater (McCartney *et al.*, 1994). In contrast, for longer-lived radionuclides (*e.g.*, ^{239}Pu, half-life = 24,000 y) there has been no significant decrease in the inventories. Indeed, the inventory of the alpha-emitting ^{241}Am nuclide will increase for several decades as a result of « grow-in » from the decay of ^{241}Pu, a beta-emitter discharged in large quantities in the 1970s (Fig. 7.1.). Further, only a small fraction of the Pu discharged annually from Sellafield is expected to leave the Irish Sea area (Pentreath *et al.*, 1986).

Attempts have been made to quantify the total environmental inventory of Pu in the water column and sediments of the Irish Sea taking into account the subtidal and intertidal seabed and seawater inventories and the advective loss *via* the North Channel (Pentreath *et al.*, 1984; Kershaw *et al.*, 1990; Woodhead, 1988). These studies have been able to account for about 78% of the reported Pu discharge and have shown that the bulk of the Pu inventory resides in the sediment compartment, with more than 90% of the observed sediment inventory of 519 TBq in offshore subtidal sediments. However, the increase in the Pu inventories at many intertidal sites (particularly in areas where tidal inundations deposit fine-grained particulates), despite the decline in discharges, is further evidence that the offshore sediments are subject to considerable mixing and reworking, and cannot be regarded as a final « sink » for Sellafield-derived radionuclides (Kershaw *et al.*, 1995a; Kershaw, 1996).

7.6.2. *Naturally-Occurring Radionuclides*

The environmental impact of industrially-introduced naturally-occurring radionuclides has been of less importance than that of the artificial radionuclides. There appears to be three sources of significance. Discharges of uranium and thorium to the Ribble Estuary from the BNFL Springfields' fuel fabrication plant have resulted in very high concentrations of nuclides such as ^{230}Th and ^{234m}Pa in the muddy sediments near the discharge outlet (Kershaw *et al.*, 1992). There is evidence that some of these inputs are exported from the estuary. Another source of naturally-occurring radionuclides has been a chemical production plant near Whitehaven (Marchon) on the Cumbrian coast, which formerly processed phosphate ore to produce phosphoric acid. The phosphate ore contained relatively high concentrations of uranium and its daughter nuclides, and its processing gave rise to mean annual discharges of about 35 tonnes (uranium) a^{-1} throughout the 1970s and the 1980s (McCartney *et al.*, 1990; Poole *et al.*, 1995). By comparison, average discharges from Sellafield are reported to amount to about 4 tonnes (uranium) a^{-1}, though these discharges contain few, if any, of the uranium daughters (Kershaw *et al.*, 1992). In 1992, modifications were made to the Marchon plant and crude phosphoric acid rather than phosphate ore became the raw material. A new waste treatment process was also introduced. These measures have resulted in very substantial reductions in the quantities of radionuclides discharged. Nevertheless, in the region around Whitehaven, elevated levels of uranium-series radionuclides have been detected in seawater, sediment and biota. For example, concentrations of ^{226}Ra of over 60 Bq m^{-3} have been measured in seawater close to the discharge point. This is about a factor of 30 higher than the expected background concentration (Kershaw, 1996).

7.7. Modelling and Future Research

In addition to the development of several 2-D and 3-D hydrodynamic models of water movement in the Irish Sea, a number of models have been designed specifically to predict the distribution of Sellafield-derived radionuclides within the Irish Sea and the resulting dose to man. In particular, box models have been developed which, for conservative tracers such as ^{137}Cs, give satisfactory agreement between predicted and observed concentrations (Jefferies and Steele, 1989; Abril and García León, 1993; Gurbutt *et al.*, 1988; 1993). More complicated is the modelling of non-conservative radionuclides, *e.g.* Pu and Am, as a set of complex mechanisms, including suspended matter dynamics, sediment composition, sediment accumulation and erosion rates, and redox reactions, have to be considered. To date, models such as the Harwell finite-difference model (Howorth and Kirby, 1988), have not been as successful in reproducing the seabed distributions of Pu and Am as they have in, for example, predicting the distribution of dissolved ^{137}Cs. There is clearly a need for further model development work in order to improve predictive capability. This should be accompanied by additional research in a number of key areas including particle-radionuclide interactions, cohesive sediment behaviour and the biogeochemistry of naturally-occurring radionuclides in the marine environment. These areas are the subject of on-going research at the present time.

References

Abril J.M. and García León M. (1993) A 2D 4-phases marine dispersion model for non-conservative radionuclides. Part 2: two applications. *J. Environ. Radioactivity* **20**, 89-115.

Aston S.R. and Stanners D.A. (1981) Plutonium transport to and deposition and immobility in Irish intertidal sediments. *Nature (Lond.)* **289**, 581-582.

Baxter M.S., McKinley I.G., MacKenzie A.B. and Jack W. (1979) Windscale radiocaesium in the Clyde Sea area. *Marine Pollut. Bull.* **10**, 116-120.

BNFL (1980-1995) Annual Reports on Radioactive Discharges and Monitoring of the Environment, 1979, 1980, 1981, 1982, 1983, 1984, 1985, 1986, 1987, 1988, 1989, 1990, 1991, 1992, 1993, 1994, (British Nuclear Fuels plc., Risley).

Boust D., Mitchell P.I., Garcia K., Condren O.M., León Vintró L. and Leclerc G. (1996) A comparative study of the speciation and behaviour of plutonium in the marine environment of two reprocessing plants. *Radiochim. Acta* (in press).

Camplin W.C., Mitchell N.T., Leonard D.R.P. and Jefferies D.F. (1986) Radioactivity in Surface and Coastal Waters of the British Isles. Monitoring of Fallout from the Chernobyl Reactor Accident (Ministry of

Agriculture, Fisheries and Food Directorate of Fisheries Research, Lowestoft) Aquatic Environment Monitoring Report N° 15, 49 pp.

Condren O.M., Mitchell P.I., León Vintró L. and Downes A.B. (1996) Plutonium and radiocaesium in western Irish Sea sediments: origin, bioavailability and ultimate fate, Irish Marine Science Symposium, Galway 6-9 September 1995, Special Publ. Royal Irish Academy (in press).

Cunningham J.D. and O'Grady J. (1986) Radioactivity Monitoring of the Irish Marine Environment, 1982-1984. 26 pp. (Nuclear Energy Board, Dublin).

Cunningham J.D., O'Grady J. and Rush T. (1988) Radioactivity Monitoring of the Irish Marine Environment, 1985-1986. 35 pp. (Nuclear Energy Board, Dublin).

Garland J.A., McKay W.A., Burton P.J. and Cambray R.S. (1989) Artificial Radioactivity on the Coasts of Northern Ireland, (Department of the Environment, U.K.) Report N° DOE/RW.89.055.

Gray J., Jones S.R. and Smith A.D. (1995) Discharges to the environment from the Sellafield site, 1951-1992. *J. Radiol. Prot.* **15**, 99-131.

Gurbutt P.A., Kershaw P.J. and Durance J.A. (1988) Modelling the distribution of soluble and particle-adsorbed radionuclides in the Irish Sea, Radionuclides: a Tool for Oceanography, (J.C. Guary, P. Guegueniat and R.J. Pentreath, Eds.) pp. 395-406. Elsevier Applied Science, London.

Gurbutt P.A., Kershaw P.J., Pentreath R.J., Woodhead D.S., Durance J.A., Camplin W.C. and Austin L.S. (1993) MIRMAID: the MAFF Irish Sea Model (Ministry of Agriculture, Fisheries and Food, Directorate of Fisheries Research, Lowestoft) Fish. Res. Tech. Rep.

Hamilton E.I. (1981) Alpha-particle radioactivity of hot particles from the Esk Estuary. *Nature (Lond.)* **290**, 690-693.

Hamilton E.I., Williams R. and Kershaw P.J. (1991) The total alpha particle radioactivity for some components of marine ecosystems, Radionuclides in the Study of Marine Processes (P.J. Kershaw and D.S. Woodhead, Eds.) pp. 234-244. Elsevier, London.

Hetherington J.A. (1976) The behaviour of plutonium nuclides in the Irish Sea, Environmental Toxicity of Aquatic Radionuclides (W. Miller and J.N. Stannard, Eds.) pp. 81-106. Ann Arbor Science, Michigan.

Hetherington J.A. (1978) The uptake of plutonium nuclides by marine sediments. *Mar. Sci. Comm.* **4**, 239-274.

Howarth M.J. (1984) Currents in the eastern Irish Sea. *Oceanogr. Mar. Biol. Ann. Rev.* **22**, 11-53.

Howells H. (1966) Discharges of low-activity, radioactive effluent from the Windscale works to the Irish Sea, Symp. on Disposal of Radioactive Wastes into Seas, Oceans and Surface Waters, Vienna. (International Atomic Energy Agency, Vienna).

Howorth J.M. and Kirby C.R. (1988) Studies of Environmental Radioactivity in Cumbria. Part II. Modelling the Dispersion of Radionuclides in the Irish Sea. (United Kingdom Atomic Energy Authority, Harwell) AERE-R 11734, 81 pp.

Hunt G.J. (1985) Timescales for dilution and dispersion of transuranies in the Irish Sea near Sellafield. *Sci. Total Environ.* **46,** 261-278.

Hunt G.J. and Kershaw P.J. (1990) Remobilisation of artificial radionuclides from the sediment of the Irish Sea. *J. Radiol. Prot.* **10,** 147-151.

IAEA (1985) Behaviour of Radionuclides Released into Coastal Waters (International Atomic Energy Agency, Vienna) pp. 1-183. TECDOC 329.

Jefferies D.F. and Steele A.K. (1989) Observed and predicted concentrations of caesium-137 in seawater of the Irish Sea 1970-1985. *J. Environ. Radioactivity* **10,** 173-189.

Kershaw P.J. (1996) Radioactive contamination of the Solway and Cumbrian coastal zone, The Solway Firth, Proc. ECSA Symposium (ECSA/JNCC, in press).

Kershaw P.J. and Baxter A. (1995) The transfer of reprocessing wastes from north-west Europe to the Arctic. *Deep Sea Res. II* **6,** 1413-1448.

Kershaw P.J., Gurbutt P.A., Young A.K. and Allington D.J. (1988) Scavenging and bioturbation in the Irish Sea from measurements of ^{234}Th/^{238}U and ^{210}Pb/^{226}Ra disequilibria, Radionuclides: a Tool for Oceanography (J.C. Guary, P. Guegueniat and R.J. Pentreath, Eds.) pp. 131-142. Elsevier Applied Science, London.

Kershaw P.J., Pentreath R.J., Woodhead D.S. and Hunt G.J. (1992) A Review of Radioactivity in the Irish Sea: a report prepared for the Marine Pollution Monitoring Management Group (Ministry of Agriculture, Fisheries and Food Directorate of Fisheries Research, Lowestoft) Aquatic Environment Monitoring Report N° 32, 65 pp.

Kershaw P.J., Pentreath R.J., Harvey B.R., Lovett M.B. and Boggis S.J. (1986) Apparent distribution coefficients of transuranium elements in U.K. coastal waters, Application of Distribution Coefficients to Radiological Assessment Models (T.H. Sibley and C. Myttenaere, Eds.) pp. 277-287. Elsevier Applied Science, London.

Kershaw P.J., Sampson K.E., McCarthy W. and Scott R.D. (1995b) The measurement of the isotopic composition of plutonium in an Irish sea sediment by mass spectrometry. *J. Radioanal. Nucl. Chem. Articles* **198,** 113-124.

Kershaw P.J., Swift D.J., Pentreath R.J. and Lovett M.B. (1983) Plutonium redistribution in Irish Sea sediment by biological activity. *Nature (Lond.)* **306,** 774-775.

Kershaw P.J., Swift D.S., Pentreath R.J. and Lovett M.B. (1984) The incorporation of plutonium, americium and curium into the Irish Sea seabed by biological activity. *Sci. Total Environ.* **40,** 61-81.

Kershaw P.J., Woodhead D.S., Lovett M.B. and Leonard K.S. (1995a) Plutonium from European reprocessing operations - its behaviour in the marine environment. *Appl. Radiat. Isot.* **46,** 1121-1134.

Kershaw P.J., Woodhead D.S., Malcolm S.J., Allingham D.J. and Lovett M.B. (1990) A sediment history of Sellafield discharges. *J. Environ. Radioactivity* **12,** 201-241.

Leonard K.S., McCubbin D. and Lovett M.B. (1995) Physico-chemical characterisation of radionuclides discharged from a nuclear establishment. *Sci. Total Environ.* **175**, 9-24.

Lovett M.B. and Nelson D.M. (1981) Determination of some oxidation states of plutonium in sea water and associated particulate matter, Techniques for Identifying Transuranic Speciation in Aquatic Environments, Ispra (International Atomic Energy Agency, Vienna) pp. 27-35. STI/PUB/613.

MacKenzie A.B. and Scott R.D. (1982) Radiocaesium and plutonium in intertidal sediments from Southern Scotland. *Nature (Lond.)* **299**, 613-616.

MacKenzie A.B., Scott R.D., Allan R.L., Ben Shaban Y.A., Cook G.T. and Pulford I.D. (1994) Sediment radionuclide profiles: implications for mechanisms of Sellafield waste dispersal in the Irish Sea. *J. Environ. Radioactivity* **23**, 39-69.

MAFF (1967-1995) Radioactivity in Surface and Coastal Waters of the British Isles, 1963-94 (Ministry of Agriculture, Fisheries and Food, Directorate of Fisheries Research, Lowestoft) Technical Reports Nos. (FRL) 1, 2, 5, 7, 8, 9, 10, 11, 12, and 13; Aquatic Environment Monitoring Reports Nos. 3, 4, 6, 8, 9, 11, 12, 13, 14, 18, 19, 21, 23, 29, 34, 38, 42 and 45.

Mauchline J. (1980) Artificial radioisotopes in the marginal seas of north-western Europe, The North-West European Shelf Seas: the Sea Bed and the Sea in Motion II. Physical and Chemical Oceanography, and Physical Resources (F.T. Banner, M.B. Collins and K.S. Massie, Eds.) pp. 517-542. Elsevier Scientific Publishing Company, Oxford.

McCartney M., Kershaw P.J. and Allington D.J. (1990) The behaviour of ^{210}Pb and ^{226}Ra in the eastern Irish Sea. *J. Environ. Radioactivity* **12**, 243-265.

McCartney M., Kershaw P.J., Woodhead D.S. and Denoon D.C. (1994) Artificial radionuclides in the surface sediments of the Irish Sea, 1968-1988. *Sci. Tot. Environ.* **141**, 103-138.

McDonald P., Cook G.T., Baxter M.S. and Thomson J.C. (1990) Radionuclide transfer from Sellafield to south-west Scotland. *J. Environ. Radioactivity* **12**, 285-298.

McGarry A., Lyons S., McEnri C., Ryan T., O'Colmain M. and Cunningham J.D. (1994) Radioactivity Monitoring of the Irish Marine Environment, 1991-92. 38 pp. (Radiological Protection Institute of Ireland, Dublin).

McKay W.A. and Pattenden N.J. (1993) The behaviour of plutonium and americium in the shoreline waters of the Irish Sea: a review of Harwell studies in the 1980s. *J. Environ. Radioactivity* **18**, 99-132.

McKinley I.G., Baxter M.S. and Jack W. (1981) A simple model of radiocaesium transport from Windscale to the Clyde Sea area. *Est. Coast. Shelf. Sci.* **13**, 59-67.

Mitchell P.I. (1989) Radionuclide monitoring in the Irish Sea, Seminar on the Radiological Exposure of the Population of the European Communities from Radioactivity in North European Marine Waters (Project Marina),

Bruges 14-16 June 1989. (Commission of the European Communities, Luxembourg), pp. 185-227. Publication XI/4669/89-EN.

Mitchell P.I., Sánchez-Cabeza J.A., Vidal-Quadras A. and Font J.L. (1987) Distribution of plutonium in inshore waters around Ireland using *Fucus vesiculosus* as a bio-indicator, Proc. CEC/CIEMAT Seminar on the Cycling of Long-Lived Radionuclides in the Biosphere: Observations and Models, Madrid 15-19 September 1986, Vol. II, Sect. 4. (Commission of the European Communities, Luxembourg), pp. 1-13.

Mitchell P.I., Sánchez-Cabeza J.A., Vidal-Quadras A., García León M. and Manjón G. (1989) The impact on Irish coastal waters of long-lived radioactive waste discharges to the Irish Sea, The Irish Sea - A Resource at Risk (J.C. Sweeney, Ed.) pp. 124-147. Geographical Society of Ireland, Dublin, Special Publication N°. 3, Ch. 12.

Mitchell P.I., Vives i Batlle J., Downes A.B., Condren O.M., León Vintró L. and Sánchez-Cabeza J.A. (1995) Recent observations on the physico-chemical speciation of plutonium in the Irish Sea and the Western Mediterranean. *Appl. Radiat. Isot.* **46,** 1175-1190.

Mitchell P.I., Vives Batlle J., Ryan T.P., Schell W.R., Sánchez-Cabeza J.A. and Vidal-Quadras A. (1991a) Studies on the speciation of plutonium and americium in the western Irish Sea, Radionuclides in the Study of Marine Processes (P.J. Kershaw and D.S. Woodhead, Eds.) pp. 37-51. Elsevier, London.

Mitchell P.I., Vives Batlle J., Ryan T.P., McEnri C., Long S., O'Colmain M., Cunningham J.D., Caulfield J.J., Larmour R.A. and Ledgerwood F.K. (1991b) Plutonium, americium and radiocaesium in sea water, sediments and coastal soils in Carlingford Lough, Radionuclides in the Study of Marine Processes (P.J. Kershaw and D.S. Woodhead, Eds.) pp. 265-275. Elsevier, London.

Nelson D.M. and Lovett M.B. (1978) Oxidation states of plutonium in the Irish Sea. *Nature (Lond.)* **276,** 599-601.

Nicholson M.D. and Hunt G.J. (1995) Measuring the availability to sediments and biota of radionuclides in wastes discharged to the Sea. *J. Environ. Radioactivity* **28,** 43-56.

O'Grady J. and Currivan L. (1989) Radioactivity Monitoring of the Irish Marine Environment, 1987. 30 pp. (Nuclear Energy Board, Dublin).

Peirson D.H., Cambray R.S., Cawse P.A., Eakins J.D. and Pattenden N.J. (1982) Environmental radioactivity in Cumbria. *Nature (Lond.)* **300,** 27-31.

Pentreath R.J. (1987) The interaction with suspended and settled sedimentary materials of long-lived radionuclides discharged into United Kingdom coastal waters. *Continent. Shelf Res.* **7,** 1457-1469.

Pentreath R.J., Lovett M.B., Jefferies D.F., Woodhead D.S., Talbot J.W. and Mitchell N. (1984) The impact on public radiation exposure of transuranium nuclides discharged in liquid wastes from fuel reprocessing at Sellafield, U.K., Symp. Radioactive Waste Management, Seattle 1983. pp. 315-329, (International Atomic Energy Agency, Vienna).

Pentreath R.J., Woodhead D.S., Kershaw P.J., Jefferies D.F. and Lovett M.B. (1986) The behaviour of plutonium and americium in the Irish Sea. *Rapp. P.-v. Reun. Cons. Int. Explor. Mer* **186**, 60-69.

Poole A.J., Allington D.J., Baxter A.J. and Young A.K. (1995) The natural radioactivity of phosphate ore and associated waste products discharged into the eastern Irish Sea from a phosphoric acid production plant. *Sci. Tot. Environ.* **173/174,** 137-149.

United Kingdom - Parliament (1993) Radioactive Substances Act, 1993. 44 pp. HMSO, London.

Vives i Batlle J. (1993) Speciation and Bioavailability of Plutonium and Americium in the Irish Sea and Other Marine Ecosystems, PhD Dissertation, 347 pp. National University of Ireland.

Walker M.I., McKay W.A., Pattenden N.J. and Liss P.S. (1986) Actinide enrichment in marine aerosols. *Nature (Lond.)* **323,** 141-143.

Woodhead D.S. (1988) Mixing processes in nearshore marine sediments as inferred from the distributions of radionuclides discharged into the northeast Irish Sea from BNFL, Sellafield, Radionuclides: a Tool for Oceanography (J.C. Guary, P. Guegueniat and R.J. Pentreath, Eds.) pp. 331-340. Elsevier Applied Science, London.

8 Time Evolution and Levels of Man-Made Radioactivity in the Mediterranean Sea

C. Papucci, S. Charmasson, R. Delfanti,
C. Gascó, P. Mitchell and J.A. Sánchez-Cabeza

The sources and levels of the most relevant anthropogenic radionuclides in the Mediterranean Sea are described and the processes controlling their distribution are discussed in detail.

The global inputs of ^{137}Cs and ^{239,240}Pu to the Mediterranean Sea are estimated to be 15 and 0.19 PBq respectively, up to 1996. The most important sources are atmospheric fallout from nuclear weapon tests and the Chernobyl accident.

^{137}Cs distribution in the water column is mainly controlled by physical processes (water mass circulation, convection) and there is a general trend to increasing concentrations in deep waters with time. Most of the ^{137}Cs is still present in the water column, where its global inventory is 13.6 PBq, while only about 10% of this amount is accumulated in sediments.

The vertical distribution of plutonium is governed not only by the physical processes active for ^{137}Cs, but also by its chemical speciation and association to particles. Its present concentration in surface water is about 1/3 of that measured in 1977, while the levels near the bottom show a clear increase (+ 30%) during the last 20 years. In open Mediterranean environments, the amount of plutonium in sediments is only few percent of the cumulative fallout deposition.

A general decrease of the total inventory of both ^{137}Cs and ^{239,240}Pu in the Mediterranean Sea is foreseen for the future, due to the absence of relevant sources, exchanges through the Gibraltar Straits (Pu), and physical decay (Cs).

8.1. Introduction

The Mediterranean Sea is a complex, deep environment, having a mean depth of more than 1400 m. It is comprised of two interacting basins, connected by the shallow Strait of Sicily. The whole Mediterranean Sea is in turn connected to the Atlantic Ocean by the narrow and shallow Strait of Gibraltar. The effect of wind, coupled with geographic variation of heat and water budgets, leads to extended processes of dense water formation and the establishment of stable and *quasi*-stable gyres, that constitute the driving forces of the general circulation.

The exchange through the Strait of Gibraltar, with the outflow being cooler and more saline than the inflow, implies that the Mediterranean must be experiencing net cooling and evaporation. It is well known, as a matter of fact, that the entire Mediterranean, and in particular its eastern part, are concentration basins, with evaporation exceeding precipitation and runoff (Béthoux, 1979). Due to the increase in salt and consequent density instabilities, deep-intermediate water is formed by vertical convection in some key-sites. In particular, in the Eastern basin, the Rhodes gyre has been known to be one of the main sites of formation of the denser Levantine Intermediate Water (LIW) (Malanotte-Rizzoli and Bergamasco, 1991) that stabilizes at depths of 200-600 m and moves westward, constituting the main « driving force » for the general circulation in the whole Mediterranean.

The picture of the circulation pattern in the Mediterranean Sea is complex, and involves a number of multiple interacting driving forces, the most relevant being:
• strong topographic and coastal influences;
• internal dynamic processes on a basin and sub-basin scale;
• intense mesoscale and seasonal variabilities; and, finally,
• winter convection processes producing deep and intermediate waters.

The general scheme can be summarised as follows: the major structure influencing the surface circulation is the light Atlantic water jet (salinity 36.5-37.5 psu) entering *via* the Strait of Gibraltar. After some meandering in the Alboran Sea, the jet proceeds along the North African coast, until the Strait of Sardinia. After crossed the Sicily sill, the Atlantic stream occupies the southern part of the Ionian basin, becoming an intensified mid-Mediterranean jet. In the area between Crete and Rhodes, extensive vertical convection gives rise to the formation of the saltier and denser Levantine Intermediate Water (salinity 38.45-38.75 psu) at 200-600 m depth (Wüst, 1961), which moves westward, passes over the Sicilian sill and enters the Western basin. After following a rather complicated path throughout the basin, finally the LIW flows, mixed with some Mediterranean Deep Water (MDW), out of the Mediterranean, crossing the Gibraltar Straits at an average depth of more than 150 m (Bryden *et al.*, 1994). The outflow of salty water from the Mediterranean settles out at about 1000 m in the North Atlantic and constitutes the main source of the salt tongue that spreads across the Atlantic Ocean, enhancing the deep convection in the Norwegian-Greenland Sea and, thus, influencing the global ocean circulation (Price *et al.*, 1993).

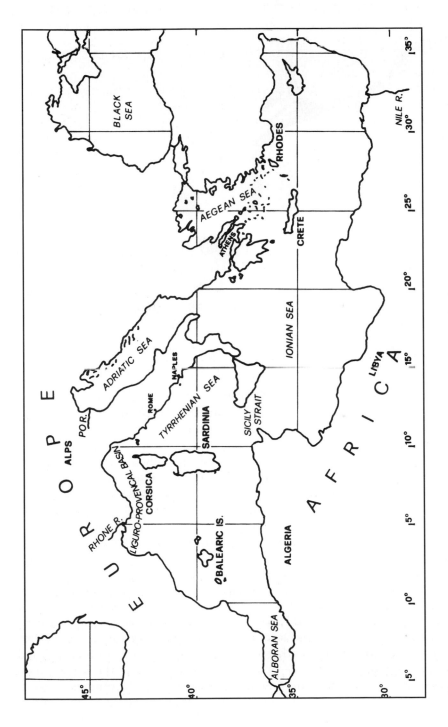

Fig. 8.1. Mediterranean basins.

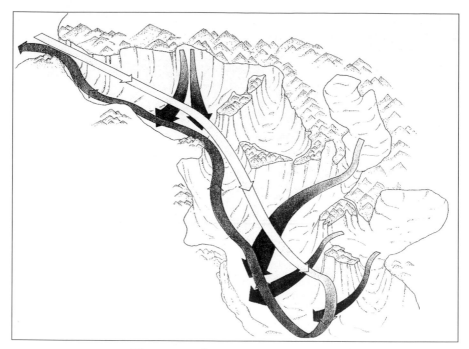

Fig. 8.2. Mediterranean conveyor belt.

The deepest Mediterranean waters are mainly formed in areas where prolonged periods of wind sharply increase the evaporation rates and produce, at the surface, a dense, well oxygenated water mass that sinks rapidly in vertical water chimneys and cones, that reach the bottom and spread all over the basin.

The Gulf of Lions, the Liguro-Provencal basin, the Adriatic Sea and the Rhode/Crete area, in particular, have been identified as the most important sites in the Mediterranean Sea where the dense abyssal water is formed (Ovchinnikov, 1966). More recently, Roether *et al.* (1996) observed remarkable changes in the deep water pattern in the Levantine Basin, with dense water masses of Aegean origin substituting the previous water mass originated in the Adriatic.

In this paper we discuss the present distribution of the most relevant anthropogenic radionuclides (^{137}Cs and transuranics) in the Mediterranean Sea and their relationship with the main oceanographic processes occurring in the area. The physical and biogeochemical processes controlling radionuclide distribution in the Mediterranean Sea are not considered to be different from those occurring in other seas. However, the study of this enclosed, deep basin gives us a unique opportunity to investigate the role of these processes in determining time-trends of radionuclide distributions, inventories and exchange fluxes with the Atlantic Ocean. In fact, the constrained, semi-enclosed nature of the Mediterranean Sea provides a laboratory basin for which accurate budgets of heat, salt, water, but also radionuclides, can be obtained comparatively easily. Furthermore, the relatively small size of the Mediterranean Sea implies ease of logistics for *in situ* investigations, resulting in valuable insights and transferable methodology for the study of global ocean processes, and for the validation of predictive models.

8.2. Sources of Artificial Radionuclides

An extensive review of artificial radionuclide inputs to the Mediterranean Sea, up to 1986, has been reported by Holm *et al.* (1988) and by UNEP (1992). The main source is atmospheric fallout deriving from nuclear weapon testing in the early sixties. Up to 1986, the total quantities of ^{137}Cs and $^{239, 240}$Pu from this source are reported to have been 10.2 ± 2 PBq and 0.23 ± 0.02 PBq, respectively. All other sources amounted to no more than 10% of these values. In particular, radionuclide input by river runoff was estimated by Fukai *et al.* (1980) to be approximately 3% of the annual delivery by dry and wet fallout. This corresponded roughly to 0.1 PBq of ^{137}Cs and 0.003 PBq of $^{239, 240}$Pu until 1986. Exchanges with the Atlantic Ocean through the Gibraltar Strait in the same period led to an additional net ^{137}Cs input of about 1.5 PBq and, in contrast, to a loss of about 0.04 PBq of ^{239,240}Pu. Exchanges with the Black Sea were less important, resulting in an increase of ^{137}Cs and $^{239, 240}$Pu supply of about 1%. From these data, the total inputs of ^{137}Cs and $^{239, 240}$Pu to the Mediterranean Sea were calculated to be 12 ± 2 and 0.19 ± 0.02 PBq, respectively, up to 1986.

The atmospheric deposition of caesium isotopes following the Chernobyl accident was significant, but a precise estimate of the total input to the whole Mediterranean is quite difficult, because its deposition was patchy, depending on the trajectories of the plumes. Moreover, measurements of caesium deposition are available mainly for the Northern Mediterranean, Aegean and Black Seas, but little is known for the Southern basins. Based on published data (UNEP, 1992; Kritidis and Florou, 1990), we have calculated the total ^{137}Cs input to the Liguro-Provencal basin, the Tyrrhenian, the Adriatic and the Aegean Seas in at least 2.5 PBq. Since 1986, there was also a significant input from the Black Sea, that, according to Egorov *et al.* (1994) is in the order of 0.03 PBq y^{-1}, *i.e.* 0.3 PBq up to 1996. No data are available for ^{137}Cs input from rivers. In addition to these contributions, the deposition of ^{137}Cs by dry and wet fallout in the period 1987-1996 must also be taken into account. If the average deposition to Italy is assumed to be representative of the whole Mediterranean basin, a total input of 0.3 PBq of ^{137}Cs is estimated from this source. Recent studies carried out at the Gibraltar Straits indicate that the amount of ^{137}Cs leaving the Mediterranean is equal to that entering with the Atlantic flow. We can then conclude that the total ^{137}Cs input to the Mediterranean Sea, up to 1996, is in the order of 15 PBq, corresponding to an increase of at least 25% during the period 1986-1996. It must be underlined that this is a lower estimate, because no data have been reported regarding the southern Mediterranean basins and Chernobyl radionuclide inputs from rivers.

The Chernobyl accident did not significantly contribute to the total plu-tonium input to the Mediterranean. The total integrated deposition of ^{239,240}Pu at Monaco following the accident was 10 ± 1 mBq m^{-2} (Whitehead *et al.*, 1988), corresponding to only about 0.01% of the previous integrated deposition from nuclear tests fallout. Based on the measurements carried out in Monaco in the course of 1978-1979 (Thein *et al.*, 1980) and assuming that since that period ^{239,240}Pu yearly deposition by rain has not signifi-cantly changed, the atmospheric input of these radionuclides, in the period 1986-1996, can be estimated to be 0.007 PBq. At the Gibraltar Straits, a net outflux from the Mediterranean of 0.63 TBq y^{-1} of ^{239,240}Pu was calculated in 1994 by Mitchell *et al.* (in preparation). Thus, a global input to the Mediterranean Sea of 0.19 PBq can be estimated for ^{239,240}Pu up to 1996.

Another source of man-made radionuclides to the marine environment is the controlled discharge of low-level liquid effluents from the nuclear installations. Among these discharges, spent fuel reprocessing plant efflu-ents represent the major source. The reprocessing plant of Marcoule (France) is authorized to discharge low-level effluents in the Rhône river, which flows into the Gulf of Lions. The discharge rates of ^{137}Cs and ^{239,240}Pu, given by Charmasson *et al.* (1994) for the period 1980-1991, have been updated to 1995, leading to total inputs of 30.2 TBq of ^{137}Cs and 0.26 TBq of ^{239,240}Pu. Although being several orders of magnitude lower than inputs from fallout, such point-source can lead to local enhancement in the concentration levels in the coastal marine environment.

A summary of radionuclide inputs into the Mediterranean Sea is shown in Table 8.I.

Table 8.I. Inputs of ^{137}Cs and ^{239,240}Pu into the Mediterranean marine environment up to 1996 through different routes.

Route	^{137}Cs (PBq)	^{239,240}Pu (TBq)	Reference
Total input up to 1986	12.0	190	UNEP, 1992; Holm *et al.*, 1988.
Fallout from Chernobyl	2.5	0.02	This work; Whitehead *et al.*, 1988
Atmospheric input, 1986-1996	0.3	7.5	This work
Marcoule reprocessing plant, up to 1995	0.03	0.3	This work; Charmasson *et al.*, 1994
Black Sea 1986-1996	0.3		Egorov *et al.*, 1994.
Exchanges with Atlantic Ocean 1986-1996	=	– 6.3	Mitchell *et al.*, paper in preparation.
Total, up to 1996	15.1	191.5	

8.3. Radionuclide Concentration in Seawater

8.3.1. ^{137}*Cs*

Many data are available for ^{137}Cs concentrations in surface seawater in the coastal environment, mainly deriving from National Networks. As an example, the time trend of the ^{137}Cs concentration in seawater at a coastal site of the Ligurian Sea in the period 1960-94 is shown in Figure 8.3.

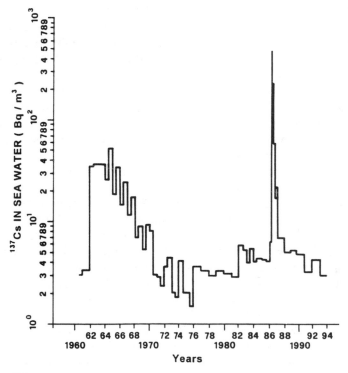

Fig. 8.3. ^{137}Cs concentration in surface seawater, La Spezia, Italy, 1960-1994.

These data show a clear decrease of ^{137}Cs levels from the early to the late sixties and a levelling off in the seventies and afterwards. An analysis of literature data shows that ^{137}Cs concentrations in open surface Mediterranean waters were not significantly different and exponentially decreased, in the period 1970-1982, from an average value of 8.4 ± 0.6 to 3.8 ± 0.4 mBq m^{-3}. These changes correspond to the decrease in radionuclide fallout from nuclear weapon testing, but are also related to radionuclide vertical transport by diffusion and convection processes, as will be discussed in the following pages.

The fallout deriving from the Chernobyl accident was unevenly distributed in the Mediterranean area and was highest in the northern (Adriatic, Liguro-Provençal) and in the eastern basins (Aegean, Levantine). Consequently, in the Ligurian Sea, an increase in the ^{137}Cs concentration in seawater of about two orders of magnitude was observed in the first days of May 1986 (Delfanti and Papucci, 1988; Whitehead *et al.*, 1988). Such an increase was also observed in the Gulf of Lions surface water in September 1986, with a gradient decreasing westward, but in December the concentrations were homogeneous over the entire Gulf (Calmet *et al.*, 1992). The decrease of ^{137}Cs levels in surface seawater after the accident was quite rapid in the North Western Mediterranean due to mixing with « uncontaminated » waters coming from the southern Mediterranean basins and from the Atlantic Ocean. In the Adriatic Sea, ^{137}Cs levels were systematically higher than in the Western Basin, due to the higher Chernobyl deposition in the area, to the general circulation pattern that brought to this basin « contaminated » waters from the Aegean and Ionian Sea, and to runoff from the major Italian rivers (Franic and Bauman, 1993; Delfanti *et al.*, 1994). In 1990, ^{137}Cs concentrations were usually ~ 5 Bq m^{-3} all over the Mediterranean Sea, except for some areas of the Aegean Sea receiving direct water input from the Black Sea (Marina-Med, 1994).

While the time trend of ^{137}Cs concentrations in surface waters is well known, especially for the coastal environment, few data are available for the vertical distributions, particularly in the Eastern Basin, and for water depths greater than 2000 m. The first systematic studies on the vertical distribution of ^{137}Cs were conducted by Kautsky (1977) in 1970 and 1974. Data reported by Fukai in 1980 show similar concentrations at depth and a slight decrease at the surface. Before the Chernobyl accident, in the period 1970-1982, average ^{137}Cs concentrations in the water column were in the order of 5.4 ± 2.1 mBq m^{-3} in the surface layer, 2.2 ± 0.6 in the LIW (300-600 m) and 1.0 ± 0.5 mBq m^{-3} in the MDW (600 m to bottom) (Fig. 8.4.).

As discussed above, the Chernobyl accident produced a sharp increase in the ^{137}Cs concentration in surface water in the Northwestern Mediterranean, in the Adriatic Sea and in the Aegean-Levantine basin. The evolution of caesium levels in the water column after the accident was controlled by physical processes. In a first phase, dilution of surface « contaminated » waters with « uncontaminated » waters coming from the southern basins and from the Atlantic Ocean took place. Subsequently, during the winter, convection processes and the formation of intermediate and deep waters induced rapid caesium transfer from surface to depth. In fact, measurements carried out at the Sicily Straits in 1993 show that the level of ^{137}Cs in the LIW entering the Western Mediterranean (3.5 mBq m^{-3}) is significantly higher than that measured before the Chernobyl accident and is very similar to the level in the Modified Atlantic Water flowing at the surface. Moreover, relative caesium concentration maxima were observed both in LIW and MDW of the Western Mediterranean in 1989 (IAEA, 1991).

Systematic studies conducted in 1991-1994 (Delfanti *et al.*, 1995) evidence an increase in caesium concentration in the Western Mediterranean Deep Waters, which average level is at present 1.7 ± 0.5 mBq m^{-3} (Fig. 8.4.). The vertical profiles of ^{137}Cs show the same trend as those of dissolved oxygen, indicating that the additional input is strictly dependent on the supply of newly formed dense waters.

Based on 1991-1994 data, the present inventory of ^{137}Cs in the Mediterranean water column is estimated to be 13.6 PBq. This corresponds to an increase, after the Chernobyl accident, of about 25% and is in good agreement with the estimated global input of 15 PBq to the whole Mediterranean.

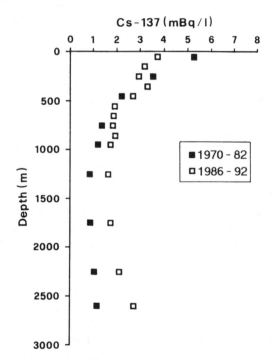

Fig. 8.4. Average ^{137}Cs vertical distributions in Mediterranean waters, 1970-1982 and 1986-1992.

8.3.2. Transuranium Nuclides

An analysis of published $^{239,\,240}$Pu levels in surface seawater for the period 1970-1994 shows, as for ^{137}Cs, a decreasing trend with time (Fig. 8.5.).

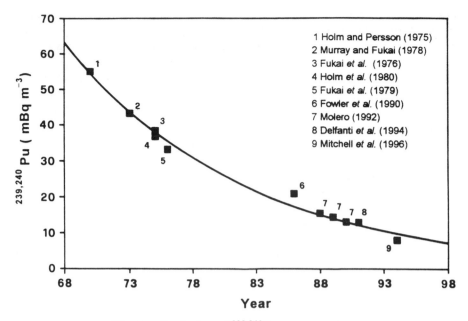

Fig. 8.5. Evolution of ^{239,240}Pu concentrations
in surface waters of the western Mediterranean.

From the exponential fit of the curve, it is apparent that plutonium decreases with a time constant of about 14.5 years. This value is in good agreement with the residence time of 12.3 years estimated by Thein *et al.* (1980), on the basis of plutonium delivery and inventories in the 0-100 m mixed layer. The removal of transuranium nuclides from surface water is controlled by the same physical processes active for ^{137}Cs, but also by the association to suspended matter and the subsequent sedimentation processes. In continental shelf waters of the Northwestern Mediterranean, about 10% of plutonium is adsorbed to suspended matter, whilst up to 45% of americium is found in the particulate fraction, in agreement with what observed in other shallow marine environments, such as the Irish Sea (Molero *et al.*, 1995a; Mitchell *et al.*, 1991). The fraction of transuranics adsorbed to the particulate phase is smaller for open waters characterized by low particle population, where typical values are about 5% for plutonium and 10% for americium (Holm *et al.*, 1980; Delfanti *et al.*, 1994; Molero *et al.*, 1995b). The mean ^{241}Am/$^{239,\,240}$Pu ratio in Mediterranean waters is presently 0.083 ± 0.014 and 0.6 ± 0.3 for the soluble and particulate fraction respectively. The ratio in the soluble fraction is much lower than the value of 0.30 reported for the integrated global fallout by Bunzl and Krackle (1988), and comparable to that estimated in the past for the Mediterranean area (Holm *et al.*, 1980). This represents an actual americium enrichment of the particulate fraction of 8 ± 4 (Molero *et al.*, 1995b). The enrichment of americium with respect to plutonium is believed to be due to the preferential association of americium to inorganic particles which, in the low productivity Mediterranean Sea, may be more abundant than the biogenic ones. As a consequence, the percentage of plutonium inventory still remaining in the water column is larger than that observed for americium.

The sinking of particles through the water column is the main mechanism determining the shape of transuranic vertical profiles, which are characterized by pronounced subsurface maxima at depths of 250-400 m. At these depths decomposition of organic matter takes place, releasing the associated nuclides to the soluble phase. Although surface plutonium concentrations have markedly decreased in the last 20 years, the activities presently observed at the depth of the subsurface maxima, around 40 mBq m^{-3}, are very similar to those (50 mBq m^{-3}) reported for the period 1977-81 by Fukai *et al.* (1980). In contrast, higher values characterize now the deep mediterranean waters: 25 mBq m^{-3} in 1992 with respect to 10 mBq m^{-3} in 1977-1981.

The analysis of the distribution of the chemical forms of plutonium in the Mediterranean water column gives a better understanding of the mechanisms controlling its behaviour. The most abundant particles occurring in surface waters are colloids (Wells and Goldberg, 1991), which presence is relevant to transport of pollutants because of their conservative behaviour in the water column. From ultrafiltration and preferential sorption on alumina beds experiments, it has been shown that the fraction of colloidal plutonium ranged from 0-30% (Mitchell *et al.*, 1991; Merino, 1993). The oxidation state distribution in filtered seawater has been examined in detail by Mitchell *et al.* (1995). In open waters, a pronounced sub-surface maximum in the Pu(V) concentration profile is observed at some few hundred metres depth. A similar maximum is apparent in the case of the Pu(IV) concentration, though it appears to occur nearer to the surface. Interestingly, the percentage of plutonium associated with particulate matter is maximum at a depth of 50 m. Below a few hundred meters, the concentration of reduced plutonium diminishes significantly. In fact, the percentage of plutonium in a reduced chemical form in the water column was found to increase from a minimum of 5-12% close to the seabed, to a maximum of over 70% at a depth of about 500 m, most if not all of this increase taking place in the upper half of the water column. Further, the percentage of plutonium in a reduced form near the seabed appeared to be independent of depth, being similar in deep waters (3000 m) and coastal shelf waters. The bulk of the plutonium inventory in the Mediterranean water column is in an oxidised form, particularly in open waters, while the quantities in particulate or colloidal form are comparatively small. It has been suggested that the reduction of oxidised plutonium by phytoplancton forming a biologically productive layer near the surface is responsible for the observed maximum in the Pu(IV) concentration profile, while some components of the bottom sediments, probably manganese dioxide, is involved either as a catalyser or as an active agent in the oxidation of Pu(IV) to Pu(V).

8.4. Sediments

Radionuclide concentrations and inventories in sediments are highly variable, being usually highest on the continental shelf and near the river mouths, and lowest in deep sea environments. [137]Cs vertical distribution and inventories in deep sea sediments were not significantly affected by the Chernobyl input. Recent data indicate that ^{137}Cs inventories in sediment cores of the Western Mediterranean, at water depths of about 1000 m were in the order of 230 Bq m^{-2}, corresponding to 5-10% of the water column inventory at the same stations (Delfanti *et al.*, 1995). Much more complex is the situation on the continental shelf and in the areas of influence of large rivers. In these areas, particularly where the Chernobyl fallout was significant (Northern Adriatic Sea, Liguro-Provencal basin), ^{137}Cs inventories show a large variability. Studies have been carried out near the mouths of some of the most important rivers of the Northern Mediterranean. The results obtained for the Rhône, the Po and some other North Italian rivers flowing into the Adriatic Sea show that high caesium concentration and inventories are found in the prodelta of the rivers. In these areas, the values reported (up to 30 kBq m^{-2}) are ten times higher than in the surronding areas (2 kBq m^{-2}). The studies show that a significant part of suspended solids, and associated radionuclides, transported by the rivers into the Mediterranean Sea are temporarily trapped in a small prodelta area, where the sedimentation processes are governed by flocculation and by particle aggregation phenomena. However, the shallow prodelta deposits are not stable and are reworked by the action of waves. There is evidence that thick layers of sediment can be resuspended and transported elsewhere (Arnaud *et al.*, 1995).

[239,240]Pu concentrations and inventories in sediments show the same trend as that reported for [137]Cs. High values, often 2 to 3 times higher than the total cumulative fallout deposition (82 Bq m^{-2}), are found in fine-grained sediments of the continental shelf (Anton *et al.* 1994; Delfanti *et al.*, 1995). In contrast, in deep sea environments that do not receive significant particulate input from the shelf, plutonium inventories are as low as a few Bq m^{-2}, being very similar to those reported for low productivity areas in the Atlantic Ocean. Intermediate values are found along the continental slope and on the walls of submarine canyons. The vertical transport of transuranic nuclides through the water column by particulate matter has been studied, using moored sediment traps, at two different sites of the Western Mediterranean: the Lacaze-Duthiers Canyon and the open waters of the Gulf of Lions (Fowler *et al.*, 1990). Although the concentrations of [239,240]Pu and [241]Am in settling particles is very similar in the two areas, the resulting fluxes range from 0.24 Bq m^{-2} y^{-1} in the Gulf of Lions to 2.6 Bq m^{-2} y^{-1} in the canyon, in relation to different mass fluxes at the sites of measurement.

The following mechanism can then be hypothesized for transuranic accumulation in sediments:
- the removal of plutonium and americium from the water column mainly takes place in areas where particle population in the water column is highest (continental shelf, river mouths, submarine canyons);
- their accumulation in sediments is strictly related to the stability of sedimentary deposits: transuranic inventories are then highest on the continental shelf and highly variable along the walls of submarine canyons, where hydrodynamic and topographic conditions favour dislocation and slumping of sediment toward the deep sea;
- in open-sea environments, where the particle population is very low, being the Mediterranean an oligotrophic sea, only a small fraction (5%) of transuranics deposited at the sea surface has reached the bottom.

8.5. Palomares

An area of particular interest is the site of Palomares, in the Southeastern coast of Spain, which received in 1966 an extra input of transuranics, due to an aircraft accident, in which an aerosol was formed from the conventional explosion of two atomic bombs (Iranzo, 1987; UNSCEAR, 1988). Immediately after the accident, the top 10 cm of soil was removed, but agricultural, underbrush and urban areas remained partly contaminated by plutonium and americium. Scarse but heavy rainy storms produced intense floods in the small local torrents, resulting in large inputs of terrigenous materials into the neighbouring Mediterranean continental shelf. The Palomares marine area presents a narrow continental shelf, indented by a main submarine canyon, with several subtributaries branches having pronounced slope. The sediment particles deposited on the continental shelf tend to be preferentially transported to the flat abyssal plains through this complex canyon system by turbidity currents.

Several sediment cores collected in the period 1985-1991 and covering the marine area near Palomares have been analysed. The results show enhanced transuranic inventories, in the range 200-1500 Bq m^{-2} of $^{239, 240}$Pu, in a limited area Southeast of the Almanzora River mouth (typical values observed in the Spanish continental shelf are in the range 25-120 Bq m^{-2}). In these cores, the ratios ^{238}Pu/$^{239, 240}$Pu (< 0.02) and ^{241}Am/$^{239, 240}$Pu (< 0.2) point to weapon grade plutonium origin. The plutonium and americium derived from the accident (identified by their isotopic ratios) in the sediment collected on the continental shelf, appear to be associated to insoluble particles, whilst plutonium and americium from 60's fallout were associated with organic matter, sesquioxides and exchangeable fraction (Romero, 1991; Antón et al., 1994; 1995).

The continental shelf in the area Cape of Gata-Cape of Palos, where Palomares is located, represents 6% of the total Spanish mediterranean continental shelf (0-50 m). Taking into account the plutonium inventories calculated from the sediment cores collected on the continental shelf, the input of the Palomares accident was estimated to be a maximum of 1.37 TBq of plutonium. As a term of reference, the inventory of fallout Pu on the total Spanish mediterranean continental shelf is estimated to be 1.6 TBq. Due both to the random distribution of plutonium and americium in the Palomares sediments and the area considered, the calculated inventory is possibly overestimated, and should be considered as a maximum value (Gascó *et al.*, 1994; Antón *et al.*, 1994).

8.6. Organisms

The analysis of the time-trend evolution of radiactivity levels in the marine organisms of the Mediterranean is practically restricted to ^{137}Cs, which is the only anthropogenic radionuclide systematically analysed by the different countries, through their own national networks for monitoring environmental radioactivity. The marine organisms for which we possess data on a large scale are: i) fish, that are essentially measured for health assessment, and ii) filter-feeder molluscs, that are sampled both for health assessment and for being bio-indicators. The ability of mussels for indicating levels of different pollutants in marine coastal environment and also their widespread distribution, led them to be major sentinel organisms (Goldberg *et al.*, 1987).

Table 8.II. reports the mean annual ^{137}Cs concentrations respectively in mussels and in fish, over the period 1985-1995, in different Mediterranean basins. These data essentially come from national networks. Data below the detection limit have not been taken into account. Therefore, the annual mean concentrations presented in the table may be accounted as a maximum level. In order to provide us against the patchy regional variations observed immediately after the Chernobyl accident, the data regarding 1986 has not been reported in the table. Unfortunately there is a lack of data regarding the southern part of the Mediterranean Sea. The coverage of the Aegean Sea is also quite poor, despite the interest in following the inputs from the Chernobyl-contaminated Black Sea. The data regarding the Gulf of Lions, that undergoes the contributions coming from the nuclear facilities along the Rhône river, have been grouped separately, as representative of a different source of anthropogenic radionuclides.

Levels reported for the period preceeding the Chernobyl accident are generally very low, and reveal quite a large discrepancy in the average concentrations between the different basins, in relation to heterogeneity both in the species sampled, representing therefore different food-habits, and the

Table 8.II.

137Cs concentrations (Bq kg⁻¹ wet weight) in mussels from different basins of the Mediterranean Sea.

^{137}Cs concentrations (Bq kg^{-1} wet weight) in mussels from different basins of the Mediterranean Sea.

Areas Years	Gulf of Lions				W Liguro-Provencal				E Liguro-Provencal				Tyrrhenian				NW Adriatic				Ionian				Aegean			
	mean	SD	n	%	mean	SD	n	%	mean	SD	n	%	mean	SD	n	%	mean	SD	n	%	mean	SD	n	%	mean	SD	n	%
1985	0.29	0.15	33	92	0.05	0.02	7	50									0.14	0.04	4		0.30	0.44	3		0.63		1	
1987	1.52	1.09	33	97	0.17	0.05	23	96					0.15	0.07	2		0.25	0.07	2		0.15	0.07	2		0.55		1	
1988	0.42	0.41	31	94	0.10	0.05	20	87	0.22	0.01	2		0.13		1		0.43	0.22	8		0.22	0.07	2		0.53		1	
1989	0.20	0.12	34	100	0.07	0.05	23	100	0.12		1		0.22	0.16	2		0.43	0.19	12		<DL		2		0.30		1	
1990	0.22	0.10	31	100	0.07	0.00	17	77	<DL		2		<DL		2		0.50	0.024	5		0.14		1					
1991	0.13	0.06	16	94	0.07	0.05	15	83					0.33		1	33	0.36	0.15	6	21	0.20	0.04	2					
1992	0.11	0.02	9	39									0.16	0.08	5	45	0.31	0.22	12	46	<DL		2					
1993	0.11	0.02	9	39	0.09	0.05	3	30																				
1994	0.16	0.03	11	33	0.10	0.02	6	35																				
1995	0.09	0.005	11	41	0.12	0.05	4	20																				

n = number of measurements above the detection limit.   % = proportions of measurements above the detection limit.

137Cs concentrations (Bq kg⁻¹ wet weight) in fish from different basins of the Mediterranean Sea.

^{137}Cs concentrations (Bq kg^{-1} wet weight) in fish from different basins of the Mediterranean Sea.

Areas Years	Gulf of Lions				W Liguro-Provencal				E Liguro-Provencal				Tyrrhenian				NW Adriatic				Ionian				Aegean			
	mean	SD	n	%	mean	SD	n	%	mean	SD	n	%	mean	SD	n	%	mean	SD	n	%	mean	SD	n	%	mean	SD	n	%
1985	0.26	0.16	12	100	0.11	0.04	7	100	0.71	0.28	2		0.27	0.20	10		0.23	0.10	16		0.20	0.12	8		0.93	0.62	2	
1987	2.42	3.06	16	100	0.56	0.25	12	100	0.30		1		0.95	0.78	2		1.55	1.34	2		0.70	0.71	2		0.37	0.31	2	
1988	1.81	2.31	19	100	0.21	0.10	11	92	0.25	0.14	5		0.33	0.05	4		0.61	0.46	11		0.40	0.34	7		0.66	0.35	2	
1989					0.13	0.04	12	100	0.17	0.09	3		0.51	0.39	3		0.37	0.2	7		0.26	0.23	4		0.9	0.00	2	
1990					0.15	0.07	11	92	0.20	0.05	3		0.15	0.02	2		0.26	0.12	3		0.13	0.03	3		0.51	0.20	2	
					0.19*	0.01	3																					
1991					0.17	0.06	9	100	0.16		1		0.5	0.38	3	60	0.29	0.10	10	71	0.29	0.02	3	60				
1992					0.13	0.02	3	75	0.18	0.07	4	80	0.68		1	100	0.27	0.12	26	79	0.17	0.03	3	100				
1993					0.24*	0.06	2																					
1994					0.25	0.08	6	100																				
1995					0.25	0.12	8	89																				

* Spanish data (Romero, 1994).

characteristics of the organism analysed (*i.e.* age, analysis on the whole organism or on edible parts, etc.). The uneven deposition of the Chernobyl fallout produced an increase in ^{137}Cs concentrations in the marine biota of the Mediterranean (Calmet *et al.*, 1988; Delfanti and Papucci, 1988; Florou *et al.*, 1987; Holm *et al.*, 1988). In Greece the ^{137}Cs concentrations in fishes were in the order of 10 Bq kg[-1] wet weight; however, in certain samples of mussels and fishes, contents up to 33 and 66 Bq kg[-1] w.w. were reported (Florou *et al.*, 1990). In Italy, ^{137}Cs contents up to 8 and 10 Bq kg[-1] w.w. have been observed, in mussels and fishes respectively. [137]Cs concentration was higher in fishes from the Adriatic Sea than in fishes from the Ligurian and Thyrrenian basins, reflecting the higher concentrations in seawater. In the same way, in the seawater along the French coast, a diminishing east-west gradient emerges in May 1986 for the different radionuclides connected with the Chernobyl accident ([103]Ru, [106]Ru, ^{137}Cs, [134]Cs), confirming the patchiness of the fallout deposition. The highest contents were observed near the Italian border, with concentrations up to 220, 70, 4 and 2 Bq kg[-1] w.w. respectively. The sharp Chernobyl signal registered monitoring over time the mussels and fishes at different locations, reveal a rapid temporal decrease of these radionuclides. The kinetics of ^{137}Cs loss from mussels have been studied by different authors using two component system. Delfanti and Papucci (1988) reported biological half-lives of 2 and 60 days, after a monitoring over 2 months, when Whitehead *et al.* (1988) and Pruchon and Charmasson (1992) found biological half-lives of 14 and 300-380 days, after a monitoring over a longer period. These values confirm that ^{137}Cs concentration bordering the pre-Chernobyl levels were observed by the end of 1989. A decrease in concentrations is also observed in the organisms collected in the Gulf of Lions, that corresponds to the Marcoule plant decreasing discharges since 1991 (Charmasson *et al.*, 1994). The concentration factors observed in fishes (*i.e.* 100) is almost systematically higher than in mussel (30). Unfortunately there is a lack of data regarding the southern part of the Mediterranean Sea. However, Romero (1994) reported values in fish of 0.59 ± 0.14 ($n = 3$) Bq kg[-1] w.w. for the Algerian basin in 1990 and 0.17 ± 0.03 ($n = 4$) for the Alboran in 1993, which are in the same range than in the other basins.

Except for some values, Table 8.II. shows an increase in ^{137}Cs concentrations, both in fishes and in mussels, in the years following the Chernobyl accident, compared to the pre-Chernobyl period. Despite the high variability expecially, for fish data, even from the same basin, we can consider that levels similar to the pre-Chernobyl period are encountered by the years 1989-1990.

8.7. Summary

More than 90% of ^{137}Cs deposited onto the surface of the Mediterranean Sea is still present in the water column, while the remaining 10% is deposited in the upper layers of the sediments. Present concentrations in surface waters are about 1/3 of those measured 20 years ago, while an increase of about 30% is observed in the mediterranean deep waters. The present inventory in the water column has been estimated to be 13.6 PBq. The actual inputs to the Mediterranean Sea are lower than decreases due to physical decay, indicating that future trends are toward a general lowering of the ^{137}Cs inventory in the Mediterranean water column.

Plutonium inventory is also going to decrease in the water column, due both to the outflow at Gibraltar and to vertical transport by association with particulate matter and incorporation into the sediment. The sites of preferential scavenging are the continental shelves and the submarine canyon systems, where plutonium (and caesium) inventories in sediment are often as high or higher than their cumulative fallout deposition. In contrast, inventories in sediments of open-sea areas are as low as few percent (*i.e.* 5%) of the deposition, in relation to the low particle population and low productivity regimes that characterize the Mediterranean Sea.

Radionuclide levels in the living organisms obviously reflect the low concentrations in seawater. The enhanced levels observed in biota after Chernobyl, are now reduced to the pre-accident concentrations, except in few areas that are still receiving radionuclide inputs either from rivers (Adriatic Sea) or from contaminated basins (Aegean Sea-Black Sea).

References

Antón M.P., Gascó C., Sánchez-Cabeza J.A. and Pujol Ll. (1994) Geochemical association of Plutonium in marine sediments from Palomares (Spain). *Radiochim. Acta* **66/67**, 443-446.

Antón M.P., Gascó C. and Pozuelo M. (1995) Chemical partitioning of plutonium and americium in sediments from the Palomares marine ecosystem. *Rapp. Comm. Int. Mer Medit.* **34**, 223.

Arnaud M., Charmasson S., Delfanti R. and Papucci C. (1995) Caesium inventories in sediment cores in areas under the influence of the Po river (Italy) and the Rhône river (France). *Rapp. Comm. int. Mer Medit.* **34**, 223.

Béthoux J.P. (1979) Budgets of the Mediterranean Sea: their dependence on the local climate and on the characteristics of the Atlantic Waters. *Oceanol. Acta* **2**, 157-163.

Bryden H.L., Candela J. and Kinder T.H. (1994) Exchange through the Strait of Gibraltar. *Prog. Oceanog.* **33**, 201-248.

Bunzl K. and Kracke W. (1988) Cumulative deposition of ^{137}Cs, ^{238}Pu, $^{239+249}$Pu and ^{241}Am from the global fallout in soils from forest, grassland and arable land in Bavaria (FRG). *J. Environ. Radioactivity* **8**, 1-14.

Calmet D., Charmasson S., Gontier G. and Daburon M.-L. (1988) The impact of Chernobyl fallout on Mytilus sp. collected from the French coast. In: IVth International symposium of Radioecology: Impact of nuclear accident on the environment, Cadarache, 14-18 March, C18-C31.

Calmet D., Charmasson S., Fernandez J.-M. and Gontier G. (1992) The impact of the fallout of the Chernobyl accident on the distribution of anthropogenic radionuclides of the northwest Mediterranean basin (seawater, marine sediments and marine organisms 1985-1988). 89 p. In: Report CEA-R-5584, CEN-Saclay, France.

Charmasson S., Arnaud M., Piermattei S. and Romero L. (1994) Sources of radioactivity in the Mediterranean Sea. Report of working group I. In: *The radiological exposure of the population of the European Community to radioactivity in the Mediterranean Sea*. Marina-Med Project (Cigna *et al.*, Eds.) pp. 11-70. Radiation Protection 70, EUR 15564 EN.

Delfanti R. and Papucci C. (1988) Characteristics of Chernobyl fallout in the Italian coastal marine environment. *Rapp. Comm. int. Mer Medit.* **31**, 311.

Delfanti R. and Papucci C. (1995) Inventories of 239,240Pu in slope and deep-sea sediments from the Ionian Sea and the Algerian Basin. *Rapp. Comm. int. Mer Medit.* **34**, 225.

Delfanti R., Papucci C., Salvi S., Vives i Batlle J., Downes A. and Mitchell P.I. (1994) Distribution of Cs-137 and transuranic elements in seawater of the Western Mediterranean Sea (Algerian Basin, Balearic Sea). In: *Proc. Marina-Med Seminar on the Radiological Exposure of the Population of the European Community from Radioactivity in the Mediterranean Sea* (Cigna *et al.*, Eds.) pp. 427-439. Rome, 17-19 May 1994, EUR-Report 15564 EN.

Delfanti R., Papucci C., Alboni M., Lorenzelli R. and Salvi S. (1995) ^{137}Cs inventories in the water column and in sediments of the western Mediterranean Sea. *Rapp. Comm. int. Mer Medit.* **34**, 226.

Egorov V.N., Polikarpov G.G., Stokozov N.A., Kulebakina L.G. and Lazorenko G.E. (1994) Distribution of artificial radionuclides in water, bottom sediments and hydrobionts of the Black Sea following the Chernobyl NPP accident and assessment of ^{137}Cs input to the seas of the Mediterranean basin through the Bosporus. In: *The radiological exposure of population of the European Community to radioactivity in the Mediterranean Sea*. Marina Med Project (Cigna *et al.*, Eds.) pp. 363-392. Report EUR-15564-EN, 1994.

Florou H., Kritidis P., Synetos S. and Chaloulou Ch. (1987) Aspects radioecologiques par les polluants radioactifs en milieu marin. In: *Congr. Intern. Radiat.* Prot. assoc., Rome, Italy, 12-13 October 1987.

Florou H., Kritidis P. and Probonas M. (1990) ^{137}Cs in marine organisms - Ten year studies in the Greek marine environment. *Rapp. Comm. int. Mer Medit.* **32**, 293.

Fowler S.W., Ballestra S. and Villeneuve J.P. (1990) Flux of transuranium nuclides and chlorinated hydrocarbons in the northwestern Mediterranean. *Continental Shelf Research* **10**, 1005-1023.

Franic Z. and Bauman A. (1993) Radioactive contamination of the Adriatic Sea by ^{90}Sr and [137]Cs. *Health Physics* **64**, 162-169.

Fukai R., Ballestra S. and Vas D. (1980) Distribution of caesium-137 in the Mediterranean Sea. In: *Managment of Environment*. Wiley Eastern Ltd., pp. 353-360. New Delhi, Bangalore, Bombay, Calcutta.

Gascó C., Antón M.P. and Romero L. (1994) Radioecologia de transuránidos en el Mediterraneo Español. *Radioprotección* **1**, 21-29.

Goldberg E.D., Bowen V.T., Farrington J.W., Harvey G., Martin J.H., Parker P.L., Risebrough R.W., Robertson W., Schneider E. and Gamble E. (1987) The mussel watch. *Environmental Conservation* **5**, 101-126; *Mar. poll. Bull* **6**, 101-126.

Holm E., Ballestra S., Fukai R., Beasley T.M. (1980) Particulate plutonium and americium in the Mediterranean surface waters. *Oceanol. Acta* **3**, 157-160.

Holm E., Fukai R. and Whitehead N.E. (1988) Radiocesium and transuranium elements in the Mediterranean Sea: sources, inventories and environmental levels. In: *International Conference on environmental radioactivity in the Mediterranean Area*. pp. 601-617. SNE. Barcelona.

IAEA (1991) Biennial Report 1989-91, International Atomic Energy Agency, Monaco, 79 pp.

Iranzo E. (1987) Air concentrations of [239+240]Pu and potencial radiation doses to persons living near Pu-contaminated areas in Palomares, Spain. *Health Physics* **52**, 453.

Kautsky H. (1977) Die vertikalverteilung radioaktiver falloutprodukte im westlichen mittelmeer in den Jahren 1970 und 1974. *Deutsch. Hydrol. Zeitsch.* **30**, 175-184.

Kritidis P. and Florou H. (1990) Estimation of the ^{137}Cs deposited in Aegen Cretian and Ionian Seas after the Chernobyl accident. *Rapp. Comm. int. Mer Medit.* **32**, 318.

Malanotte-Rizzoli P. and Bergamasco A. (1991) The wind and thermally driven circulation of the Eastern Mediterranean Sea. *Dynamics of Atmospheres and Oceans* **15**, 355-420.

MARINA MED Project (1994) The radiological exposure of population of the European Community to radioactivity in the Mediterranean Sea (Cigna *et al.*, Eds.) 662 pp. Report EUR-15564-EN.

Merino Pareja J. (1993) Especiación Físico-Química del Plutonio en Aguas del Mar Mediterráneo. MSc. Thesis, Universitat Autònoma de Barcelona, 106 pp.

Mitchell P.I., León Vintró L., Condren O.M., Papucci C. and Delfanti R. (in preparation). Time-trend evolution of transuranium nuclides in the western Mediterranean: mechanisms geverning the transport and fate plutonium and americium in the western Basin and the Strait of Gibraltar.

Mitchell P.I., Vives-Batlle J., Ryan T.P, Schell W.R., Sánchez-Cabeza J.A. and Vidal-Quadras A. (1991) Studies on the speciation of Plutonium and Americium in the Western Irish Sea. In: *Radionuclides in the study of Marine Processes* (Kershaw *et al.*, Eds.) pp. 37-51. Elsevier Applied Science, London.

Mitchell P.I., Vives i Batlle J., Downes A.B., Condren O.M., León Vintró L., Sánchez-Cabeza J.A. (1995) Recent observations on the physico-chemical speciation of plutonium in the Irish Sea and the western Mediterranean. *J. Appl. Rad. Isot.* **46**, 1175-1190.

Molero J., Sánchez-Cabeza J.A., Merino J., Vives i Batlle J., Mitchell P.I. and Vidal-Quadras A. (1995a) Particulate distribution of Plutonium and Americium in surface waters from the Spanish Mediterranean coast. *J. Environ. Radioactivity* **28**, 271-283.

Molero J., Sánchez-Cabeza J.A., Merino J., Pujol Ll., Mitchell P.I. and Vidal-Quadras A. (1995b) Vertical distribution of Radiocesium, Plutonium and Americium in the Catalan Sea (Northwestern Mediterranean). *J. Environ. Radioactivity* **26**, 205-216.

Ovchinnikov I.M. (1966) Circulation in the surface and intermediate layers of the Mediterranean. *Oceanol.* **6**, 48-59.

Price J.F., O'Neil-Baringer M., Lueck R.G., Johnson G.C., Ambar I., Parrilla G., Cantos A., Kennelly M.A. and Sanford T.B. (1993) Mediterranean outflow mixing and dynamics. *Science* **259**, 1277-1282.

Pruchon A.S. and Charmasson S. (1992) Étude de l'élimination de [134]-Cs et [137]-Cs provenant des retombées de l'accident de Tchernobyl chez *Mytilus sp.* prélevées à Nice. *Rapp. Comm. int. Mer Medit.* **33**, 277.

Roether W., Manca B.B., Klein B., Bregant D., Georgopoulos D., Beitzel V., Kovacevic V. and Luchetta A. (1996) Recent changes in eastern Mediterranean deep waters. *Science*, **271**, 333-335.

Romero L. (1991) Estudio del transporte tierra-mar de elementos transuránidos. Aplicatión al accidente de Palomares (Almería) de 1996. Colección de la Universidad Complutense de Madrid. Ph. D. Dissertation, 300 pp.

Romero L. (1994) ^{137}Cs and [210]Po measurements in the Mediterranean Sea along the coast of Spain. Annex 2.1 Report of Working Group 2. In: The radiological exposure of the population of the European Community to radioactivity in the Mediterranean Sea. Marine-Med Project (Cigna *et al.*, Eds.) pp. 91-98. Radiation Protection 70, EUR 15564 EN.

Thein M., Ballestra S., Yamato A. and Fukai R. (1980) Delivery of transuranic elements by rain to the Mediterranean Sea. *Cosmoch. Geoch. Acta* **44**, 1091-1097.

UNEP (1992) Assessment of the state of pollution of the Mediterranean Sea by radioactive substances. MAP Technical Reports Series No. 62, Athens, 60 pp.

UNSCEAR (1988) United Nations Scientific Committee on the effects of Atomic Radiation. *Report to the General Assembly.* 654 pp. United Nations, New York.

Wells M.L. and Goldberg E.D. (1991) Occurrence of small colloids in sea water. *Nature* **353**, 342.

Whitehead N.E., Ballestra S., Holm E. and Huynh-Ngoc L. (1988) Chernobyl radionuclides in shellfish. *J. environ. Radioactivity* **7**, 107-121.

Wüst G. (1961) On the vertical circulation of the Mediterranean Sea. *J. Geophys. Res.* **66**, 3261-3271.

9 Natural and Man-Made Radionuclides in the Black Sea

K.O. Buesseler and H.D. Livingston

A review is presented of current knowledge on natural and artificial radioactivity in the Black Sea. The unique features of this partially closed basin – an upper layer which is freshened by input from rivers overlying a major anoxic deep water mass – are shown to affect the levels and distributions of many radionuclides. Artificial radionuclides from atmospheric nuclear weapons tests and from the Chernobyl accident are major man-made sources. Both natural and artificial radionuclides are discussed in the context of their geochemical properties, *i.e.* as water or particle tracers. In particular the rapid transfer of uranium and plutonium to Black Sea sediments contrasts strongly with the behavior of these elements in most of the world ocean. The time-series evolution of both the bomb testing and Chernobyl-derived soluble tracers in the upper 500 m of the Black Sea are discussed in the context of upper water circulation and deep mixing. Finally, the radioecological situation in the Black Sea is contrasted with other ocean basins, and the very large dominance of natural radionuclides in terms of human radiation exposure is noted.

9.1. Introduction

As with any oceanic basin, a wide variety of natural and man-made radionuclides can be detected in the waters, sediments and biota of the Black Sea. In contrast to other oceanic settings however, the Black Sea is unusual in that it is the world's largest anoxic basin. As such, it has been extensively studied due to the unique geochemical processes that occur across the oxic/anoxic interface and in the sulfidic deep waters. Due to the stability of these anoxic conditions, the Black Sea can also be used as an analog to ancient anoxic seas. Anoxia is established due to restricted mixing between the brackish surface layers (salinities ≤ 18 ppt in upper 100-150 m) and the deeper waters (≈ 22 ppt, max. depth = 2200 m). Riverine fluxes are dominated by inflow from the Danube and the rivers along the N boundary, and outflow is restricted to the narrow and shallow Bosphorus Straits in the

SW Black Sea. Mediterranean waters flow into the Black Sea as an undercurrent in the Bosphorus Straits. The general cyclonic circulation pattern leads to a doming of the isopycnal surfaces in the central basin, and a deepening of the depth of sulfide onset along the margins. The Black Sea is an ideal setting for mass balance studies since characterization of the inflows and outflows can be made. Radionuclides can be valuable tracers of both natural and anthropogenic processes in this basin, given their known sources and behavior.

For radiochemists, the low redox conditions in the Black Sea provide an interesting site to study redox transformations of radionuclides with multiple oxidation states. In addition, soluble tracers, such as ^{137}Cs, ^{90}Sr and ^3H introduced from weapons testing and the Chernobyl accident to Black Sea surface waters, can be used to estimate physical exchange rates between the surface and deeper layers. Finally, radionuclides can be used to date the deposition record that has been well preserved in the deep sediments. In this paper we will provide an overview of the sources and behavior of radionuclides in the Black Sea. An emphasis will be placed on those radionuclides whose behavior in the Black Sea contrasts most sharply with other oceanic settings, either due to the low salinities or changing redox environment which is characteristic of this basin.

9.2. Input of Radioisotopes to the Black Sea

The input of radioactivity to the Black Sea from natural and artificial sources is derived from atmospheric fallout and inflow of water from both rivers and Mediterranean inflow through the Bosphorus. However, the unique oceanographic characteristics of the Black Sea affect the behavior and relative activities of these radionuclides making their distributions very different from other seas and the open ocean.

9.2.1. Naturally Occurring Radionuclides

Perhaps the most important observation on Black Sea natural radioactivity derives from the effects of the huge freshwater inflow and relatively small saline inflow of water from the Mediterranean. As most Black Sea salinities lie in the range 18-22 ppt, the average salinity is almost one half that of the open ocean. Accordingly, the concentrations of many the naturally occurring radionuclides in seawater, ^{40}K, ^{87}Rb, ^{235}U, ^{238}U, etc., are correspondingly lower in proportion to open ocean levels. On the other hand, atmospheric input of natural radionuclides should not differ significantly from their input to the open ocean at the same latitude.

9.2.2. Atmospheric Nuclear Weapons Testing

Direct input of artificial radioisotopes from fallout of the products of the atmospheric nuclear weapons tests, in the 50's and 60's especially, would have had the same time history and deposition rate as found at other locations of similar latitude. As the 45° N latitude band of maximum fallout runs across the Black Sea, it must have received high levels of global fallout. By the end of 1985, fallout deposition at this latitude has been shown (Juzdan, 1988) to be 1.84 GBq km^{-2} for ^{90}Sr (which would be equivalent to 2.77 GBq km^{-2} for ^{137}Cs) and, from soil inventories (Hardy *et al.*, 1973), 81.4 MBq km^{-2} for ^{239,240}Pu. According to Eremeev *et al.* (1993), average Black Sea surface ^{137}Cs activities in 1977 were about 17 Bq m^{-3}. Buesseler *et al.* (1991a) estimated the pre-Chernobyl level of ^{137}Cs in Black Sea surface water in 1986 to be 9 Bq m^{-3}. In a later paper, Buesseler and Livingston (1996) made a more accurate estimate using a salinity normalization technique and put the pre-Chernobyl ^{137}Cs at 18 ppt (a typical salinity in the mixed layer) to be about 14 Bq m^{-3}. From a few near surface ^{90}Sr measurement in ^{134}Cs free water, the corresponding pre-Chernobyl ^{90}Sr in surface water at 18 ppt would be about 18 Bq m^{-3}. From data on samples collected in 1988, Buesseler and Livingston (1996) estimate corresponding pre-Chernobyl ^{137}Cs and ^{90}Sr levels to be 14.8 and 19.0 Bq m^{-3} respectively. Surface levels of ^{137}Cs and ^{90}Sr in 1976 for open western Black Sea water reported by Eremeev *et al.* (1993) are in reasonable agreement, at 16.7 and 20.1 Bq m^{-3} respectively.

9.2.3. Chernobyl

The Black Sea received substantial amounts of fallout from the April 1986 Chernobyl accident. In fact, the levels of ^{137}Cs there are second only to the Baltic Sea in terms of marine areas affected by this source. In addition to the Cs isotopes, short lived reactive species such as ^{144}Ce and ^{106}Ru have been observed. The initial deposition pattern was quite patchy (Eremeev *et al.*, 1993; Vakvlovsky *et al.*, 1994) but subsequent mixing and circulation has both spread out and reduced this initial surface concentration pattern. Vakulovsky *et al.* (1994) report average levels of ^{137}Cs in surface waters declining from 159 Bq m^{-3} in summer 1986 to 26 Bq m^{-3} in 1991. Since they did not report their sampling positions nor actual data, it is impossible to know what this average means. Our data track higher than this, with average surface values in the open northwestern Black Sea in 1990 and 1992 of 64 and 52 Bq m^{-3} respectively (Buesseler *et al.*, 1991a; Buesseler and Livingston, 1996).

9.2.4. Rivers vs. Atmospheric Sources

The massive freshwater inflow to the Black Sea, primarily in the northwest, greatly modifies the initial composition of Black Sea artificial radionuclides derived from both global weapons fallout and from Chernobyl. Soluble radionuclides, especially ^{90}Sr and tritium, are preferentially transported in rivers to the Black Sea in higher concentrations than exist in the open Black Sea by direct fallout from these sources. Prior to the Chernobyl input, when the only source was global fallout, the freshwater input from the various large rivers reduced the ratio of ^{137}Cs to ^{90}Sr in the affected surface waters from the fallout ratio of about 1.5 to values of 1 or less. The reduction was inversely proportional to salinity, of course. Following the Chernobyl accident, the same process took place, but the influence of a ^{90}Sr rich signal from the Dnepr river, in particular, controlled the low salinity water ratios. A large amount of ^{90}Sr from intensely contaminated areas around the Chernobyl plant leads to the particularly high levels in the Dnepr, compared to other large rivers like the Danube (Polikarpov *et al.*, 1992). So, in recent years, Black Sea waters exhibit a range of ^{137}Cs to ^{90}Sr ratios. These range from high values in open Black Sea surface waters – up to 4-5 soon after the ^{137}Cs rich input arrived (Buesseler *et al.*, 1991a) – to values less than one in the low salinity waters fed by the Dnepr (Polikarpov *et al.*, 1991). Deep water values still show the fallout ratio closer to 1.5 derived from the effects of local fallout and inflowing Mediterranean water through the Bosphorus. In addition, the Chernobyl Cs isotope input was readily characterized by the presence of ^{134}Cs with a ^{134}Cs to ^{137}Cs ratio of 0.53 (Buesseler *et al.*, 1991a). Use of this ratio allowed the determination of the fraction of the observed ^{137}Cs levels in Black Sea waters which came from fresh Chernobyl input or from the older global fallout source (Buesseler *et al.*, 1991a; Buesseler and Livingston, 1996).

9.3. Geochemical Behavior
of Radionuclides in the Black Sea

As discussed in the previous section, the Black Sea contains both naturally occurring and man-made radionuclides in measurable quantities. As summarized by Chesselet and Lalou (1988) at the first Cherbourg meeting (1-5 June, 1987), these radionuclides can broadly be broken down into the « swimming or diving » radionuclides. One radionuclide may fit both categories depending upon the time scales one is interested in and the geochemical setting. For example, ^{7}Be is a rather soluble tracer in off shore waters and the open ocean (*i.e.* a « swimmer »), but is quite rapidly scavenged in nearshore settings (a « diver »). The Black Sea is unusual as well in that a single radionuclide may have widely differing geochemical properties depending upon whether one is interested in the surface oxic or deep anoxic waters. This is particularly important for elements with more than one redox state, such as U and Pu (see below).

9.3.1. Soluble Radionuclides

As in other ocean basins, the main anthropogenic radionuclides that have been used as water circulation tracers are ^{3}H, ^{14}C, ^{90}Sr and ^{137}Cs. In addition ^{134}Cs from Chernobyl has been studied.

9.3.2. Tritium

Although tritium has been widely used in ocean tracer studies, there have been relatively few Black Sea tritium studies reported in the Western literature. Early measurements in 1965 and 1975 were reported by Ostlund (1974) and Top and Clark (1983). Russian studies were summarized by Eremeev et al. (1993). All these sets of data point to some analytical problems. Both Ostlund (1974) and Top and Clark (1983) reported occasional non-zero tritium concentrations in deep waters. But much higher deep water values were reported in papers cited by Eremeev et al. (1993), eg. Vakulovsky et al. (1982). Newer data reported by Top et al. (1991) do not include any more high values. Neither in their data, the chlorofluorocarbon data reported by Bullister and Lee (1995), nor in deep ^{90}Sr measurements shown in this paper by Buesseler and Livingston (1996), is there any evidence of measurable signals below about 500 meters. The data shown in Figure 9.1. from Top et al. (1991) are likely to be the best Black Sea tritium depth distributions available at the present time. It can be seen that the tritium distribution is relatively similar to ^{90}Sr in deep waters but shows relative enrichment in waters at depths above the 21.5 salinity isohaline (Fig. 9.1.). Both tritium and ^{90}Sr from bomb fallout have entered the Black Sea from direct deposition and riverine input. However, additional input is possible for tritium alone through recycled tritium caught up in the hydrological cycle (evaporation and precipitation). In the ocean this has been recognized as a factor producing additional delayed tritium deposition relative to ^{90}Sr (Livingston et al., 1985). This may be the most likely explanation for the Black Sea upper water tritium enrichment.

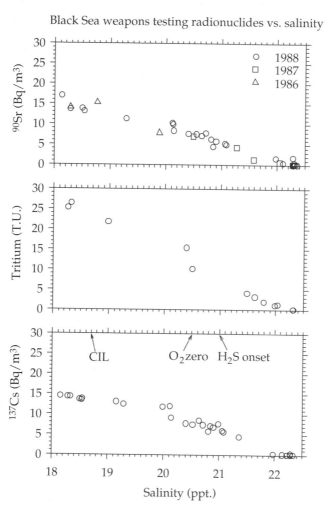

Fig. 9.1. Profiles of ^{90}Sr, ^{3}H and ^{137}Cs against salinity – Black Sea 1986-1988. Total ^{90}Sr data corrected for Chernobyl ^{90}Sr by subtracting Chernobyl ^{137}Cs multiplied by 8.6 (maximum 1986 surface value). Correction usually < 10%. Total ^{137}Cs corrected for Chernobyl ^{137}Cs (calculated by dividing the measured ^{137}Cs by the ^{134}Cs/^{137}Cs of 0.53). Approximate depths of the Cold Intermediate Layer (CIL), O_2 zero, H_2S onset and maximum depth of tracer penetration are around 40-70, 80-170, 100-250 and 500 meters, respectively.

9.3.3.   Carbon-14

Carbon-14, produced by both natural processes in the atmosphere and in nuclear weapons fallout, has been used in the oceans in gas exchange, tracer and water mass dating studies. Results summarized by Eremeev *et al.* (1993) suggest that the Black Sea to sea to air flux of CO_2 is in the range 22-44 Mtons of CO_2 per year. Radiocarbon ages reported by Ostlund (1974) for Black Sea deep water suggest the bottom waters are 2000 ± 200 years old.

9.3.4.   Pre- and Post-Chernobyl Evolution of Black Sea Depth Distributions of ^{90}Sr and Cs-Isotopes

Pre-Chernobyl profiles of ^{137}Cs and ^{90}Sr in the Black Sea have been recon-structed (Fig. 9.1.) using techniques mentioned earlier (Buesseler *et al.*, 1991a; Buesseler and Livingston, 1996). Basically, these profiles represent the evolution of mixing on the bomb fallout signal deposited on the Black Sea surface, plus the continued freshwater input of ^{90}Sr in river water. The influence of the freshwater input can be seen through comparison of the ratios ^{137}Cs/^{90}Sr. They average 0.94 (range from 0.78 to 1.15, n =10) in near surface water (salinity 18.3 – 21 ppt) to ratios averaging 1.38 ± 0.15 in deep water (salinity > 21 ppt) – which is indistinguishable from the fallout input ratio of 1.5 – the lower ratios being a function of decreasing salinity in the near surface waters.

Buesseler and Livingston (1996) describe a set of time-series measure-ments of Chernobyl ^{137}Cs profiles in the western Black Sea. Presented nor-malized to salinity, they show the rapid mixing of the Chernobyl signal in the surface mixed layer, the Cold Intermediate Layer (CIL) and across the strong pycnocline into the upper anoxic water zone. Figure 9.2. shows the temporal evolution of total ^{137}Cs (from both Chernobyl and weapons testing sources) from 1987 to 1992 and one can see the contrast with the weapons testing profile estimated for 1986 (Fig. 9.1.). Presumably the gradient of the Chernobyl profile will approach that of the weapons testing profile after two decades of mixing.

9.3.5.   Riverine Input of Chernobyl ^{90}Sr to NW Black Sea Shelf Waters

The large influx of ^{90}Sr in the Dnepr River from Chernobyl, mentioned ear-lier, has been noted in time-series measurements made at the mouth of the river (Polikarpov *et al.*, 1992). Concentrations of ^{90}Sr in river water rose from pre-Chernobyl levels of around 10 Bq m^{-3} to a maximum of about 700 Bq m^{-3} in spring 1987. The pattern of concentrations showed maxima each spring and minima each winter. The annual input to the Black Sea declined from a maximum of 14.7 TBq in 1987 to 9.9 TBq in 1989. The unique source of ^{90}Sr represented by the Dnepr river was recognized through comparison of the concentrations and fluxes of ^{90}Sr between the Danube and Dnepr. Dnepr concentrations in 1988 were 1-2 orders of magnitude higher than found in the Danube, whereas Danube fluxes were 15% of those of the Dnepr. The magnitude of the Dnepr concentrations and fluxes, while not of radioecological significance, constitute an unique and substantial tracer of the circulation of this freshwater source in the western Black Sea basin.

The first indication that the Dnepr ^{90}Sr input to the northwest Black Sea could be detected away from the river mouth was reported by Polikarpov *et al.* (1991). They presented data for the western Black Sea and Aegean Sea on surface concentrations of Cs and Sr radionuclides in 1988. Sr-90 concentrations in the northwest Black Sea were in general twice as high as those in the central part. They noted that this was a consequence of the very high ^{90}Sr concentrations observed in the Dnepr river and estuary. In similar fashion, ratios ^{137}Cs/^{90}Sr were 2-3 times lower in the northwest relative to central regions.

A further refinement of these observations and the implications for water mass tracing has been described by Buesseler and Livingston (1996). Measurements at both shelf regions near the Danube and Dnepr inflow and in offshelf stations in the northwest Black Sea in 1990 were reported. The relationship of the river ^{90}Sr signal to the observed concentrations and ratios was examined by plotting the observed concentrations or ratios against salinity. When ^{137}Cs/^{90}Sr ratios were plotted against salinity, three distinct mixing process were revealed.
- Mixing of the high ^{90}Sr low salinity Dnepr river/estuary end member with Black Sea coastal water.
- Off shelf intrusions of this river derived high ^{90}Sr signal into sub-surface waters.
- Mixing of the high ratio (3-4) open Black Sea water with deeper water of bomb fallout origin and ratio (1.4).

Some of the same influence of the rivers on ^{137}Cs can be seen in 1990 and 1992 – shown here in Figure 9.2. at salinities < 18 ppt. Further work underway by Stokosov and Buesseler (1996), shows that it is possible to estimate the contributions of Danube, Dnepr and surface Black Sea water in this region using data such as these.

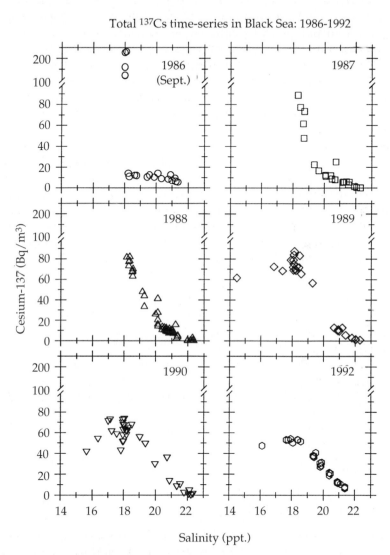

Fig. 9.2. Time-series of total ^{137}Cs for the Black Sea from 1986 (post-Chernobyl) through 1992. All data taken from this laboratory.

9.4. Particle-Reactive Radionuclides

In this section we focus on the behavior of the more particle-reactive isotopes with an emphasis on those radionuclides with a geochemistry that is
strongly influenced by the unique low redox setting of the deep Black Sea.
For the artificial radionuclides, this group includes the long-lived Pu isotopes, derived from both weapon's testing and Chernobyl fallout, as well as
short-lived particle-reactive radionuclides such as ^{144}Ce, ^{141}Ce, ^{106}Ru, and
^{103}Ru studied most recently after the Chernobyl accident. For the natural
radionuclides, U-series isotopes and their decay products (Th, Ra, and Pb
isotopes) have also been used to study scavenging process in this basin.

Shortly after the early atmospheric weapons tests, Osterberg *et al.* (1963)
detected short-lived fallout ^{141}Ce, ^{144}Ce and ^{95}Zr in deep Pacific sea-
cucumbers. This finding led them to conclude that at least some fraction of
fallout radionuclides were rapidly transported to the deep ocean, at rates far
exceeding simple Stokes settling velocities. Immediately following the
Chernobyl accident, sediment trap studies in the Black Sea were used to
quantify these same sinking particle fluxes. These studies suggested that the
residence times with respect to removal on sinking particles were on the
order of 60, 70, and > 300 years for ^{106}Ru, ^{144}Ce and ^{137}Cs, respectively
(Buesseler *et al.*, 1987; 1990). In confirmation of these rapid removal rates, one
could detect a decrease in the relative ratio of ^{106}Ru and ^{144}Ce to ^{137}Cs in
Black Sea surface waters (Livingston *et al.*, 1988). Such studies provide con-
venient time-scales of particle-removal and scavenging processes that can be
used to model pollutant transport and sedimentation fluxes in general.

The cycling of redox sensitive elements across the shallow oxic/anoxic
interface can strongly influence the residence time of a given radionuclide.
This contrasts sharply to other marine basins, where most of the water column is oxygenated, and anoxic conditions are restricted to sediment pore
waters and deeper layers after burial. Redox cycling can have an impact on
those elements with their own redox sensitive geochemistries, such as Mn,
Fe (Spencer *et al.* 1972; Lewis and Landing, 1991), and those radionuclides
such as U, Pu whereby redox transformations produce a more or less soluble species. In addition, co-precipitation reactions that accompany the
cycling of Mn and Fe across redox boundaries can influence the removal of
radionuclides such as ^{106}Ru and ^{234}Th (Buesseler *et al.*, 1991b) as well as stable elements such as phosphorus (Shaffer, 1986 ; Buesseler *et al.*, 1994).

The cycling of U, in the Black Sea is thought to involve both oxidized
and reduced forms. In oxidized seawater, U is thought to exist as a soluble
uranyl carbonate species in the U(VI) oxidation state, and under these conditions, U is known to be conservatively distributed as a function of salinity
(Ku *et al.*, 1977). Under reducing conditions such as exist in the sulfidic deep
water of the Black Sea, U(IV) may predominate, and this form is much more
particle-reactive in seawater. Studies by Anderson *et al.* (1989) suggest that
U exists in an unstable U(VI) form in the deep Black Sea, with a relatively

short residence time for removal (200 years). In fact, a sharp break in the ^{238}U-salinity relationship is observed in the Black Sea at a salinity around 21.6 ppt, or at depths of elevated sulfide concentration (Wei and Murray, 1991). In these deep sulfidic waters, ^{238}U is 30-60% lower than one would find at a similar salinity in oxic marine basins. Sediment and pore water U were measured in the Black Sea by Barnes and Cochran (1991) in a study of U geochemistry. They used the depletion in pore water U with depth to calculate the diffusional flux of U into the deep sediments. This flux agreed within uncertainties with U removal determined from measurements of solid phase authigenic U accumulation. All of the evidence thus points to removal of U in the deep Black Sea, similar to that which has been observed in other anoxic inlets and fjords (Todd et al., 1988). These data suggest that while the sediments underlying anoxic regions of the worlds oceans represent only a small fraction of the total area (0.4%), they can account for 20% of the oceanic U balance (Barnes and Cochran, 1991).

The aquatic chemistry of Pu in the Black Sea can be expected to be quite complex, due to the four possible oxidation states of Pu in natural waters (III, IV, V, VI) and the widely differing chemical properties expected for each form. In general, there is a clear relationship between the oxidation state of Pu and its affinity for particle surfaces, with the more reduced Pu species having a much higher particle reactivity than the more oxidized forms. In the Black Sea, one would expect therefore that the more reduced and highly particle reactive forms would dominate in the deep anoxic waters. This is indeed what Sanchez et al. (1991) found in two Pu oxidation state profiles collected in 1988. They determined that about 70% of the Pu was in the reduced oxidation states (III/IV) in the surface waters (total ^{239,240}Pu = 6-8 μBq l^{-1}). Subsurface waters from the upper 100 m were dominated by oxidized forms (V/VI). Below the oxic/anoxic interface (approx. 150 m at the stations sampled) they found low activities of reduced Pu, but could not detect any oxidized Pu above errors (<1-2 μBq l^{-1}). The total watercolumn inventory of Pu is 7-9 Bq m^{-2}, or only approx. 10% of the expected inventory of weapons testing fallout Pu in the 40-50° latitude band (Hardy et al., 1973). This is in sharp contrast to the Atlantic or Mediterranean Seas, where 90% or more of the Pu inventory is found in the water column (Fukai et al., 1987; Cochran et al., 1987). In the Atlantic, > 85% of the Pu is found in the oxidized form using these same techniques (Cochran et al., 1987). We can thus attribute the low watercolumn inventories in the Black Sea to the predominance of the reduced forms of Pu, and hence its faster rate of removal relative to other marine settings. Lower than expected watercolumn Pu implies a higher Pu sedimentary inventory, and this has now been confirmed in at least at one site (Buesseler and Benitez, 1994; and see below).

The Pu results presented by Sanchez et al. (1991) and those reported by Livingston et al. (1988) represent samples collected in the post-Chernobyl era, and one should ask the question to what extent the Chernobyl accident contributed transuranics, such as Pu, to the Black Sea. The presence of short lived ^{242}Cm (half-life = 163 days) in dissolved and particulate samples collected in June and September of 1986 from the Black Sea (Livingston *et al.*, 1988), suggests that Chernobyl transuranics were indeed deposited in this basin (Tab. 9.I.). A clear indication of Chernobyl Pu is seen in the measured ^{238}Pu/^{239,240}Pu activity ratios. Global fallout is characterized by a ^{238}Pu/^{239,240}Pu ratio near 0.04 (post SNAP 9A releases in 1964; Perkins and Thomas, 1980), while Chernobyl debris has an elevated ratio near 0.47 (Aarkrog, 1988). The measured surface ^{238}Pu/^{239,240}Pu ratios in 1986 were near 0.25, suggesting that approximately half of the Pu activity found in surface waters is from the more recent Chernobyl source. This Chernobyl Pu was not detectable in any of the subsurface waters however. In « Chernobyl free » waters collected from 110 m in September 1986 (« Chernobyl free » based upon the lack of Chernobyl ^{134}Cs, see previous discussion), the ^{238}Pu/^{239,240}Pu ratio appears to be similar to global fallout, as expected (Tab. 9.I.). ^{240}Pu/^{239}Pu atomic ratios determined by mass spectrometry corroborate these ^{238}Pu data quite well. The same 110 m sample is characterized by a ^{240}Pu/^{239}Pu atom ratio near 0.18, which is the isotopic signature measured world-wide from global fallout Pu (Krey *et al.*, 1976; Perkins and Thomas, 1980). As with ^{238}Pu, elevated ^{240}Pu/^{239}Pu ratios (> 0.30) are found in surface waters. Assuming a mixing ratio of 50:50 for Chernobyl and weapons testing Pu (from ^{238}Pu), and a weapons testing ^{240}Pu/^{239}Pu ratio of 0.18, this suggests an end-member Chernobyl ^{240}Pu/^{239}Pu atomic ratio around 0.42. This highly elevated ratio is expected due to the build-up of the

Table 9.I. Plutonium and Curium Data.

Location	Sampling Dates*	Depth	Type	^{239,240}Pu (µBq l^{-1})	^{238}Pu/^{239,240}Pu (activity ratio)	^{240}Pu/^{239}Pu (atom ratio)	^{242}Cm (µBq l^{-1})
offshore	June	surface	part	1.18 ± 0.13	0.25 ± 0.09	bd	22.50 ± 1.83
Black Sea			diss	15.67 ± 3.00	0.24 ± 0.04	0.22 ± 0.06	21.33 ± 2.50
	Sept.	surface	part	0.27 ± 0.07	bd	bd	5.75 ± 0.83
			diss	8.68 ± 0.92	0.26 ± 0.07	0.33 ± 0.05	20.67 ± 2.05
	Sept.	110 m	part	1.08 ± 0.35	bd	0.18 ± 0.04	bd
				8.78 ± 1.95	bd	0.15 ± 0.01	bd
nearshore	June	surface	part	0.60 ± 0.18	bd	0.19 ± 0.02	bd
Black Sea				6.08 ± 3.00	0.19 ± 0.05	0.32 ± 0.04	bd
	Sept.	surface	part	0.20 ± 0.12	bd	0.22 ± 0.04	0.90 ± 0.48
			diss	12.25 ± 1.35	0.23 ± 0.04	0.35 ± 0.04	33.40 ± 2.83
Atlantic	1978	surface	total	22.17 ± 4.50	0.04 ± 0.01	0.18 ± 0.01	bd
				Bq kg^{-1}			Bq kg^{-1}
Kefken Island	Sept.		total	0.40 ± 0.002	0.04 ± 0.01	0.17 ± 0.03	0.05 ± 0.02

bd = below detection   *All sampling dates were in 1986, unless otherwise noted.

higher masses of Pu in the core of the Chernobyl reactor. While most of the total Chernobyl releases were attributed to the loss of gases and volatiles during the accident, non-volatile components were also released. In fact, Chernobyl fallout in the Black Sea area is characterized by relatively high ^{106}Ru/^{137}Cs and ^{144}Ce/^{137}Cs ratios, compared to the Baltic Sea or more northerly sites (Livingston et al., 1988).

While Chernobyl Pu can thus account for up to 50% of the Pu in the shallowest samples, total Chernobyl Pu inventories would be quite small with respect to global fallout Pu, which has been preferentially removed to the deeper watercolumn and sediments. In 1987, one soil sample was collected from Kefken Island in the southern Black Sea, and both ^{238}Pu and ^{240}Pu/^{239}Pu data are indistinguishable from global fallout (compare soil to Atlantic surface waters – Tab. 9.I.). While just above detection, the measured ^{242}Cm activity in this soil sample is too low to indicate measurable Chernobyl Pu.

9.4.1. Sediment Records

It has been long known that the lack of mixing and the seasonal nature of particle deposition leads to the formation of light and dark layers in deep Black Sea sediments (Ross and Degens, 1974; Müller and Stoffers, 1974). The light layers are composed primarily of shells from the coccolithophorid E. Huxleyi, while the dark layers are enriched in lithogenic matter (Hay et al., 1990). The sediments represent a unique repository of the historical deposition records for a wide range of natural and man-made compounds. This is due to the complete lack of bioturbation effects, which in most other marine settings causes a partial or complete smearing of the input record over many cm depth, or over a time-scale of decades to > centuries. Resolution is thus limited only by sampling resolution (1-3 varves per mm) and sample size. Radionuclide data for ^{210}Pb and ^{14}C suggest that recognizable varves are not formed annually, hence sedimentation rates determined based upon varve counting may be overestimated (Buesseler and Benitez, 1994; Calvert et al., 1991; Crusius and Anderson, 1992; Jones and Gagnon, 1994). Using fine-scale sampling in a deep Black Sea core (6-8 samples per cm depth), the peak in fallout Pu from the 1960's can be identified, as well as double peaks for ^{137}Cs from both weapons testing and Chernobyl sources (Buesseler and Benitez, 1994).

Overall, it appears that long term mass accumulation rates in the deep Black Sea have increased from approximately 35 to 65 g m^{-2} yr^{-1} (14 to 26 cm/1000 yr at a porosity of 90%) sometime between the last millennium (dated by ^{14}C) and the last century (dated by ^{210}Pb) (Buesseler and Benitez, 1994). In the shelf and margin regions, accumulation rates are much higher, and ^{210}Pb profiles suggest rates of 0.1-1 cm yr^{-1} (Anderson and Fleisher, 1991). One additional advantage in studying chronologies in Black Sea sediments, is that from east to west across the entire deep Black Sea basin, one can visually identify strongly correlated varve couplet sequences (Ross *et al.*, 1970; Lyons, 1991). Thus from a single chronology at one site, it is possible to date major horizons in other cores over time scales of the past few thousand years, throughout the so-called Unit 1 sediments (*i.e.* past 1600-3200 years – Jones and Gagnon, 1994; Calvert *et al.*, 1991; Arthur *et al.*, 1994). In some cores, fine-grained turbidite layers interrupt this sequence, but they do not apparently erode the general layering or varve correlation between cores (Arthur *et al.*, 1994). The processes which trigger and deposit these turbidites layers are not well understood.

Sediment radionuclide inventories can used to examine the mass balance of a given radionuclide. In the central deep Black Sea, inventories of ^{210}Pb are in approximate balance with its source (from ^{226}Ra decay and removal in the watercolumn and atmospheric delivery- 50-100 dpm cm^{-2} Moore and O'Neill, 1991; Buesseler and Benitez, 1994). As stated above, for Pu, the low redox setting in the deep waters results in considerable enhancement of Pu removal. A sedimentary Pu inventory of 75 Bq m^{-2} was found in the central basin (Buesseler and Benitez, 1994). Together with the watercolumn inventory of 7-9 Bq m^{-2}, the total Pu inventory balances the expected weapons testing fallout at these latitudes (81 Bq m^{-2}) and one does not need to invoke any significant Chernobyl contribution to the total Pu balance for this basin.

9.5. Summary

9.5.1. *Comparisons with Other Basins*

The Black Sea has unique features compared to other ocean basins. It has a large freshwater inflow, a huge volume of anoxic deep water and has received significant fallout from the Chernobyl accident. As a result of the latter, a recent report (IAEA, 1995) shows that 1990 surface ^{137}Cs concentrations are only higher in the Baltic and Irish Sea when compared with other global ocean basins – see Table 9.II.

9.5.2. *Comparison of Human Radiation Doses from Black Sea Radionuclides*

The IAEA report (1995) mentioned above also provides a comparison between radiological doses to humans from natural as opposed to artificial radionuclides. This report was based on the conclusion that the highest dose to man from natural radionuclides in the ocean came from the consumption of ^{210}Po from seafood. The corresponding highest dose from artificial radionuclides came from the consumption of ^{137}Cs in seafood, especially fish. The appropriate doses were calculated for the major FAO (Food and Agricultural Organization of the UN) fishing areas for both these nuclides. The Black Sea was included as part of FAO region 37 – which includes the Mediterranean. Because of this, the Black Sea ^{137}Cs doses can be higher than the average for region 37 (the ^{137}Cs water levels were about 7 times higher). But the low fish catches in the Black Sea offset this and hence the estimated values of 6 man Sieverts (^{137}Cs) may not be low by more than a factor of 2 or so. It is hardly relevant compared to the estimated doses of 700 man Sieverts for ^{210}Po. Also, doses from either or both radionuclides are considerably higher in other ocean areas such as the North Pacific and North Atlantic.

Table 9.II. Typical Surface Concentrations of ^{137}Cs in Surface Ocean Waters in 1990.

Basin	Average ^{137}Cs Bq m^{-3}
Baltic	125
Irish Sea	55
Black Sea	52
North/Barents Sea	10 – 12
Arctic	7.6
Mediterranean	5.4
North Pacific	4.0
North Atlantic	2.9
Indian Ocean	2.9
South Pacific	1.6
South Atlantic	1.4
Antarctic	0.4

Acknowledgments

Our own studies and this review have benefited greatly from our collaboration with the very many colleagues we have found in the countries surrounding the Black Sea. In particular, we acknowledge and thank our colleagues at the Institute of Biology of the Southern Seas and the Marine Hydrophysical Institute, Sevastopol, Ukraine and the University of Izmir and Institute of Marine Sciences in Turkey. For our own fieldwork in the Black Sea, we acknowledge with thanks the expert technical assistance of J. Andrews, S. Casso, and M. Hartman. Support for these studies has been provided by the US National Science Foundation and the US Environmental Protection Agency. This is contribution number 9258 from the Woods Hole Oceanographic Institution.

References

Aarkrog A. (1988) The radiological impact of the Chernobyl debris compared with that from nuclear weapons fallout. *J. Environ. Radioact.* **6**, 151-162.

Anderson R.F. and Fleisher M.Q. (1991) Uranium precipitation in Black Sea sediments. In: *Black Sea Oceanography* (E. Izdar and J.W. Murray, Eds.) pp. 443-458. Kluwer Academic Publishers, Netherlands.

Anderson R.F., Fleisher M.Q. and LeHuray A.P. (1989) Concentration, oxidation state, and particulate flux of uranium in the Black Sea. *Geochim. Cosmochim. Acta* **53**, 2215-2224.

Arthur M.A., Dean W.E., Neff E.D., Hay B.J., King J. and Jones G. (1994) Varve calibrated records of carbonate and organic carbon accumulation over the last 2000 years in the Black Sea. *Global Biogeochem. Cycles* **8**, 195-217.

Barnes C.E. and Cochran J.K. (1991) Geochemistry of uranium in Black Sea sediments. *Deep Sea Res.* **38**, S1237-S1254.

Buesseler K.O. and Benitez C.R. (1994) Determination of mass accumulation rates and sediment radionuclide inventories in the deep Black Sea. *Deep Sea Res. I* **41**, 1605-1615.

Buesseler K.O. and Livingston H.D. (1996, in press) Time-series profiles of ^{134}Cs, ^{137}Cs and ^{90}Sr in the Black Sea. In: *Sensitivity of North Sea, Baltic Sea and Black Sea to Anthropogenic and Climatic Changes*. NATO Advanced Research Workshop, Varna, Bulgaria, 14-18 November 1995.

Buesseler K.O., Livingston H.D., and Casso S.A. (1991a) Mixing between oxic and anoxic waters of the Black Sea as traced by Chernobyl caesium isotopes. *Deep Sea Res.* **38**, S725-S745.

Buesseler K.O., Livingston H.D. and Casso S.A. (1991b) Ruthenium-106 in the Black Sea. In: *Black Sea Oceanography* (E. Izdar and J.W. Murray, Eds.) pp. 229-243. Kluwer Academic Publishers, Netherlands.

Buesseler K O., Livingston H.D., Honjo S., Hay B.J., Konuk T. and Kempe S. (1990) Scavenging and particle deposition in the southwestern Black Sea — Evidence from Chernobyl radiotracers. *Deep Sea Res.* **37**, 413-430.

Buesseler K.O., Livingston H.D., Honjo S., Hay B.J., Manganini S.J., Degens E.T., Ittekkot V., Izdar E. and Konuk T. (1987) Chernobyl radionuclides in the Black Sea sediment trap, *Nature* **329**, 825-828.

Buesseler K.O., Livingston H.D., Ivanov L. and Romanov A. (1994) Stability of the oxic-anoxic interface in the Black Sea. *Deep Sea Res. I* **41**, 283-296.

Bullister J.L. and Lee B.-S. (1995) Chlorofluorocarbon-11 removal in anoxic marine waters. *Geophys. Res. Lett.* **22**, 1893-1896.

Calvert S.E., Karlin R.E., Toolin L.J., Donahue D.J., Southon J.R. and Vogel J.S. (1991) Low organic carbon accumulation rates in Black Sea sediments. *Nature* **350**, 692-695.

Chesselet R. and Lalou C. (1988) The use of natural radionuclides in oceanography: An overview. In: *Radionuclides: A tool for oceanography*

(J.C. Guary, P. Guegueniat and R.J. Pentreath, Eds.) pp.1-11. Elsevier Applied Science, London.

Cochran J.K., Livingston H.D., Hirschberg D.J. and Surprenant L.D. (1987) Natural and anthropogenic radionuclide distributions in the northwest Atlantic Ocean. *Earth Planet. Sci. Lett.* **84**, 135-152.

Crusius J. and Anderson R.F. (1992) Inconsistencies in accumulation rates of Black Sea sediments inferred from records of laminae and ^{210}Pb. *Paleoceanography* **7**, 215-227.

Eremeev V.N., Chudinovskikh T.V. and Batrakov G.F. (1993) Artificial radioactivity of the Black Sea, UNESCO Reports in Marine Science 59, UNESCO/Chernobyl Project, France, 95 p.

Fukai R., Yamato A., Thein M. and Bilinski H. (1987) Oxidation states of fallout plutonium in Mediterranean rain and seawater. *Geochem. J.* **21**, 51-57.

Hardy E.P., Krey P.W. and Volchok H. (1973) Global inventory and distribution of fallout plutonium. *Nature* **241**, 444-445.

Hay B.J., Honjo S., Kempe S., Ittekkot V.A., Degens E.T., Konuk T. and Izdar E. (1990) Interannual variability in particle flux in the southwestern Black Sea. *Deep Sea Res.* **37**, 911-928.

IAEA (1995) Sources of radioactivity in the marine environment and their relative contributions to overall dose assessment from marine radioactivity (MAR DOS), IAEA-TECDOC-838, Vienna, Austria.

Jones G.A. and Gagnon A.R. (1994) Radiocarbon chronology of Black Sea sediments, *Deep Sea Res. I* **41**, 531-557.

Juzdan Z.R. (1988) Worldwide deposition of ^{90}Sr through 1985. Environmental Measurements Laboratory Report EML-515, Department of Energy, N.Y., USA.

Krey P.W., Hardy E.P., Pachucki C., Rourke F., Coluzza J. and Benson W.K. (1976) Mass isotopic composition of global fall-out plutonium in soil. In: *Transuranium Nuclides in the Environment*, IAEA-SM-199/39 (IAEA, Vienna) pp. 671-678.

Ku T.L., Knauss K.G. and Mathiew G.G. (1977) Uranium in the open ocean, concentration and isotopic composition. *Deep Sea Res.* **24**, 1005-1917.

Lewis B.L. and Landing W.M. (1991) The biogeochemistry of manganese and iron in the Black Sea, *Deep Sea Res.* **38**, S773-S803.

Livingston H.D., Buesseler K.O., Izdar E. and Konuk T. (1988) Characteristics of Chernobyl fallout in the Southern Black Sea. In: *Radionuclides: A tool for oceanography* (J.C. Guary, P. Guegueniat and R.J. Pentreath, Eds.) pp. 204-216. Elsevier, Essex, U.K.

Livingston H.D., Swift J.H. and Östlund H.G. (1985) Artificial radionuclide tracer supply of the Denmark Strait Overflow between 1972 and 1981. *J. Geophys. Res.* **90**, 6971-6982.

Lyons T.W. (1991) Upper Holocene sediments of the Black Sea: Summary of Leg 4 box cores (1988 Black Sea Oceanographic Expedition). In: *Black Sea Oceanography* (E. Izdar and J.W. Murray, Eds.) pp. 401-441.

Moore W.S. and O'Neill D.J. (1991) Radionuclide distributions in recent Black Sea sediments. In: *Black-Sea Oceanography* (E. Izdar and J.W. Murray, Eds.) pp. 257-270. Kluwer, Boston, U.S.A.

Müller G. and Stoffers P. (1974) Mineralogy and petrology of Black Sea basin sediments. In: *The Black Sea—Geology, chemistry, and biology* (E.T. Degens and D.A. Ross, Eds.) pp. 200-248. American Association of Petroleum Geologists, Memoir 20.

Osterberg C., Carey A.G. Jr. and Curl H. Jr. (1963) Acceleration of sinking rates of radionuclides in the ocean. *Nature* **200,** 1276-1277.

Ostlund H.G. (1974) Expedition 'Odysseus 65': Radiocarbon age of Black Sea deep water. In: *The Black Sea—geology, chemistry, and biology* (E.T. Degens and D.A. Ross, Eds.) pp. 127-133. American Association of Petroleum Geologists, Memoir 20 (1974).

Perkins R.W. and Thomas C.W. (1980) Worldwide fallout. In: *Transuranic elements in the environment* (W.C. Hanson, Ed.).

Polikarpov G.G., Kulebakina L.G., Timoshchuk V.I. and Stokozov N.A. (1991) ^{90}Sr and ^{137}Cs in surface waters of the Dnieper River, the Black Sea and the Aegean Sea in 1987 and 1988. *J. Environ. Radioact.* **13,** 25-28.

Polikarpov G.G., Livingston H.D., Kulebakina L.G., Buesseler K.O., Stokozov N.A. and Casso S.A. (1992) Inflow of Chernobyl ^{90}Sr to the Black Sea from the Dnieper River. *Estuarine Coastal Shelf Sci.* **34,** 315-320.

Ross D.A. and Degens E.T. (1974) Recent sediments of Black Sea. In: *The Black Sea—Geology, chemistry, and biology* (E.T. Degens and D.A. Ross, Eds.) pp.183-199. American Association of Petroleum Geologists, Memoir 20.

Ross D.A., Degens E.T. and MacIlvaine J. (1970) Black Sea: Recent sedimentary history. *Sci.* **170,** 163-165.

Sanchez A.L., Gastaud J., Noshkin V. and Buesseler K. (1991) Plutonium oxidation states in the southwestern Black Sea: Evidence regarding the origin of the cold intermediate layer. *Deep Sea Res.* **38,** S845-S854.

Shaffer G. (1986) Phosphate pumps and shuttles in the Black Sea. *Nature* **321,** 515-517.

Spencer D.W., Brewer P.G. and Sachs P.L. (1972) Aspects of the distributions and trace element composition of suspended matter in the Black Sea. *Geochim. et Cosmochim. Acta* **36,** 71-86.

Stokozov N.A. and Buesseler K.O. (1996) Mixing model for the NW Black Sea using Sr-90 and salinity as tracers, in prep.

Todd J.F., Elsinger R.J. and Moore W.S. (1988) The distributions of uranium, radium and thorium isotopes in two anoxic fjords, Framvaren Fjord (Norway) and Saanich Inlet (British Columbia). *Marine Chem.* **23,** 393-415.

Top Z. and Clark, W.T. (1983) Helium, neon, and tritium in the Black Sea, *J. Marine Res.* **41,** 1-17.

Top Z., Östlund G., Pope L. and Grall C. (1991) Helium Isotopes, neon and tritium in the Black Sea: A comparison with the 1975 observations. *Deep Sea Res.* **38,** S747-S760.

Vakulovsky S.M., Krasnopevtsev Y.V., Nikitin A.I. and Chumichev V.B. (1982) Distribution of ^{137}Cs and ^{90}Sr between water and bottom sediments in the Black Sea, 1977. *Oceanology* **22,** 712-715.

Vakulovsky S.M., Nikitin A.I., Chumichev V.B., Katrich I.Y., Voitsekhovich O.A., Medinets V.I., Pisarev V.V., Bovkum L.A. and Khersonsky E.S. (1994) Caesium-137 and Strontium-90 contamination of water bodies in the areas affected by releases from the Chernobyl nuclear power plant accident: An overview. *J. Environ. Radioact.* **23,** 103-122.

Wei C.-L. and Murray J.W. (1991) ^{234}Th/^{238}U disequilibria in the Black Sea. *Deep Sea Res.* **38,** S855-S873.

10

Radioactivity in the Baltic Sea

H. Nies and S.P. Nielsen

The Baltic Sea is the largest brackish water of the world, though it covers a mere 0.1% of the world oceans. It is unique in many ways, *e.g.* by its flora and fauna. This is primarily due to its limited exchange of water with the world oceans through the Danish Straits in the Belt Sea. The hydrographic condition, *i.e.* salinity and temperature distribution, is controlled by the water inflow of high salinity water from the North Sea through the Belt Sea beneath the halocline and brackish water outflow at the surface. There is a stable halocline and thermocline throughout the entire Baltic with its different basins. This prevents the direct vertical exchange between surface and deep water and, consequently, also the exchange of soluble pollutants or dissolved oxygen. Therefore, a typical feature is the oxygen depletion in deep water layers of the basins.

The highest salinities are found in deep layers of the western Baltic Sea with values up to 20 PSU. Lowest salinities are found in the Gulf of Finland and the Bothnian Bay with salinities between 3 to 5 PSU.

Radioactive substances have been studied for many years in the Baltic Sea in international cooperation in the group MORS (Monitoring of Radioactive Substances) under the umbrella of the Helsinki Commission (HELCOM, 1994). The group MORS prepared a detailed Joint Evaluation Report which is presently published. The data presented here are mainly based on this report.

10.1. Contamination of the Water of the Baltic Sea Prior to the Chernobyl Accident

Artificial radioactivity in the Baltic Sea are due to the following:
- Global fallout from the nuclear weapon tests primarily during the sixties, whereas, part of the radionuclides deposited directly to the sea surface

and part of it being discharged into the sea indirectly *via* river run-off
from land territory;

- Liquid discharges from western Europe nuclear reprocessing plants at La
  Hague (F) and Sellafield (UK) by means of the transport of contaminated
  water from the North Sea through the Belt Sea;
- Direct discharges from nuclear power plants and other nuclear facilities
  such as research centres;
- Fallout from the accident at the Chernobyl nuclear power plant in April
  1986.

The main sources of contamination with Tritium, Sr–90, Cs–137 and plutonium isotopes before 1980 for the Baltic Sea were the global fallout. From
the seventies, the contamination from the nuclear reprocessing plant at
Sellafield due to the inflow of subsequently contaminated water from the
North Sea became more important. This lead to an almost linear correlation
between the Cs–137 activity concentration and salinity (IAEA, 1986a) (Fig.
10.1a.). The distribution of the Cs–137 and Sr–90 activity was studied in the
entire Baltic Sea in 1983. The results showed that the Cs–137 concentrations
generally increased with depth being higher in bottom waters in correspon-
dence with the vertical stratification of saline water in the Baltic Sea. This
again reveals the source of Cs–137 being the saline water from the North Sea
with the discharges from the reprocessing plant at Sellafield. Such a correlation was not found for Sr–90 (Fig. 10.1b.) because the discharges of Sr–90
from the plants La Hague and Sellafield were significantly lower and, consequently, the salinity relationship was completely different. The mixing
line between the fresh water run–off and sea water in the Gulf of Finland
and the Bothnian Bay even shows that the supply of Sr–90 from the rivers is
lower than the concentration in sea areas with higher salinity.

Figure 10.2. presents the surface water contamination by Cs–137 from a
survey in May 1983. This survey is based on a station grid of about 100 stations. Generally, the concentration increased with increasing depth according to the increase of the salinity.

Taking into account the activity ratios of Cs–134/Cs–137 in the discharges from the European reprocessing plants (*e.g.* MAFF annual reports),
the actual concentrations of Cs–134 in the area of the entrance to the Baltic
should not exceed values of more than 1 Bq m^{-3} before 1986. The time of
transport of contaminated sea water from the Irish Sea to the entrance of the
Kattegat is about four years. This can be seen in Figure 10.3. which shows
the temporal trend of Cs–137 and Sr–90 at a station in the western Baltic.
The highest annual discharges of Cs-137 at Sellafield in 1975 were registered
by the peak concentration in 1980 at this station. Thus, the transport time
between the Irish Sea to the western Baltic is in the order of 4 to 5 years.

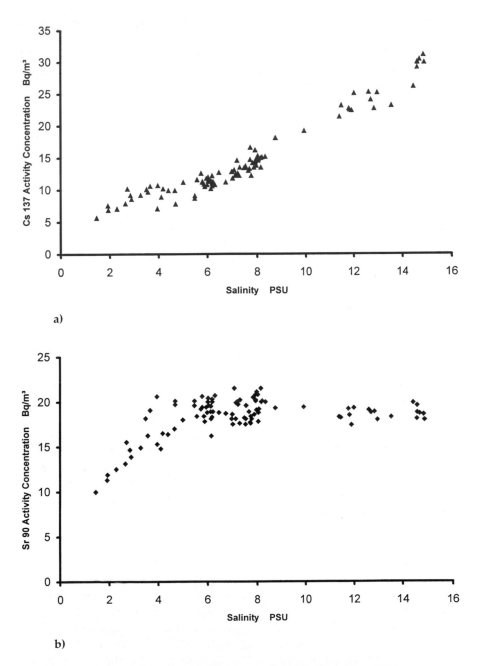

a)

b)

Fig. 10.1. a) Cs–137 / Salinity correlation in May/June 1983.
Different subareas of the Baltic Sea show slightly different correlations
(IAEA, 1986a). b) Sr–90/Salinity relationship in May/June 1983.
Activity concentrations at salinities below 4 PSU are located
in the Bay of Bothnia.

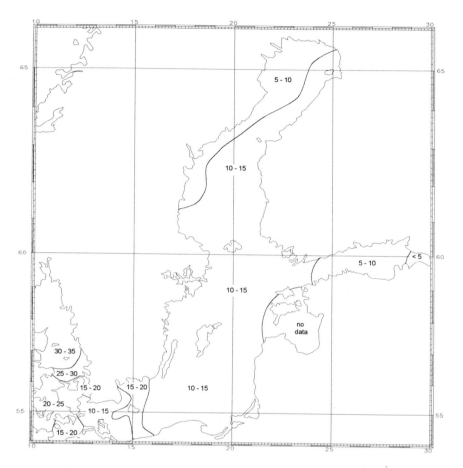

Fig. 10.2. Cs–137 activity concentration (Bq m^{-3}) in surface water
in May/June 1983. The concentration increases
with depth depending on the salinity.

Tritium was mainly deposited to the Baltic by direct aerial fallout or by river run off from the drainage area after the atmospheric nuclear weapons tests. Consequently, before 1984 there existed a strong negative linear correlation with salinity, showing the source in fresh water and river run-off. However, the Tritium concentration decreased almost continuously by physical decay from about 6 kBq m^{-3} in surface water of the western Baltic in 1980 to less than 3 kBq m^{-3} in 1992, because there was no new supply from nuclear tests and the supply due to natural cosmic ray production is negligible. Near the nuclear power stations and other nuclear facilities, Tritium was detected at levels higher than those mentioned above.

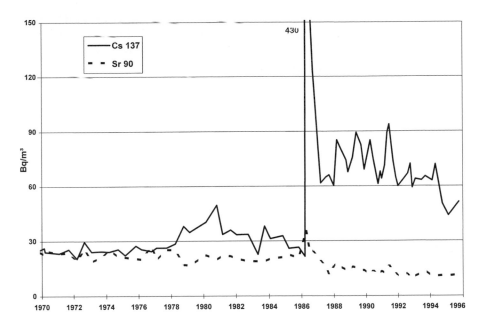

Fig. 10.3. Temporal trend of the Cs–137 and Sr–90 activity concentration between 1970 and 1995 at the position « Schleimündung » in the western Baltic (Belt Sea).

In the vicinity of nuclear power stations and other nuclear facilities, a few more activation and fission nuclides such as Mn–54 and Co–60 could be detected at very low levels, primarily in sediment samples.

Most recent information by the Russian Federation (Yablokov *et al.*, 1993) about dumping of liquid radioactive waste in the Baltic Sea has obviously not created any significant concentration in seawater. The total amount dumped was 0.007 TBq. No information is given about the date and area of dumping.

10.2. Deposition of the Chernobyl Fallout over the Baltic Sea

During the Chernobyl accident in April 1986, plumes of contaminated air masses moved from the accident area to the Baltic region. During this period more than 20 different radionuclides were detected in the fallout. Many radionuclides, such as Sr–89, Zr/Nb–95, I–131, Te/I–132, Ba/La–140, detected also in sea water, due to the short half–lives, decayed within several days or months. At longer term, the Chernobyl contamination can be unequivocally identified in the environment by means of its characteristic activity ratio Cs–134/Cs–137 which was measured at the initial period of deposition. The amount and composition of the release is described in detail also in the IAEA Report about the accident (1986b).

The main contamination from the Chernobyl fallout was detected in the southern part of the Bothnian Sea. The contamination corresponds directly with the contamination measured on adjacent land areas in Sweden, Finland, former USSR, Poland, Denmark and Germany. An entire survey of the Baltic was carried out in October 1986. The data were reported by Gavrilov *et al.* (1990), HELCOM (1989), Ilus *et al.* (1987), Nies and Wedekind (1988) and Nies (1988).

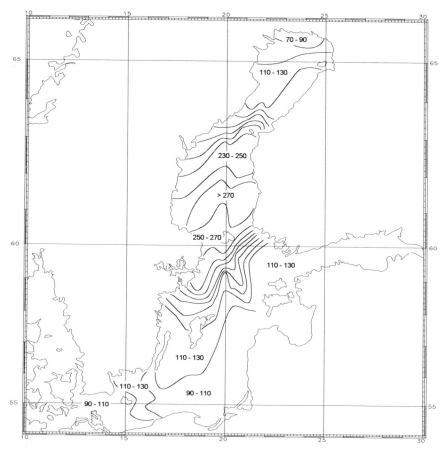

Fig. 10.4. Cs–137 contamination (Bq m^{-3}) of the surface water of the Baltic in summer 1989.

The fallout of Chernobyl was scattered very unevenly over the area of the Baltic Sea (HELCOM, 1989). The range of Cs–137 concentration measured in May and June 1986 was between 40 Bq m^{-3} (Arkona Sea) and 5 200 Bq m^{-3} (northern coastal area of the Gulf of Finland). In general the concentrations of radionuclides were lowest in the southern parts of the Baltic Sea and in the Bothnian Bay. Most contaminated sea water areas were in the Bothnian Sea, in the Gulf of Finland and in the Mecklenburg Bight. A substantial difference was obvious between coastal and open sea areas, so that the concentrations were higher near the coast (STUK, 1987). The activity ratio Cs–134/Cs–137 after the accident was measured to be in the range of 0.5 that corresponded to the theoretical value for the fuel of Chernobyl NPP (IAEA, 1986b).

By the end of 1988, the Caesium concentrations were in great extent smoothed out due to mixing processes in the Baltic Sea and river water input. Nevertheless, Cs–137 contents essentially vary in the different sea areas. This can be seen in Figure 10.4. which illustrates the Cs–137 distribution in surface water in 1989. In 1991 in the surface waters of the eastern part of the Baltic Proper, the Cs–137 content varies from 100 to 130 Bq m^{-3}, being (120 ± 10) Bq m^{-3} on average.

An insignificant increase of Sr–90 and alpha–emitting plutonium isotopes activity concentrations were observed during the first year after the accident in those parts of the Baltic Sea where high deposition occurred. In general the Pu–239,240 concentrations in the Baltic Sea are very low, in average less than 10 mBq m^{-3}. The radioactive contamination of the Baltic Sea after the Chernobyl accident has been dominated by the caesium isotopes 134 and 137 in its typical and fairly constant activity ratio of 0.54. This activity ratio gives the opportunity to identify the Chernobyl signal also in the outflow from the Baltic, *e.g.* in the Norwegian Coastal current.

10.3. Temporal Evolution of the Chernobyl Contamination in the Baltic Sea

Figure 10.3. shows the temporal trend of the Cs–137 and Sr–90 activity concentration in surface water at a position in the Belt Sea (Schleimündung) from 1970 to 1995. The first maximum of Cs–137 in 1980 is due to the maximum annual discharge at Sellafield in 1975 revealing the time of transport of contaminated water to this position between four to five years. The concentrations of Cs–137 changed dramatically after the deposition of the Chernobyl fallout. The seasonal variation with increasing levels in spring and decreasing levels to autumn and winter are explained by the penetration of higher contaminated surface water from the northern Baltic due to higher fresh water input by snow melting and wet deposition in spring and, consequently, higher output of surface water from the Baltic. The opposite effect takes place during autumn and winter. However, the highest levels were recorded at this position in 1991. Since then the activity concentration of Cs–137 shows a decreasing trend.

The initial contamination of the surface layer penetrated rapidly into deeper waters in those areas with the lack of the stable halocline. In 1991 in the deep water layer of the Baltic Proper, the caesium concentrations were still lower than in surface water. For example at the Gothland Deep the Cs–137 activity concentrations in the surface and deep water were 120 and 25 Bq m^{-3}, respectively.

During the following years after 1986, the contamination of the water in the Gulf of Finland have decreased more rapidly than those of the Bothnian Sea. This is due to both the river water run–off from Neva, Luga, and Narva from less contaminated land areas and higher water exchange rates between the Gulf of Finland and the Baltic Proper than between that one of the Bothnian Sea. The contaminated water moved into southern direction, which lead to increasing Cs–134 and Cs–137 activity concentrations in initially less contaminated areas .

The distribution of Cs–137 in May 1994 both, in surface water and in vertical profiles is shown in Figure 10.5. The highest values are mostly still measured at the surface but the contamination has penetrated significantly into deep layers. This is valid in particular for those areas with less pronounced halocline, *e.g.* Northern Baltic Proper and Bothnian Sea.

The Cs–137/Salinity relation of a survey in May 1994 is displayed in Figure 10.6a. This figure reveals the mixing of water between different areas contaminated at mainly two different levels:

- A significant high and large range contamination of water with low salinity which may be related to coastal areas in the Bothnian Sea and,
- the deposition on the central Bothnian Sea and Baltic Proper.

The Cs–137/Salinity correlation for the values from the Bothnian Sea is not well established indicating that the Cs–137 concentration covers a large range over a small salinity distribution ($r = -0.19$). Concentrations of Cs–137 in surface water of the Bothnian Sea are still higher than compared to other parts of Baltic Sea with values above 110 Bq m^{-3}. The correlation, however, in the Baltic Proper and, in particular in the western Baltic and Belt Sea is well established:

$$A_{Cs-137} = 125.1 - 4.17 \times S \qquad (r = -0.88)$$

While the concentrations of Sr–90 increased only slightly in 1986 but in a short period they returned to pre–Chernobyl level (at about 20 Bq m^{-3}). The Sr–90 activity concentration A_{Sr-90} is less strongly dependent on the salinity (Fig. 10.6b.):

$$A_{Sr-90} = 17.907 - 0.304 \times S \qquad (r = -0.87)$$

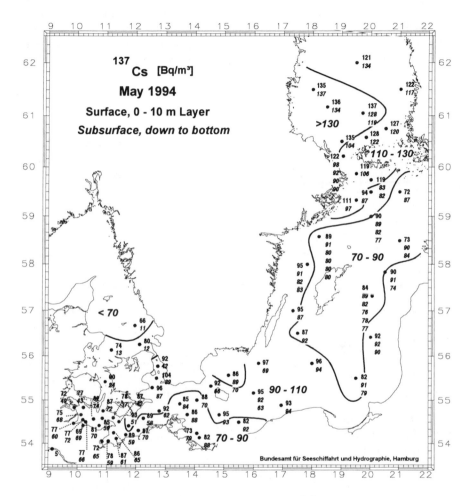

Fig. 10.5. Cs–137 contamination of the water.
The vertical profiles of the concentration are indicated down to bottom water
(20 m, 50 m, 100 m ... bottom water).

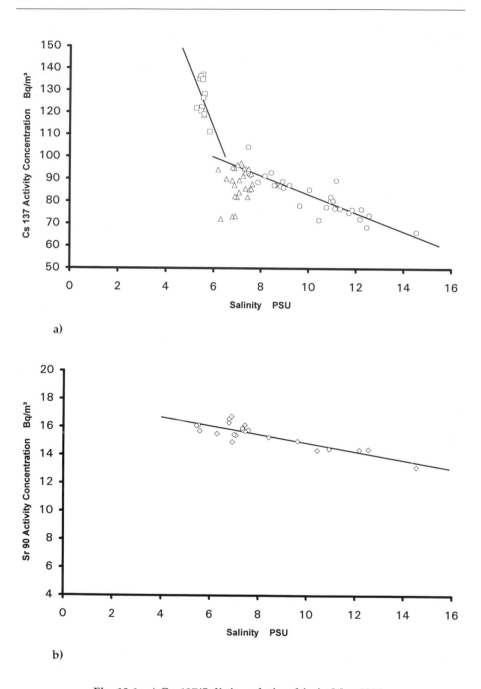

Fig. 10.6. a) Cs–137/Salinity relationship in May 1994.
(○): Data in the western Baltic and Belt Sea; (□): Data in the Bothnian Sea;
(△): Data in the Baltic Proper. b) Sr–90/Salinity relationship in May 1994
(Data from Belt Sea to Bothnian Sea).

10.4. Contamination of Sediments

Bottom sediments reflect in general the relative contamination of a sea area. Therefore, a great deal of monitoring work has been dedicated to the analysis of bottom sediments. The sediments have been sliced in vertical layers in order to establish the historical deposition of various radionuclides. Most sediments in the Baltic contain fine grain material with high capability of radionuclide absorption. The relative contamination level of the different subareas in the Baltic were also reflected in the sediment contamination.

Although the deep layers beneath the halocline were almost not contaminated in 1986 initially after the Chernobyl accident, the Chernobyl signal was detected in the sediments even in the Baltic Proper and the Bothnian Sea at relatively great depths. This shows the relevant transport of Cs–isotopes by sinking particulate matter. One reason might also be that the deposition of the Chernobyl fallout occurred partly in particulate form. The sedimentation rate were estimated in different areas of the Baltic between 0.5 and 2.5 mm a^{-1} (Ilus *et al.* in: HELCOM, 1996).

The comparison of the sediment inventory in the subareas shows the highest levels in the Gulf of Finland and the Bothnian Sea. The highest specific activity of Cs–137 was measured in the surface sediment layer during 1987 in the eastern part of the Gulf of Finland with 3.4 kBq kg^{-1} (dry weight) and the total inventory at this station of 43 kBq m^{-2} during 1990. At a station in the central Bothnian Sea, the maximum values were 1.4 kBq kg^{-1} and 21 kBq m^{-2}, respectively, in 1990 (Ilus *et al.* in: HELCOM, 1996). The levels in the western Baltic were significantly lower. At a station in the Lübeck Bight the highest level in the top 2 cm layer was measured about 150 Bq kg^{-1} and the inventory amounted up to 3 kBq m^{-2} (Nies *et al.*, 1990).

In addition to the two typical Chernobyl Cs–isotopes, other radionuclides from Chernobyl could be detected, such as Ru–106, Sb–125 and Ag–110m in sediments. Radionuclides originating from nuclear power stations were only detectable at the direct vicinity of these plants.

10.5. Inventories

Some attempts have been made to estimate the inventories of the main radionuclides in the water of the Baltic Sea on the basis of observation data. Several results were estimated by the HELCOM expert group MORS already in 1988. That estimates showed that the inventory of Cs–137 in the Baltic water mass was 324 TBq during 1983; 4 620 TBq by September 1986; and 3 700 TBq during August 1987. The Sr–90 inventory was 416 TBq in 1983; 460 TBq in October 1986; and 391 TBq in August 1987. A later review on the data by the group MORS came to the data given in Table 10.I. The unusual decrease in 1988 is probably caused by the lack of the observation data during this period from the most contaminated areas. It must be stated that these estimates were done in a very simplified approach and give only an indication of the level.

Table 10.I. Cs–137 Inventories in the Baltic Sea Water.

Year	Inventory (TBq)
1985	325
1986	4300 – 5000
1987	3700
1988	1800
1989	2300
1990	2100

Acknowledgments

This paper is based on the Joint Evaluation Report « Radioactivity in the Baltic Sea, 1984 –1991 », prepared by the Group of Experts of HELCOM MORS under the chairmanship of the authors. The Report will be published in 1996. Significant contributions to this paper have been given by Y. Panteleev (Russia), T. Ikäheimonen and E. Ilus (Finland).

References

Gavrilov V., Gritchenko Z.G. and Ivanova L.M. (1990) Sr–90, Cs–134, and Cs–137 in Waters of the Baltic Region in the USSR (1986 – 1988). *Radiochemistry* **32**, 171–179 (in Russian).

HELCOM (1989) Three years observations of the levels of some radionuclides in the Baltic Sea after the Chernobyl accident. Baltic Sea Environment Proc., No. 31.

HELCOM (1994) Nies H., Monitoring of Radioactive Substances in the Baltic Sea. In: HELCOM Seminar for Experts from Estonia, Latvia, Lithuania and Russia on the Implementation of HELCOM Arrangements, other International Instruments and Related Matters. Riga, Sept. 1993. Baltic Sea Environment Proc. No. 59, pp. 61-70. Helsinki.

HELCOM (1996) Radioactivity in the Baltic Sea, 1984 – 1991. Joint Evaluation Report of the Expert Group MORS. Baltic Sea Environment Proceedings. In press.

IAEA (1986a) Study of Radioactive Materials in the Baltic Sea. Report of the final research coordinated meeting on the study of radioactive materials in the Baltic Sea, organized by the International Atomic Energy Agency and held in Helsinki, Finland, 24–28 Sept. 1984. IAEA–TECDOC–362, Vienna, 1986.

IAEA (1986b) Summary Report on the Post–Accident Review Meeting on the Chernobyl Accident. Report by the International Nuclear Safety Advisory Group. Safety Series No.75–INSAG–1. Vienna, 1986.

Ilus E., Sjöblom K.–L., Aaltonen H., Klemola S. and Arvela H. (1987) Monitoring of Radioactivity in the Environs of Finnish Nuclear Power Stations in 1986. STUK–A67. Supplement 12 to Annual Report STUK–A55, Helsinki, Finland.

Ilus E., Niemistö L. and Bojanowski R. (1996) in HELCOM, 1996: Radioactivity in the Baltic Sea, 1984 – 1991. Joint Evaluation Report of the Expert Group MORS. Baltic Sea Environment Proceedings. (In press)

Nies H. and Wedekind Ch. (1988) The Contamination of the North Sea and Baltic Sea by the Chernobyl Fallout. In: *Radionuclides: A Tool for Oceanography*. (J.C. Guary, P. Guéguéniat and R.J. Pentreath. Eds.) pp. 227-239. Elsevier Applied Science, London and New York.

Nies H. (1988) The Radioactive Contamination of the Baltic Sea during the Years 1983 to 1987 and its Radiological Consequences. *Dt. Hydrogr. Z.*, **41**, 39-44.

Nies H. (1989) The Distribution of the Chernobyl Fallout over the Baltic Sea and its Change during 1987 and 1988 in Seawater. Baltic Sea Environment Proceedings, No. 31; Three Years Observation of the Levels of some Radionuclides in the Baltic Sea after the Chernobyl Accident. pp. 31–51, HELCOM, Helsinki.

Nies H., Albrecht H., Rechenberg V., Goroncy I., Dahlgaard H., Weiß D. and Brügmann L. (1990) Intercomparison of Sediment Sampling Techniques by means of Radionuclide and Heavy Metal Analysis. *Dt. hydrogr. Z.* **43**, 27–53.

STUK (1987) Finnish Studies on Radioactivity in the Baltic Sea after the Chernobyl Accident in 1986. Supplement 11 to Annual Report STUK-A55. Finnish Centre for Radiation and Nuclear Safety, Helsinki.

Yablokow A.V., Karasev V.K., Rumyantsev V.M., Kokeyev M.E., Petrov O.I., Listsev V.N., Yemelyanenkov A.F. and Rubtsov P.M. (1993) Facts and Problems Related to Dumping of Radioactive Waste at Seas Bordering to the Territory of the Russian Federation. 108 pages Moscow (in Russian).

Impression : EUROPE MEDIA DUPLICATION S.A.
F 53110 Lassay-les-Châteaux
N° 4648 - Dépôt légal : Septembre 1996